Mrs Blakemore
14 Devonshire Ro
Bexleyheath
Kent
DA6 8DS

RUDOLF

British Heart
Foundation

Cover photograph of Sanctuary of St. Anselm's Church,
West Hill, Dartford, by Martine Wates

*Dedicated in gratitude
to the memory of Arthur McGuinness.
His generous bequest to St. Anselm's Church
has enabled the work of restoration to go forward
and has sponsored the publication of this book.*

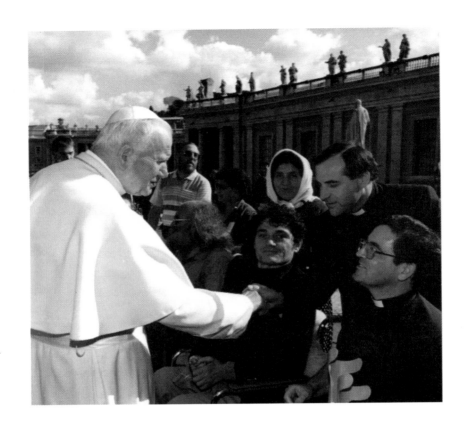

Pope John Paul II greeting Father William Saunders
at a General Audience at St. Peter's
following World Mission Sunday, 1994,
at which time he imparted his Apostolic Blessing
on the Parish of St. Anselm in Dartford.

St. Anselm's

and the Catholic Life of Dartford

Sheila Whitehead

Sheila Whitehead

STAP 2000
DARTFORD KENT

Published in 2000 in Great Britain by
STAP 2000
St. Anselm's Church, 89 West Hill,
Dartford, Kent, DA1 2HJ

ISBN 0-9538216-0-9

Artwork and Typesetting by WHM Photosetting
Printed by G. Morbin, Sidcup, England

Contents

Acknowledgements

When Bishop John Jukes visited St. Anselm's in 1993, he asked for the history of the parish to be written. I had been interested in Dartford's medieval priory for many years and I asked Father David Gummett whether he thought it would be possible to combine the two stories. He encouraged me to make the attempt.

It was not as simple as it seemed. The Church had been here for about a thousand years even before the Priory was founded. When Father William Saunders came to Dartford in 1994, he suggested that I should begin at the beginning. I have done this and a picture has emerged of 'something of great constancy', of the Church living out her life through all the vicissitudes of war and peace, suffering sometimes to the point of extinction or near extinction, but returning like an unquenchable flame to draw people to Christ, from one century, and one millennium, to another.

I owe a debt of gratitude to many people for their generous assistance: to the late Sister Mary Albert Hughes, O.P., to her Community at Carisbrooke, and to Father Bede Bailey, O.P., to Brother Ferruccio Bortolozzo, O.F.M.Cap., and Father Eric Mead; to Father Michael Clifton, Monsignor George Stack, and Father Ian Dickie; to the late Sister Norah Browne and to Sister Dolores Heys, of the Sisters of Charity of Our Lady of Mercy; to Father Stephen Haylett, Father Steven Fisher, Dr. John Burne, and Miss Lisa Johnstone; to Mrs. Joan Bond of the Catholic Central Library, Miss Pat Stevens and her colleagues at the Dartford Reference Library, and Mr. Peter Boreham and his colleagues at Dartford Museum; to Professor Michele Ranchetti and his wife Hazel, to Mrs. Joan Kelly, and Mrs. Angela Reynolds. I owe a debt of gratitude also to Mr. Brian Wates, to the

Rev. Dennis and Mrs. Mary Barratt, who have given much thought and care to the artwork and typesetting, and, not least, to my sisters, Barbara and Marion, without whose support I should not have finished in time for the Millennium.

I owe a very special debt to Brother Thomas More Mann, O.F.M.Cap., and to Father William Saunders. Brother Thomas More has given me much help in connection with the beginnings of St. Anselm's, and has allowed me to use materials from his own far more scholarly research. I am most grateful to him for this great generosity. Father Saunders has helped me in many ways. He first told me that Bishop Challoner had visited Dartford and he has generously offered information and ideas and suggestions. I am grateful for his thoughtful guidance and for his encouragement and support as the history which I thought would be only a few pages in length has turned into a book. I wish to thank him also for his kindness in offering the photograph of his audience with Pope John Paul II – with the Pope's blessing on the Parish of St. Anselm – to be the frontispiece I had asked him for; and for his generosity in writing the Foreword.

And I thank in advance the readers of our history, who, as I hope and trust, will together support its publication.

The Illustrations

I wish to thank the photographers who have been to great trouble to provide the illustrations, and I also thank all those who have kindly given permission to reproduce copyright material.

The Frontispiece (*Pope John Paul II greeting Father William Saunders*; photo: A. Mari) is by courtesy of *L'Osservatore Romano* Photo Service. *St. John's Jerusalem* and *Remains of the Chapel of the Knights Hospitallers* (photos: Duncan Pearson) are by courtesy of the National Trust. *Playtime at Our Lady's School, St. Anselm's Church (1975), St. George's Church, Interior of St. George's,* and *The Catholic Oratory,* are also by Duncan Pearson. *The Priory of the Blessed Virgin Mary and St. Margaret, Virgin,* is by courtesy of Groundwork Kent Thames-side. *Reredos of the Martyrs' Altar, Tyburn Convent* (photo: Martine Wates) is by courtesy of the Tyburn Benedictines; *Statue of Our Lady of Walsingham* is by courtesy of the Administrator of the National Shrine; *Bishop Richard Challoner* and the *Prayer for the Beatification of Richard Challoner* are by courtesy of the Administrator of Westminster Cathedral; and *Bishop Challoner's Notes of his First Visitation* by courtesy of the Westminster Diocesan Archivist. The mementoes of *The Opening of the Franciscan Mission, Father Buckley's Four Lectures,* and *The Opening of St. Anselm's, Spital Street,* with the photo of *The Gateway,* are by courtesy of the Librarian, Dartford Library Local Collection. *Dartford Purchase, Dr. George Winham,* and *Father Dudley preparing for the Road,* are by courtesy of the Southwark Diocesan Archivist; *Father Buckley's Church with the Old School* and *St. Anselm's Church, Spital Street,* are by courtesy of Father William Saunders; and *St. Vincent's School* is by courtesy of the Presentation Brothers. *St. Vincent's Church* is by Father Patrick Zammit, *Father John Sandom's Ruby Jubilee Mass* is by Michael Sheppard; and the illustration of the *Seven Sentences of St. John Fisher* was kindly contributed by John Wilkinson. *Jubilee Praise* is reproduced by permission of Father Saunders and Phyl Lloyd and was kindly printed by Hugh Greer.

Foreword

It is with great joy that I write the Foreword to *St. Anselm's and the Catholic Life of Dartford* by Sheila Whitehead, published in the year of the Great Jubilee 2000.

A jubilee year is one of jubilation and at Dartford our jubilation is ever greater for three reasons: first the Church of St. Anselm has the special privilege of being an indulgenced church; second, the building is twenty-five years old this year and celebrates its silver jubilee on October 30th, 2000; third, the old St. Anselm's at Spital Street, now no more, was blessed on December 8th 1900, and the Catholics at Dartford remember with pride what would have been the centenary of the old church. All this in the year of the Great Jubilee.

To commemorate the Great Jubilee I wrote a hymn, *Jubilee Praise*, with music by Phyl Lloyd and arranged by Sheila Whitehead. The first line is, 'God's people give praise in our Jubilee days.' This book recalls the generations of praise by Catholics in Dartford.

May this new millennium be the start of both a new evangelisation and an ever greater praise to God by a new generation of Catholics.

William D. Saunders

Fr. William D. Saunders
Parish Priest of St. Anselm's, Dartford.
Lourdes, France,
Memorial of Our Lady, Queen and Mother,
22nd August 2000.

ix

Chapter 1

The First Thirteen Centuries

St. Anselm's, facing the old Roman road from Dover to London, may not be far from a very old Catholic church indeed, older perhaps than the chapel at Lullingstone.

Springhead, the Roman town of Vagniacis, also on the Roman road, near Southfleet, with seven pagan temples drawing pilgrims from far and wide, overshadowed Dartford for the first three centuries of Roman occupation.[1] It had its origins in an even earlier Celtic shrine at the spring. In the fourth century, when the Empire officially adopted Christianity after the conversion of Constantine, Springhead dwindled and Dartford grew in importance. There may already have been a nucleus of believers living nearby, perhaps among the legionaries and the slaves and freedmen.

In the large Roman cemetery overlooking the Roman road down East Hill towards Dartford, pagan graves have been found which are thought to date from the second and third centuries, and also fourth century – or perhaps earlier – Christian graves. Much of the cemetery has still to be excavated. Some of the graves, near East Hill House, are apparently focused on a central point and it has recently been suggested that they may be grouped in front of a sanctuary, either a temple mausoleum or a Christian church. They lie along an arc, facing east. So the remains of our first church may be hidden there.[2]

Christianity had put down deep roots in Roman Britain during the centuries of persecution, long before Constantine proclaimed the 'Peace of the Church' in 313. The Church in Britain was already well organised and Bishop Restitutus of London was one of three British bishops known to have attended the Synod of Arles in 314.

1

A hundred years later, after the Romans had left, most of the Britons in the area were forced to flee before the Anglo-Saxon invaders. It was the beginning of a new Dark Age. It is doubtful whether any memory of Christianity could have lived on through the next century and a half, even among Britons who had survived the slaughter and remained as slaves. The Jutish kings of Kent claimed descent from, and worshipped, Woden. Paganism, and pagan temples, had returned.

When St. Augustine and his brother monks, sent by Pope Gregory the Great, arrived in Thanet in 597 to bring the Gospel to the English, the 'Good News' spread like wildfire. King Ethelbert was well disposed; he had married a Frankish princess who was already a Christian. Queen Bertha used to pray in the little church of St. Martin of Tours built by the Romans in Canterbury. At the king's invitation, St. Augustine celebrated Mass there and on the Feast of Pentecost that same year, June 2nd 597, Ethelbert was baptised, together with ten thousand of his followers, as Pope Gregory stated in a letter to the Patriarch of Alexandria.

Within seven years Augustine had, as Archbishop of Canterbury, consecrated Mellitus Bishop of London and Justus Bishop of Rochester.[3] (The king was 'Bretwalda', at least nominally overlord, of the Southern English, including the Kingdom of Essex, of which London was the chief town.)

There were no parish churches as yet, but Mass would have been said in those early years in the fields in Dartford, and later beside a cross. By 742, there is known to have been a church at the ford of the River Darent. This Saxon church was probably first built of timber and later rebuilt in part timber and part stone. Some Saxon stonework in the present Church of the Holy Trinity may have come from this earlier building.

Little can be said with any certainty about Dartford during the Dark Ages, but as the Kingdom of Kent yielded first in the eighth century to Mercian domination, then to Wessex, and eventually to Danish and Norman invaders, the church must always have been a haven of peace and true civilisation in a turbulent world.

Domesday Book, compiled for William the Conqueror in 1086, records that by then there were also three chapels in Dartford. One is thought to have been on the site known as the Castle, where a Saxon cresset lamp and pot have been found. It is where the priory now stands; the land was one of the four demesnes or manors of the kings of Kent and they would almost certainly have had a chapel there. There is also a tradition that a convent existed there in Saxon times and that the nuns were murdered in a Danish raid.[4] The second chapel would have been St. Edmund's, beside the Roman, and later Saxon, burial ground. The third has not been identified; one suggestion is that it was the 'little chapel' of St. John the Baptist at Weston Cross within the parish of Holy Trinity mentioned in the will of John Totenham in 1474. The location of Weston Cross is not known.[5] It is tempting to wonder whether it was on West Hill, close to the present St. Anselm's.

As the town grew, century by century, so did Holy Trinity. The Norman church was built by Gundulf, the Bishop of Rochester – the 'builder bishop' who was also employed to supervise the works at the Tower of London. (He was, incidentally, a loyal friend of St. Anselm – both were Benedictine monks from Bec – and held in warm regard by him.) Holy Trinity was both a church and a strong defence against continuing Danish raids. After the martyrdom of St. Thomas Becket, when Canterbury became one of the greatest shrines in Christendom, Dartford enjoyed considerable prosperity as streams of pilgrims broke their journey here. Many hostelries flourished in the town and the earliest extension to the church was made into a chapel dedicated to St. Thomas.

The body of Henry V, who died in France, rested overnight at Holy Trinity on its journey to Westminster Abbey. His knights kept vigil and a Requiem Mass was said by the Bishop of Exeter before the cortège proceeded to London.[6] A large retinue accompanying Cardinal Wolsey on an embassy to France in 1527 halted in Dartford. There were many other occasions when the church sped the humble and the great on their way.

In the Middle Ages, Holy Trinity had two chantries and a number of other altars. Beside the River Darent there was also St. Catherine's Hermitage. The hermit helped travellers across the ford. At his profession, he promised before God and the Saints to direct his conduct and conversation according to the Rule of St. Paul the First Hermit. William Temple, 'singleman', professed by St. John Fisher at Bromley, was the last of the line.[7] We do not know what became of him.

On East Hill, St. Edmund's Chantry Chapel was built probably on the site of the ancient Saxon chapel. At the foot of West Hill was the leper hospital, dedicated to St. Mary Magdalen, of which some records survive. It seems, as we might expect, to have had its own chapel and cemetery.

At Sutton-at-Hone, a Commandery of the Knights Hospitallers, now known locally as St. John's Jerusalem, was founded in 1199, originally to house thirteen poor men and three chaplains. The Knights always spoke of the sick as 'our lords the sick', and treated them with great deference, such as sick pilgrims receive at Lourdes today. Their beautiful chapel, part of which has survived, had seven altars, perhaps for chantry Masses or possibly for the seven 'Tongues', or Provinces, of the Order, as in Valletta. A manuscript in Valletta lists hundreds of gifts to the Knights at Sutton, including twelve pence to be paid at Easter 'for the maintenance of the light of the Holy Cross' and a rent of sixpence, granted by Geoffrey de Heilonde, for a lamp 'to be kept up before the altar of St.

Nicholas for ever'. The charities of Simon the miller, Reynold the carpenter, and Margery the laundress are among those recorded.[8]

Henry VIII dissolved the English Province of the Knights Hospitallers (the Knights of Malta) in 1540. The Grand Prior in Clerkenwell died on the day of the Dissolution, it was said of a broken heart. Sutton fell into the hands of Sir Maurice Denys, who added 'St. John's' to his name.

In 1346, the Dominican Priory of the Blessed Virgin Mary and St. Margaret, Virgin, was given its charter by Edward III in fulfilment of a vow made by his grandmother, Queen Eleanor of Castile. The king made a grant of land in Dartford, the site of the old 'Castle', for the construction of a monastery, and also provided a house for the Dominican friars who would act as chaplains to the nuns. The foundation dates from 1356 (the Black Death had intervened), when Mathilda, the first Prioress, accompanied by Father John de Woderowe, the king's Dominican confessor, came from Poissy with four nuns to their new Priory in Dartford, where ten English girls awaited them. So the new community was born.[9]

The Order of Preachers, known as Dominicans, had been founded by Dominic Guzman, a Spaniard, early in the thirteenth century. His first community had consisted of a group of nine women, nearly all converts, whom he established in a monastery at Prouille, a village in the south of France. St. Dominic worked tirelessly to bring people back to the Church and, believing that his preaching would come to nothing without the support of prayer, he called on the Sisters to help him. He guided them in faith and holiness and gave them a rule of contemplative life. At about the same time a number of men joined him and so later the first community of friars came into being. The Black Friars, as they were called, spread rapidly across Europe and beyond and by 1337 numbered 12,000.

St. Dominic's ideal of communities of friars and nuns providing mutual support became the pattern except in

England where there were eventually over fifty friaries but the only Sisters were those in Dartford. The friars ministered to them as Dominic had intended while the nuns gave them much practical assistance. They saw to the accounts of the Province, offered hospitality to travellers, and ran a school. But their most important work was prayer, particularly in the Eucharist and the Day and Night Hours of the Divine Office. Grace flowed from the prayer as from a fountain, nourishing the community and radiating out to the world.

St. Mary's and St. Margaret's was a wealthy priory but throughout its existence the nuns lived their strict rule faithfully.[10] Nearly two centuries later, while in the Tower, St. John Fisher wrote two spiritual treatises for his half-sister, Elizabeth White, a nun in Dartford. He compares her life, in *The Ways to Perfect Religion*, with that of the hunter, who, too, must fast and make real sacrifices from early morning until late into the night in order to win the sought after prize. If she is as earnest in her longing for Christ as the hunter is for the hare, he assures her, her life of prayer and penance will seem easy.[11]

Princess Bridget Plantagenet came to the school as a child of ten and later she was received into the community, remaining until her death in 1517, content all her life to be a simple nun. She was the seventh and youngest daughter of Edward IV and was a sister of the two young princes murdered in the Tower. We read, too, of a Franciscan Observant friar in the sixteenth century whose mother sent him for his early education to 'the good nuns in Dartford'. Later, at Cambridge, to his mother's dismay, Friar John George became one of the few Observants to swerve in their loyalty to Queen Catherine. His mother warned him angrily not to come home 'unless you change your condition, or you shall be as welcome "as water into the sheep"'.[12]

We see from the homely bequests of townspeople how they loved the Priory. John Joyner left his 'grete bras potte' and four pence for the light that burned perpetually before Our Lady's altar. Rose Pitt bequeathed 'twenty pence and a candlestick'.[13] John Dunkin, an Anglican, wrote in 1844 in his *History and Antiquities of Dartford* of the unblemished memory left by the nuns.

The struggle of Henry VIII to obtain his divorce from Catherine of Aragon cast a terrible shadow over the Priory. The four years leading up to the Dissolution were a time of sorrow and anguish for the nuns, who have been known since the sixteenth century as 'The Sisters of the Martyrs'.[14]

On June 19th 1535, Blessed William Exmew and Blessed Sebastian Newdigate, Carthusian monks of the London Charterhouse, were hanged, drawn, and quartered at Tyburn. They were among the king's first innocent victims. Their only offence was their refusal to take the Oath of Succession, which denied the authority of the Pope. They were brothers of Sister Elizabeth Exmew and Sister Newdigate at the Priory.[15] (We do not know the fate of two other brothers of Sister Newdigate who were Knights Hospitallers.)

Sister Elizabeth White mourned the death of St. John Fisher, beheaded on Tower Hill on June 22nd. Sister Agnes Roper was sister-in-law to St. Thomas More's favourite daughter, Margaret Roper.[16] He was beheaded on July 6th. Two years later, on June 8th 1537, Sister Alice Davy's brother, Blessed John Davy, a Carthusian deacon, starved to death in Newgate.

For fifty years the Sisters' own lives were to be a daily martyrdom of exile, poverty, and, at times, active persecution.

At the dissolution of the Priory in 1539, the nuns were sent away. Most received pensions of £2 or £5 a year. The buildings were torn down and the rubble used for the manor house that Henry VIII built for his own use. Later, it was given to Queen Anne (Anne of Cleves).[17]

A martyrdom which 'struck every mind with horror and astonishment' on account of its 'unparalleled barbarity' was that of Blessed Margaret Pole, who was over seventy years old when her execution took place on May 27th 1541 (now the Feast of St. Augustine of Canterbury). For her 'crime' of being a Plantagenet princess and the mother of Cardinal Pole, she was beheaded at the Tower without even a trial. Her last words were, 'Blessed are they who suffer persecution for righteousness' sake.'[18] One of her gentlewomen, Sister Felice, had become a nun at the Priory. Two other Sisters, Beatrice Marshall and Margaret Mountenay, may also have been her attendants.[19] Blessed Margaret was a cousin of Princess Bridget, whose early death at the age of thirty-seven spared her from experiencing the torment of these years.

The Reformation brought an end to the familiar forms of Catholic worship. All that many held dearest was taken from them. In Kent, the stripping of the altars and church furnishings was rigorously carried out. The ruins of chantry chapels such as St. Edmund's and of the monastic houses must at the time have seemed the picture of desolation.

It is likely that many will have welcomed the return of the Mass under Mary Tudor in 1553. But now rigour was matched with rigour and cruelty with cruelty: again instigated by the monarch. Those who denied the teaching of the Catholic Church were tried for heresy and Protestants died for the new faith as Catholics had for the old.

The full horror of it was brought home to Dartford when a linen weaver of the town, Christopher Waid, was burned at the stake near the Brent on East Hill. At his martyrdom, on July 19th 1555, he prayed: 'Show me a token for good, that they which hate me may see it and be ashamed, because Thou, Lord, hast spoken to me, and comforted me.'[20]

We can imagine the confusion and bewilderment of the scene and how it will have seared the faith of those who knew Christopher Waid, his friends and neighbours.

The nuns were reunited in Mary's reign, first at King's Langley. Queen Anne, who had become a Catholic, died in 1557.[21] After her death, Queen Mary returned the Manor House to the Dominicans by patent of September 8th 1558 and they came 'home' to Dartford. But, 'How sad was their homecoming! . . . The very tombstones had been taken up from cloister and church and used to pave a new water culvert',[22] and there was little left to recognize. The life of prayer was resumed for a few months, but Mary died on November 17th. Queen Elizabeth's Visitors arrived in Dartford in June 1559. The Oaths of Supremacy and Uniformity, now demanded of all priests and religious, were tendered first to Father Richard Hargrave, their President and the Dominican Provincial, then to each of the nuns separately. They all refused. Within eight days, the Visitors sold all the property of the convent before their eyes, at a very low price, then departed and gave the nuns twenty-four hours to leave.

The Spanish Ambassador shipped the pathetic little band, two priests, nine nuns, and a postulant, along with some nuns of the Order of St. Bridget, first to Antwerp. They eventually found refuge with some Dutch Dominican Sisters, living in extreme poverty, in a ruinous convent on an island in the Scheldt estuary, where there was a shortage even of fresh water. Three of the Dartford nuns were over eighty and the youngest fifty.[23]

The refugees were forced to sell their few possessions, and only after pleas to the Pope and a reminder to the king of Spain who had promised them pensions, and appeals to other benefactors, was their plight lessened.

A letter from the Prioress lists their names:

'Our father, father Richard Hartgrave, our ghostely father
Brother John Anthonye our chapleyne
Dame Elyzabethe Cressener, prioresse
Sister Katheryne Clovill

9

Sister Elizabeth White
Sister Elizabeth Exmeu
Sister Elizabeth Seygood
Joan Courtysse
Sister Katheryne Efflyne
Sister Mary Benthum
Sister Heleyne Bostocke
Sister Katheryne Garrett'.[24]

Father Godfrey Anstruther, O.P., in a moving account of the exile, confirms that all these Sisters belonged to the old Priory at Dartford and he adds some vivid details:

'Elizabeth White was half-sister of St. John Fisher, and so like him in appearance that Queen Mary recognised her at sight. To her he dedicated his two best-known treatises, *A Spiritual Consolation* and *The Ways to Perfect Religion*, both written in the Tower while he was awaiting death. In the next twenty-four years she must have learnt them almost by heart, and perhaps she carried them into exile with her. Words which he had written on the threshold of eternity must have taken on a new meaning as she looked out to sea towards the Kentish coast: "What may I do to get some help at this most dangerous hour? Where may I seek succour? Where may I resort for my comfort? My body forsaketh me, my pleasures are vanished away as the smoke, my goods will not go with me . . . All these worldly things I must leave behind; if any comfort shall be, either it must be in the prayers of my friends or in mine good deeds that I have done before."

'There was another nun who numbered a brother among the English martyrs. Elizabeth Exmew was sister to William Exmew, a monk of the London Charterhouse, who was executed three days before John Fisher. She had been turned out of Dartford in 1539, being one of the senior sisters who got an annual pension of £5. In 1555, she was 'living continently' with Elizabeth Seygood whose pension was only 40s. They had chosen for their home the little town of Walsingham in Norfolk, with its deserted priory and desecrated shrine.

'Through the good offices of Margaret, Duchess of Parma, who had recently been appointed Regent of the Spanish Netherlands, the royal pension was eventually established, but meanwhile their needs were desperate.'[25]

Father Richard Hargrave was renowned in Europe for his saintliness. He died in 1566, and in 1568 the island convent closed for ever and the nuns moved to Bruges. By 1573, only three were left and in 1574 they joined their Flemish sisters in the Convent of Engelendael, 'the valley of the angels', outside Bruges. Civil war and religious persecution forced them into hiding and they took refuge in private houses within the city.

Elizabeth Cresner died on April 27th 1577, 'deprived of the last poor comforts of religious life'. Catholic worship was restored in 1584. Elizabeth Exmew died on February 6th 1585 and was buried with full ceremonies by the Dominican Fathers of Bruges. Father Godfrey again comments: 'With her death, the English Province of the Second Order of St. Dominic, after two and a half centuries of prayer and penance, after fifty years of dispersion and exile, became extinct.'[26]

Chapter 2

Penal Times

Under Elizabethan law, it was a criminal offence to be a Catholic and high treason to be a priest or even to harbour one. Forty-two Catholic priests and lay men and women martyred in the sixteenth and seventeenth centuries for refusing to give up their faith have been canonised and a further two hundred and forty-two beatified. There were about three hundred others; some of these were put to death but most of them died in prison. Life imprisonment was at times meted out to Catholic priests even late into the eighteenth century.

There were still converts. Thomas Tilden, born in 1622, was one. He was the son of a Dartford tanner. He was ordained priest and was appointed President of Lisbon College. Using an alias, 'Dr. Godden', he came to London and worked as Archdeacon in secret, and later returned as chaplain to Catherine of Braganza. In the Titus Oates conspiracy, that caused the death of about thirty-five innocent Catholics, he was falsely accused of hiding the body of Sir Edmundbury Godfrey, whose murder in 1678 'raised the curtain' for anti-Catholic riots. He was forced to flee to Paris and became chaplain to an English convent there, where his niece, Petronilla Tilden, was a nun. It is not known whether she, too, was from Dartford. 'Dr. Godden' again returned to London and could work more openly under the Catholic King James II. He died in 1688, ten days before the king fled from England, and was buried on November 30th in the cemetery attached to the Queen's Catholic Chapel at Somerset House.[1] Some of his royal sermons were published in King James's time.

Under an Act of William III, a reward of £100 was granted to any informer who obtained the conviction of a Catholic bishop, priest or schoolmaster. Catholics were debarred from inheriting or purchasing land and liable to forfeit their estates to their next Protestant heirs. In spite of this, the Catholic population of England doubled between 1714 and 1780.

We next hear of Catholics in Dartford in the course of Bishop Challoner's visitation of Kent in 1742. Richard Challoner, 'one of the brightest men that was ever bred in Douay',[2] had returned to England in 1730 from the College which had wanted him to be its President, and he was consecrated bishop at the convent in Hammersmith in 1739, assisting Bishop Petre, whom he later succeeded as Vicar Apostolic for the London District. The District extended across ten counties and the Isle of Wight and the Channel Isles, with jurisdiction also in the American colonies and British islands in the Caribbean.

He lost no time in embarking on a thorough visitation of his vast District, beginning with London, then going westwards to Hampshire and later to Bedfordshire. In July 1742, he set out for Kent. His notebooks record his visits but with very little detail: they could have fallen into the wrong hands. Mass Centres in Kent were few and far between, and most were in the Canterbury direction. Returning from Canterbury and Chatham, he came to Dartford. He notes that there were thirteen Catholics in Farnborough (which may have been a coded reference to Farningham) and Dartford together. There were no confirmation candidates. The priest serving them he calls 'Westbrook', which is thought to be the alias of Father Darrell, whose Kentish mission field was widespread.[3]

The Church in England at this time has been compared to a patchwork quilt, with many contrasting colours and much variation of light and shade. Bishop Challoner preached openly in the Sardinian embassy chapel and visitors to London went to hear him also at the Ship Tavern in Little Turnstile. The London of Dr. Johnson was more tolerant than the world that Shakespeare knew. There was revulsion in many quarters at the idea of taking evidence from informers, even though the penal laws could be invoked at any time, and often were. Fifteen priests and nine Catholic teachers were prosecuted and at least four Mass-houses closed for a time in the spring of 1767 alone, causing 'a major disruption of London Catholic life'.[4]

It was the need for manpower for the Canadian and British armies that prompted the passage of the First Relief Act in 1778. The Act, which allowed recruits to take a simple oath of allegiance to the Crown, brought about the end of the persecution of priests and their congregations, and allowed Catholics to inherit property. Bishop Challoner required his clergy and recommended their congregations to pray, in gratitude, for the King and Queen by name and for all the Royal Family. But the Act was followed by the backlash of the Gordon Riots of 1780. Gordon chose St. George's Fields, where St. George's Cathedral now stands, to assemble the divisions of the extremist Protestant Association, who spent a week setting fire to Catholic and other property in London and to the prisons, holding the capital to ransom. The gentle old bishop, now nearly ninety, sought by a frenzied mob, was persuaded to take shelter in Finchley but he later returned to his simple lodgings in Gloucester Street, near Queen Square. The chapel of the Sardinian Embassy and the other embassy chapels, and the Ship Tavern, were among the many Mass Centres that had been destroyed.

Bishop Challoner died a few months later, on 12th January 1781. He was buried in the parish church in Milton with the blessing of the Anglican rector, who described him as 'a very pious and good man, of great learning and extensive abilities'.[5] On 1st May 1946, his remains were translated to Westminster Cathedral to the Chapel of St. Gregory and St. Augustine. Cardinal Basil Hume, who promoted the cause for his beatification, now lies close by him, in the same chapel.

The Cardinal once said that Bishop Challoner's gift as a superb administrator was perhaps even more important for the

Church than the earlier witness of the martyrs. The bishop is remembered also for his tireless pastoral work, visiting both the greatest and the humblest Catholic families in his ten counties, but happiest when he was ministering to the poor in London, in hospitals, prisons and in the crowded alleys where they lived; his almsgiving was proverbial. He sustained his people not only with the sacraments and with his preaching but also by his writings; his catechism and much-loved prayer book, *The Garden of the Soul*, are said to have found their way into almost every Catholic house in the country. We have as yet only one slight thread of evidence of his ministry in Dartford and that of his priests, but if there were still a few Catholics surviving here to the time of the First Relief Act it seems probable that they will have been joined by others when the persecution came to an end. We should be proud to remember him as our bishop.

The Second Relief Act, in 1791, granted freedom of worship to licenced public churches.[6] With Catholic Emancipation in 1829, authorisation was no longer required, and many of the grievous civil disabilities that Catholics suffered were removed. They were still not allowed to teach, so that priests could not be educated in Britain. The Act looked forward to the 'gradual suppression and final prohibition' of all religious Societies, Orders and Communities, and the early Catholic directories say little of the presence of monks, friars, or nuns. Any who entered the realm must register.

A proclamation issued by Queen Victoria in June 1852 shows that the suspicion had not disappeared. Any 'Roman Catholic Ecclesiastic' taking part in a religious procession or wearing the habit of a religious order, or ceremonial dress, in the street would be regarded as a danger to the peace and security of the Queen's dominions and punished accordingly.[7]

Chapter 3

Capuchin Mission

When the First Relief Act was passed, Bishop Challoner had commented quietly to his friends, 'There will be a new people.' Irish Catholics seeking work in England were already bringing new life to the Church. In 1829, there were 20,000 in the neighbourhood of St. George's in Southwark, and over the next generation moving appeals were made for help in the work of the priests, who were few but indefatigable. The 'angel guardians' of the thousands of Catholics who could not be accommodated for Mass in the little chapel at Webb Street in Southwark 'turn imploringly', the Directory tells us, to well-wishers, 'and ask from your jewellery, your rich viands, your amusements, wherewith ground may be purchased, a church, with convent and schools, erected – souls fitted for heaven.'

Nearer home, 'many Catholics' were reported to be living within reach of the house of Augustine Applegarth in Crayford, where from 1840 Mass was said once a month by Father Nightingale. We may believe that Dartford Catholics were among them: people would happily walk further to Mass at that time. When St. Mary of the Crays opened in Crayford in 1842, the congregation was described in another appeal as 'scattered'.

An extremely hostile letter to the *Maidstone Journal* in 1851 stated that there were 100 Catholics living in Dartford.[1] That year, a local newspaper reported, in friendly terms, that a Franciscan 'monk' from Piedmont, said to be living in Northfleet and engaged on a dictionary, Father Maurice of the Order of Capuchins, had opened a mission station on East Hill, at St. Ronan's, a terrace of early Victorian cottages built on the site of the old Roman cemetery and overlooking Darenth Road. A number of Irish families lived there.[2]

The Capuchins are a branch of the great family of Friars Minor, who live a life of poverty and self-sacrifice in the footsteps of their founder, St. Francis of Assisi. Englishmen have always been 'drawn under the spell of St. Francis' simple evangelical way of life, embraced by him in imitation of the Poor Christ on earth.'[3] Since Blessed Agnellus of Pisa first arrived in Dover in 1224 with his 'little band of beggars' (three of whom were English), there had nearly always been a strong Franciscan presence in England until the end of the eighteenth century, the friars in penal times facing imprisonment and in some cases death for their faith. There were always Capuchins among them until 1802, when Father Arthur O'Leary died. He was an Irish missioner, who had built the original St. Patrick's Church in Soho Square. There are few, if any, records of Capuchins in England for the next fifty years.

Dartford had for long been notorious for anti-Catholic outbursts of the extreme kind known as 'Kentish fire'. The Restoration of the Catholic Hierarchy in 1850 was greeted with organized abuse and a noisy procession to the Brent, where effigies of Pope Pius IX and Cardinal Wiseman were burnt.[4] As a more lasting protest, following an impassioned local campaign which was backed up by an appeal in the national press, the first memorial to Christopher Waid, intended to be as impressive as the Martyrs' Memorial at Oxford, was erected on high ground at St. Edmund's. It was unveiled in 1851, to increasing recriminations against Catholics.[5]

Father Maurice was one of the first Capuchins, perhaps the very first, to come to England after Catholic Emancipation. He was from Cossato, a town in the foothills of the Alps, some sixty miles from Turin, towards Lake Orta. It is in the Diocese of Biella and today it has four parishes.

Fra Pier Maurizio, whose secular name was Giuseppe Antonio Aguggia, was born on 1st January 1815, the son of Gian Maria Aguggia and his wife Caterina née Demargarita. He received the Capuchin habit on October 20th 1835 in Turin at the Friary of Madonna di Campagna and was professed there as a friar on October 20th the following year. He studied for the priesthood at Moncalieri under Fra Guglielmo dalla Piovà, who afterwards became a great missionary bishop among the Gallas people of Ethiopia. Father Maurice, as Fra Pier Maurizio is for us, was ordained priest on June 9th 1838 in Turin and was authorised to hear confessions while he continued studying Philosophy and Theology for the next four years. In September 1842 he completed his course and was allowed to preach. He spent a year at the Friary of Villafranca Piemonte and in September 1843 he left for the French Province of the Capuchins.

We know that in 1846 he received an 'obedience' from the Capuchin Minister General. Perhaps this means that it was then that he was chosen for the English Mission. In the 1850s, while already in England, he published two books in France, the first, which is polemical, claiming to be the work of 'a locksmith on retreat'. The second *Petit Jardin Eucharstique*, is devotional; he gave a copy of it to a lady in Swanscombe who was receiving instruction.[6]

St. Ronan's is not mentioned in Directories. In 1853, Father Maurice was chaplain to the Sisters of the Christian Retreat when they moved to Manor House, Kennington, from Peckham. He was not invited to join another Capuchin, also from Piedmont, in setting up a friary in Peckham – the first in England since the Reformation – on the grounds that Father Maurice was subject to different Superiors. In 1857, he was in Peckham as chaplain to the Sisters at Nazareth House. It is possible that he returned to France the following year. In 1860, he was in Wales, at Pantasaph, the mother house of the Capuchins of the English and Welsh Mission. In 1861, at the invitation of Father O'Sullivan he went to live at Gravesend, to care for a recently opened mission on Galley Hill, Swanscombe.

The Galley Hill Chapel, which served 250 humble Catholics, was only 'a small room fitted up for the celebration of Mass', but it had aroused national interest because of a supposed Carmelite connection. In the thirteenth century, the Carmelites, a small community of hermits living on Mount Carmel, had been forced by Moslem attacks to seek safer places to live. They came eventually to England, some to Aylesford, and in 1247 St. Simon Stock, a Kentishman, was elected the first Prior General of the White Friars, as they were known. He is said to have had a vision of Our Lady, who touched his scapular and promised her protection to whoever wore one, and there was a tradition that he had seen the vision in the neighbourhood of Greenhithe and Swanscombe. Thomas Walmesley, a prominent Catholic who had a deep longing for the love of Mary to be revived in the country once called her Dowry, became the benefactor and supporter of the Galley Hill mission and later supported the church in Greenhithe. He had hopes at one time of establishing the White Friars nearby. So the chapel, and later the church, were dedicated to Our Lady of Mount Carmel.[7]

Cambridge was later thought to have a claim to have been the place where St. Simon had the vision, and, in the event, when the Discalced Carmelites returned to England in 1862 it was in Kensington that they opened their first house. Even so, Father O'Sullivan convinced Cardinal Wiseman that it had taken place here, at Galley Hill.

The chapel had been opened in 1860 by Father Driscoll, who had since left Gravesend, and whose death by drowning off the coast of Queensland was a very sad loss to the Church. In May 1861, Father Morris began saying Mass at the chapel. Galley Hill at that time was in the country, 'fresh as a rose' to the eyes of a tourist, he tells us, its woods and fertile fields reflected in the tranquil waters of the Thames. Many of his congregation were Irish immigrants working at the cement factory and struggling for a living. Their lives were far from idyllic. His first success was in persuading them not to get involved when pub fights broke out over religion, as happened frequently. At first they thought he had joined forces with their persecutors but they remained loyal to him as their priest. He made his presbytery in part of the house where the chapel and school were, and moved in later in the year, with the authorisation of his Superiors.

He had first asked the congregation if they would help him They were pleased that he wanted to live among them and share their poverty, and they promised to do so. He made vouchers for one pound loaves and asked them to take turns to sign them so that he could present them at the baker's and they would pay. The chapel was so crowded that people were touching him during Mass and the little children, only half clad, would make their way up to him and fall asleep lying on his feet, so that he had to be careful how he moved.

His contacts grew. He loved children and they loved him, which helped him in getting to know their parents. He put up notices offering to teach Italian and French for a small fee (or free of charge), which also helped him in making contacts and (sometimes) in making ends meet.

The foreigner with the long beard must have been a conspicuous figure. Out of doors he dressed as an English gentleman, wearing his habit only in church or at home – something unknown on Galley Hill for centuries. Appearing in it in his (back) garden brought him undesired attention and catcalls: an orgy of curiosity. He was advised to stay indoors on November 5th. (They had nicknamed him Guy Fawkes.) He was philosphical about the abuse; the children knocking at his door for tuppence for a beer for the pope (on their bonfires) one day were asking him for pictures, crosses, and rosaries the next, the gift of his benefactors in France. Something he found much more painful was the vicar's refusal even to let him into the cemetery for funerals of his parishioners. The vicar had the law on his side at that time and could claim the fee – he even called the police to prevent Father Maurice saying any prayers at the graveside. He also disliked being accused of having Fenian sympathies. He had great hopes of the English but did not find them tolerant.

He made it his study never to retaliate or engage in religious arguments but always to win people's affection, and he soon found that they trusted him. He said it was also the way of English priests, and their strength.

The tradition that Our Lady had appeared to St. Simon Stock at the foot of Galley Hill and had there made her promise meant much to him and comforted him in his difficulties. There was a spring near the cement works known to non-Catholics as Lady's Fount, and to Catholics as Our Lady's Fount. Its waters were said to be unpolluted and safe to drink at all seasons. He wanted to build a shrine to Our Lady and to invite wearers of the Carmelite scapular across the world to contribute a few pence each, and so make it a gift to England.

In 1863, the tiny chapel closed and Father Maurice and his congregation moved to Greenhithe, where, helped by an appeal that Father O'Sullivan made in *The Tablet*, he had secured a group of three small cottages, which were made into a church, a school , and his presbytery. He celebrated his first Mass there on Christmas Day, 1863, 'in very great poverty and sickness', he writes in the baptismal register, but with very great gratitude to God, 'who uses the most worthless for his most sublime purposes'. He signs the Latin entry, touchingly, 'Fr. Petrus Mauritius a Cossato, ordinis capuccinorum'.[8]

Father Coleburt knew of a tradition that before St. Anselm's opened Mass was said in Dartford at the Gateway, near the railway station, in one of the two thatched cottages just behind the entrance to the present Glaxo-Wellcome buildings, which were certainly still standing early this century. It would have been more central than St. Ronan's. Father Maurice writes that on the first visit he made to Dartford from Our Lady of Mount Carmel he asked the ticket collector at the station how to get to the Catholic church and was told the nearest one was in Crayford. He had come to 'render some services' to various people. He may have been looking for someone at the Gateway. Was it perhaps served from Crayford at that time?

On coming to Greenhithe he had immediately begun looking for a property in Dartford for a daughter church. He said he had made over a hundred enquiries, but as soon as he mentioned his plans for a Catholic chapel he was invariably shown out. A gentleman who had conducted the negotiations for the purchase at Greenhithe came to the rescue in Dartford, too, avoiding any reference to a church.

Father Maurice knew of five hundred baptised Catholics in Dartford at that time, very few of whom were Mass goers. He was certainly working among them again. The Mission at St. Ronan's had not been allowed to die out.

Eventually, on September 15th 1865, the Feast of Our Lady of Sorrows, George Arnold of Gravesend (who, incidentally, was also a very generous benefactor of Westminster Cathedral) purchased for the Diocese a group of houses in Hythe Street to be used as a church and a school. (Franciscans own no property.) The price was £600.[9] Father Maurice began saying Mass there before Christmas. On January 20th Dartford experienced its worst floods for fifty years. The Cranford at that time was an open stream flowing through Hythe Street, which was also known as the Waterside. A fire had to be kept burning for several weeks before the 'damp inconvenient room' that was Father Maurice's first chapel here was fit to receive Bishop Grant.[10]

The bishop chose for its patron an earlier 'learned monk from Piedmont' (as the local newspaper had described Father Maurice in 1851) when he officially opened the first St. Anselm's at 'half past eleven a.m.' on Thursday, March 8th, 1866.[11]

It was within a few yards of the old Dominican Priory, on land that had perhaps once belonged to it, that the humble

Franciscan Mission thus put down its roots, exactly three centuries after the death of Father Richard Hargrave.

Perhaps it was fortunate that Father Maurice was still living in Greenhithe. The reputation of Dartford had sunk low, and the prejudice and hostility he encountered were exceptional even for those days. Meetings were held to try to force him out but he had every claim to the church and land. Later, he tried to forget the humiliations and annoyances of those first months. Father O'Sullivan stood by him and he overcame the strong temptation to leave.

In mid-February a school had opened beside the chapel. Miss Nicholas, the governess, had previously opened a school in Northfleet. She was offered eleven shillings (55p) a week and a house (beside the chapel), and was expected to add to her income by means of evening classes, music lessons, and private tuition. She was required to set up a choir at St. Anselm's and play the harmonium at Father Maurice's two churches on Sundays. The choir, which is still flourishing today, probably sang for the first time on Easter Sunday, March 25th.

A young girl was paid three shillings a week to assist with teaching sewing to the girls at the school. The children's weekly pennies and the Sunday collections together did not cover these costs and Father Maurice asked the bishop for help from the Poor Schools Committee.

The little chapel was eventually furnished with a very good wooden altar. Archbishop Amigo stated in 1918 that it was 'brought by the Capuchins, probably from Italy', though it has since been suggested that it is Flemish. It was later moved to Father Buckley's church and then to Spital Street, for the Sacred Heart chapel. The carved oak frontal, representing the Eucharist surrounded by angels, has now been incorporated into the marble altar in our present church. Father Maurice had no tabernacle in Dartford. Later, a gentleman of Tunbridge Wells, Mr. B. M. Zuluetta, presented the Mission with the

Stations of the Cross and through the good offices of Mr. Edward W. Tordiffe of Dartford they were put in the chapel on Rosary Sunday.

Edward Tordiffe was a young man who lived in Highfield Road and worked at the London and County Bank in Dartford. He was a convert, a devout Catholic who gave half his yearly income (£160) to support Father Maurice's charitable work among the poor and the sick and to help with the expenses of the church, and the school and house. He started a subscription fund for an extension to the chapel and he shared in Father Maurice's dream of inviting the Sisters of St. Vincent de Paul to Dartford – a dream that was never realised. He was apparently the only person of means in an extremely poor mission. His name appears frequently as sponsor at baptisms; Father Maurice wrote warmly of the support he gave him.

Father Maurice had many friends in France. He wished to help Edward Tordiffe who was making such sacrifices but he wrote that he was so poor that St. Francis would not refuse to recognize him as one of his children. His friend Count Emmanuel du Haïs, and his 'noble wife' had twice visited him at Greenhithe and had been moved at the sight of the poor little church and given him generous assisstance. Ladies working for the missions in Paris gave a monstrance, others in Arras a chasuble. Benedictine nuns in Orleans supplied gifts for the repository. Franciscan Tertiaries in Paris gave a cope, and he was especially touched when the Poor Clares in Amiens sent generous gifts including altar linen and a chalice, 'finding in their poverty', he writes, 'the means of relieving mine'.

So, somehow, the Mission survived. Repairing the roof at Greenhithe and putting up shutters to protect the windows at Dartford meant asking the bishop to help find the £9. Some Catholic families would not send their children to school (education became compulsory only in the 1870s) but Father Maurice insisted, unconventionally, on accepting non-Catholics as they helped 'pull down the deadly prejudices against us'. He sought a Catholic home for a blind boy and his blind father who were both in the workhouse. In January 1867, in spite of difficulties, he wrote to Bishop Grant, in a shaky hand: 'You said sometimes that you were satisfied with Greenhithe. It is more than I can say but Dartford will be one of the best jewels in your administrative crown. Don't be worried for some sacrifices you have done or will do. One day you will be very glad of the new foundation.'

In February he was asking the bishop's permission, 'if I am alive . . . to have a trip over France', to raise money for his 'church or churches . . . I think I must do so if I will have something suitable for Dartford at least.'[12]

People were becoming much nicer. They noted that the children at his school, Catholics and Protestants, were behaving better. Non-Catholic children were asking to make their first Holy Communion at his church; he was very careful to ensure that they did not hurt their parents' feelings. In July 1869 he again showed his confidence in Dartford when he wrote for the *Franciscan Annals*, 'God in his mercy deigned to bless this mission. It produced fruits of salvation that were truly woderful.' He described the school as 'magnificent . . . attended by more than eighty children, of whom at least half belong to Protestant parents.'

He really loved the people for whom he laboured so tirelessly. Many of the Irish immigrants might, understandably, have fallen away over the years and become quarrelsome and even violent, but he said that they still had an underlying self-respect and faith. There were also many, as he had seen in Peckham as well as in this area, who 'would forever be the admiration of earth and heaven' on account of their faithfulness and enormous efforts for the Church. He believed it was by the dispensation of Providence that the flood of emigration from Ireland to the United States and Australia was enabling Catholicism to become established there, and that the same was true of Britain. His thoughts were in line with Bishop Challoner's on this 'new people'. Similarly, he had suffered from English intolerance but he loved English people too for their kind hearts – their 'very kind hearts' – and hoped that God would be gracious to them. He quoted Pius IX as saying that the English Mission was the least of his worries as God himself was at work among the English. He even wrote in the *Annals*, 'If God comes to our aid, Dartford will soon be a Catholic town.'

One purpose of his visit to France was to find a teacher. He was known as an educationist and he had been approached by a group of about thirty factory workers in Erith and asked to set up a school there for their children. They obtained a room and he said he would help them if they could guarantee the teacher's wages. When the school opened he began saying Mass there twice a week and thus it was also the opening of a new Mission. Erith first appears in the Directory the following year, 1868.

Some of his group of supporters were seeking to strengthen their own faith and allegiance to the Gospel by following the example of St. Francis. They had been meeting together unofficially and they asked Father Maurice to say Mass for them in the small house in Cross Street, Erith, where the teacher lived. The Mass seems to have set the seal on their wish to become Franciscans. The first Tertiary Fraternity in Kent was established in Greenhithe, at the friary, in 1871, and served the whole neighbourhood including Dartford. It was not until 1876 that a second Fraternity was officially established by Father Cherubino in Erith, where the friars were then living, although it is listed in the 1872 Directory.[13]

The Third Franciscan Order, open to all, was founded by Francis himself nearly eight centuries ago. St. Elizabeth of Hungary, St. Thomas More, St. Vincent de Paul, Dante, Christopher Columbus, Michelangelo, and every Pope this century except John Paul II (who is a Carmelite Tertiary) are numbered among its members. But worldwide there are millions of Secular Franciscans, as they are now called, and most, of course, are ordinary, everyday folk trying to be better Christians. They include several members of St. Anselm's. The Erith Fraternity of the S.F.O. is the oldest lay institution in the area.

So, in 1868 we find Father Maurice working in Greenhithe, Northfleet, Dartford, and Erith, where the first recorded baptism took place on January 30th. That year he began to be helped by Father William.

'You cannot imagine how the Fathers work,' is the comment of Henry Bourne, the father of Cardinal Francis Bourne, who brought his family to live in Greenhithe in March 1868. 'Young Frank', then nearly seven, was an altar server at Our Lady of Mount Carmel during the next two years. A letter from Henry to his elder son describes the material poverty and spiritual zeal of the friars. Of the poverty he writes, 'Nobody who is not here can realize what it is; the church itself merely a tumbledown cottage, the vestments beyond repair.' But he rejoiced that after a silence of 300 years the Catholic liturgy for Holy Week had returned to Greenhithe. 'We have had Tenebrae and the Maundy Thursday and Good Friday Offices done as our extreme poverty would admit.' Saying Mass at St. Anselm's must have been only a small part of the friars' obligations. Henry Bourne admired them not only as priests but as men, and enjoyed their company. 'When they came to his table,' the Cardinal's biographer tells us, 'the conversation was in English, French, and Italian, with threats to little Frank that Father Maurice would soon take him in hand for Latin.'[14]

In 1869, after eight years in Greenhithe, during seven of which he had been on his own, he was forced to leave. His presbytery had by now become a monastery, with a Superior, three Capuchin Fathers, and a Brother. He hoped that other men would see the need for labourers in the Lord's vineyard: there was so much to be done. He trusted, too, that Our Lady of Mount Carmel would continue to watch over his missions and that she would one day provide a shrine nearby (a dream that was eventually realised at Aylesford), where her help would be invoked by 'this people whom she loves and whom I have loved after her and who have not been indifferent to my affection'.

He tells us, 'I have never experienced any sorrow so great as that of my separation from my dear missions in the county of Kent, but the good God wishes it to be so: in this, may he be blessed for ever!'

Between 1867 and 1870 he wrote a series of articles on the English Mission for the *Franciscan Annals*, on which much of this account has been based. They are simple, outspoken, direct, and witty, and give some glimpses of the sacrifices his work entailed. During the same period he issued in instalments *A Homely Life of St. Francis*, which he had translated from the French.

He went from Greenhithe to Chester and then to Pantasaph. In 1870 he received permission to return to Piedmont to visit a nephew. That year, the *Homely Life* was published in book form, signed and dated from Chester. The Introduction makes sad reading. Within his Order he had encountered enormous opposition. He said that the only real cost was that it had broken his heart. There were many problems in the Church and among the friars at that time because the bishops were letting in priests from France and Belgium who were all wanting their own way. In 1872, now in Dublin, he requested permission to live alone in a house and in February 1873 he became a secular priest in Ireland. Even so, he is probably the 'Maurice, Rev. Fr., cap' listed in the Irish Directory in the later 1870s.

In 1884, Bishop Guglielmo Massaia, the Fra Guglielmo of Piovà who had once been his Lector, was made a Cardinal, and Father Maurice published a short work in praise of his 'greatly loved' teacher, written, he says, by 'the least of his pupils'. It contains a poem in Latin and a sonnet.[6] It was printed in Turin. Perhaps Father Maurice had returned to Madonna di Campagna; he was approaching seventy.

We may one day learn the story of the last years of the priest who founded St. Anselm's and the churches in Greenhithe, Northfleet, and Erith. Father Maurice had never spared himself. No sacrifice had been too great in his struggle to 'rebuild God's Church' in the spirit of St. Francis. He was one of 'The Saints who toiled from place to place, Spreading the Gospel of God's grace'. We may trust that in his heavenly homeland he still intercedes for us all. In Dartford he is remembered particularly in the Copperfields Oratory, which is on the site of his chapel.

In 1869, Bishop Grant had confided the North Kent, or Thames, Mission, which included St. Anselm's, to the Capuchins. Their friary moved temporarily from Greenhithe to Northfleet and later to Erith, where their greatest benefactor, James de Lacy Towle, was most concerned to find that they were living in conditions that were just too primitive – and would not rest until they had a home. The first resident friar in Erith lived in a shed beside the church while it was being built, and later the friars paid an exorbitant rent for a flat. The Capuchin Provincial Curia or Office for England, Scotland and Wales was established in Erith while Father Louis Pellecetti was Provincial. It returned there in 1969 and Erith is now the settled centre of the Order in Great Britain.

St. Anselm's came under the care successively of Father Louis Pellecetti of Castelferretti, Father Anthony Sansone of Montelupone, and Father Liborius Contigiani of Urbisaglia. During the Franciscan period there was, of course, no resident priest in Dartford: St. Anselm's was served from the friary.

True to their missionary vocation, Capuchins of the English Province were already setting out for India. St. Anselm's, no longer seen as missionary territory in the strict sense, was handed over to diocesan priests in 1882. The last friar to leave was Father Angelo and a letter from Father Modestus in Pantasaph to Bishop Coffin in December that year explains the difficulty and asks when he will be able to return to Chester. 'We are very short of Fathers at present,' he tells the bishop, 'as since I last saw your Lordship, three have received their obediences to go to India.'[15]

St. Anselm's has never completely lost touch with the Capuchins. Until quite recently, friars came to say Mass when priests were ill or on holiday, and there are still many friendly contacts with Our Lady of the Angels.

Meanwhile, the Presentation Brothers had come to Dartford. Their Congregation had been founded in Waterford in 1802 by Edmund Rice, a prosperous businessman whose young wife had died after giving birth to a premature and handicapped daughter. He referred later to his loss as 'the dregs of misery and misfortune', but the tragedy had deepened his sympathy for the needy, especially for the poor and disadvantaged children of Waterford, and he realized that God was calling him to devote his life and wealth to their care and education. Soon the Presentation Brothers and the Christian Brothers, the two Congregations he founded, had opened schools all over Ireland.[16]

In 1875, a Presentation Brother from Cork, who was returning from extended sick leave in Belgium, met Father Sylvester Donnelly and visited an Industrial School that he had opened on Bishop Danell's behalf on Tanner's Hill, Deptford. It was for children in need of care and protection who had been through the courts for minor offences. Begging in those days was an offence. Brother Augustine showed such interest in the school that his Congregation was invited to take it over and he was asked to take charge. (One of Blessed Edmund Rice's favourite sayings was, 'Providence is our heritage'.) In 1878, the School, now named St. Vincent's, moved to spacious grounds on Temple Hill, Dartford's most northerly and exposed hill, that looked across bleak farmland and marshes towards the Thames.[17]

There were loud protests against 'the establishment of popery on the hill',[18] but St. Vincent's grew and a chapel was later built, which became a Mass Centre for the newer part of the town. St. Vincent's was for long a model of its kind, 'an exceptionally high-class school' in the eyes of the Home Office, and it attracted official visitors from abroad. It also became the parent foundation of the Presentation Order in England and from it Brothers went out over the next century to found missions across the world: to Ghana, the West Indies, Canada, Peru, and other far distant places.

In 1879, one of the first Ursuline Convents, if not the first, to come to the Diocese of Southwark was established at 23 Tower Road, in a house that is still standing. The Ursuline Institute was founded by St. Angela Merici in Brescia in 1535, originally with the purpose of educating poor girls as Christians. She was a Franciscan Tertiary and her Institute had Franciscan ideals. The Sisters are believed to have opened a little school at the Convent in Tower Road before moving to West Hill, a few steps away. A flourishing shoot sprang from this humble beginning, which eventually gave St. Anselm's Parish both Our Lady's Primary School and the Coleburt and Coldart Centres.

Chapter 4

Diocesan Mission

After the Franciscans left, St. Anselm's became a separate mission. There was a caretaker period, looked after first by Father Peter Kernan and later by Father C. de Latte. In the autumn of 1884, Father Edmund Buckley was appointed Rector.

Born in 1853, Father Buckley had been ordained in 1880. He was a Southwark diocesan priest, although he was from Middlesex, and had studied for the priesthood at Hammersmith.

Dartford now had a population of 10,000, double that of 1850, with three hundred Catholics. An extension costing £48 had been built to the 'damp, inconvenient room' that served as the church, but it still 'barely accommodated sixty people'. As Father Buckley was the first resident priest of the mission, there was as yet no presbytery and he lived at 7 Midland Villas in St. Alban's Road, a fair walk from the church.[1]

In his three years in Dartford, the school and church were rebuilt and a presbytery erected in Hythe Street. The second St. Anselm's – the first to be purpose-built – stood further back from the road, about where the *Squirrels* café is now, and remained in use long after it ceased to be a church. The builder of the new presbytery boasted in Dartford of the £300 profit he had made on it.[2]

The twenty-first annual report of St. Anselm's School (1886 to 1887) is confident and optimistic. Under Miss Dempsey, the energetic headteacher, numbers had risen from forty to eighty-six, and the new school, alone among the schools of Dartford, had obtained the 'Excellent Merit Grant'. We learn that the Sisters of St. Ursula, 'who have recently established themselves in Dartford', now had charge of the Infants: later they ran both schools. Father Buckley offered a weekly Mass for the benefactors of the mission. He concluded, 'There can be no work more dear to the Sacred Heart of our Divine Lord than the Christian Education of our children.'[3]

In 1888, the Sisters moved to their Convent at the top of West Hill, a homely, welcoming house on the corner of the present King Edward Avenue. St. Ursula's, now first listed in the Directory, attracted a high proportion of non-Catholic children. It is still remembered affectionately by ladies in Dartford who were pupils there before the Sisters left in 1923.

For Father Buckley adult education also was a priority. In 1887, the year of Queen Victoria's Golden Jubilee, everyone in the town, including the schoolchildren, was called on for a contribution for the new Martyr's Memorial, needed to replace the 1851 Memorial, which had been built of a soft stone and was by now crumbling. A barrage of anti-Catholic speeches was given great prominence in local newspapers. But they also reported in detail a series of Sunday evening lectures given by Father Buckley in the new church, in which he offered a vigorous and lucid exposition of Catholic doctrines that had been lampooned from other pulpits. He invited Protestants in the packed congregations to meet him and discuss their differences openly.

When the new Memorial to Christopher Waid and two other Kentish martyrs was unveiled on October 31st 1888, the Rev. A. Sturge, Founder and first Minister of Dartford's first Baptist church, in Highfield Road, who was also Chairman of the School Board, was the one speaker to strike a kindly note. He paid tribute to Sir Thomas More, 'a good Catholic', who, too, had 'suffered martyrdom for the grand principle that kings had no right to impose creeds on their subjects'.[4] It was a friendly, ecumenical gesture.

In the 1880s, the Metropolitan Asylums Board and the City of London opened hospitals in and around Dartford for the mentally ill and handicapped, and for smallpox and fever patients. Smallpox patients were brought, first in 1881, to camps in rural Darenth.

In 1884, two hospital ships, the *Atlas* and the *Castalia*, moored at Long Reach, were opened, river ambulances bringing the sick down the Thames, and the camps were then used for convalescence.[5]

During the very severe smallpox epidemic that year, there were constant calls to the ships. A supply priest, Father Wehn, who came to help in July when the epidemic was diminishing, described the bleak life of the camps. 'The wind is blowing very much and it is in the tents much like on board a ship.' A German patient overcome by the unhoped-for consolation of Mass, had sobbed continuously. Father Wehn visited the ships daily, ministering to the Catholic patients and staff. In the camps, there was a daily celebration of Mass, and Rosary and 'a little instruction in the evening'.[6]

Since coming to Dartford, in addition to serving St. Anselm's and St. Vincent's, Father Buckley had been visiting the City of London Asylum at Stone, the Metropolitan District Asylum and Schools at Darenth, the *Atlas* and *Castalia* at Long Reach, the Smallpox Convalescent Camps at Darenth, and the Dartford Union Workhouse on West Hill – without any help. In January 1886, he wrote to Bishop Butt, who had decided to send an assistant priest, that he 'always had the fear that a stronger man could do all the work' but that he had 'broken down almost entirely with the lungs – the exposure does not suit me'.[7] The mission was still extremely poor, collections averaging about five shillings (25p) a week, but it was growing. Father Thomas McMahon joined Father Buckley later that year. When Father Buckley left – eventually for Bermondsey – at the end of 1887, himself financially impoverished but with a wonderful record of achievement for so short a time, he would have been pleased to read the comment of Father Robert Collinson, his successor, that 'everything looked very well, except' (perennially, of course) 'the finances.'[8]

The new Rector's first impression was that Dartford was 'a very promising mission. There were about 40 at Holy Communion yesterday and both services on Sunday fill well; in the evening there are always a good many Protestants. The school seems flourishing. There are about 100 names on the books, and last week we had 83, which considering the state of the roads is a very creditable number.'

Problems arose when in a few years the school buildings were again condemned and the church, now much too small, looked dreary and dilapidated.

The scourge of smallpox continued and there were periods when Father Collinson's day had to be fitted round visits to the ships. 1892 was the worst year in their history and in 1893, his last year in Dartford, he wrote, 'It is hardly safe to absent myself for half a day during the epidemic as the trap from the ships comes to me rather frequently, and the cases have to be attended to at once.'[9]

The situation had not changed when Father Charles Turner took over later that year. He adds a wry comment, writing in October 1894, 'If Providence did not send us a sick call to the ships on Saturday night, I could not meet Monday morning's bills.' By January 1895 the financial situation was truly desperate. 'There is but sevenpence halfpenny in the bank,' he announces, while he owes '£6 for coals, bought in the Summer, £8 for candles for church, about £5 to various tradesmen in the town, and the clothes I am wearing are not yet paid for.'[10] The teachers and the housekeeper had to be paid. There were the seven hospitals to be visited, as well as the schools, which now included the Darenth Asylum School. The priests were saying Mass for the Brothers at St. Vincent's and for the Sisters at St. Ursula's. They struggled on.

Father John Wallace, Father Turner's successor, was faced with an urgent need to build a new school and a church which would accommodate '300 at least, if not 400'. The school, on the

Hythe Street site, was completed in 1899. Already in 1892, on the advice of Edward Fooks, a site in Spital Street had been purchased for the church for £2,530. Mr. Fooks' grandfather had once had a house there but the site was now occupied by the post office, two shops, and stables. Not until August 1899 could Mr. Welch be persuaded to give up his tenancy of the post office.[11]

The church cost £2,000 and was the gift of Edward Fooks. He wrote that he had only one desire in offering it, 'the glory of God and the salvation of souls'. The foundation stone, brought to our present church in 1974, was laid by Bishop (afterwards Cardinal) Francis Bourne on February 24th 1900. The architect was F.A. Walters, who designed St. John's Seminary, Wonersh, with its Chapel of the Sacred Heart, and Buckfast Abbey. (The then Father Bourne had been the first Rector of Wonersh.) St. Anselm's was built of red brick and neo-gothic in style. It stood opposite the present Copperfields shopping precinct on a site now covered by the Priory Shopping Centre. There was a large garden behind, where the new presbytery was later built. Father Wallace lived in Essex Road.

He blessed the church on Saturday, December 8th, 1900, in the evening, the Feast of the Immaculate Conception. The next day, the first Solemn High Mass was celebrated in the presence of Bishop Bourne, with Canon Murnane preaching the sermon. Afterwards, Mr. Fooks entertained the bishop and clergy to lunch.[12]

Edward Fooks had two sons who became priests for Southwark. Each year at St. Anselm's, a Foundation Mass is said for him and for his family. His little church in the heart of the town, although it soon became so crowded and uncomfortable (it seated only 185), was much loved, and it served three generations of Catholics.

During the opening years of the twentieth century, it could be said that smallpox in London, after a fierce struggle, was largely defeated in the hospitals of the Metropolitan Asylums Board in Dartford. The terrible epidemic of 1902 was too great for the ships to cope with. Long Reach Hospital was built and replaced them before the epidemic finally petered out. In that year, 802 victims were buried in nine months at the newly opened Joyce Green Cemetery. The disease spared neither young nor old; some whole families were wiped out.[13] Although only a small proportion of the sick were Catholics, the demands on the priests were heavy and constant, and their presence will surely have brought comfort to everyone in the wards.

Later that year, Father Wallace left Dartford. Father John Moynihan came for two years, then Father William Thompson from 1904 to 1906. He was followed by Father James Mahoney, who remained until 1916.

In 1903, Bishop Francis Bourne left Southwark to become Cardinal Archbishop of Westminster. One of his last acts before his departure was to appoint the Sisters of Mercy to assist at Our Lady of Mount Carmel in Greenhithe, the village where his family had lived for a brief period until the death of his father in 1870. The Sisters were warmly welcomed and the congregation increased rapidly after their arrival.[14]

Greenhithe had had a new church in 1875. It had been served from Northfleet and then for a few years from Walworth where the future Bishop Peter Amigo was priest. It was entrusted to St. Anselm's in 1906, remaining with us until 1937, when it returned to Northfleet parish. Father Mahoney was impressed by the genuineness of the people at Greenhithe, remarking that 'A deaf and dumb man could get on famously with them'.[15] The church has not survived. The foundations gave way and it had to be demolished, but it is still spoken of nostalgically as a peaceful and prayerful church in a village that had once been very pretty and full of character but suffered much blight over a long period from the pollution of cement works. Greenhithe is now reviving, though greatly changed.

Father Mahoney was keen to improve the liturgy at St. Anselm's. He encouraged the choir and obtained an organ. 'The people are very nice,' he writes, 'and quite good at church going so far . . . Dartford seems to agree with my curates and both are going great guns. They are both very good and earnest men, which is a blessing for their poor rector!!!'[16]

In the four tragic years of the First World War, St. Anselm's mourned the loss of members of its congregation on active service. A number of Belgian refugees who had arrived in Dartford met with friendship and support in the parish. The ten o'clock Mass on Sundays was first put on for their benefit. Among them was an artist who, in gratitude for the kindness he had experienced, designed and painted new Stations of the Cross for St. Anselm's, which have been preserved in the West Hill church.

The hospitals were largely converted to meet wartime needs. In 1915, in addition to British wounded, there were nearly four hundred wounded prisoners of war at the Lower Southern Hospital. Father Mahoney said Mass for them and brought them the sacraments. His successor, Father Henry Plummer, who came in 1916, had to struggle to learn enough German to minister to the prisoners, and he describes the plight of dying men whose afflictions were compounded by tetanus.[17]

St. John's Jerusalem, Sutton-at-Hone, on the site of the Commandery of the Knights Hospitallers (Knights of the Order of St. John of Jerusalem or Knights of Malta)

Remains of the Chapel of the Knights Hospitallers

*Priory of the Blessed Virgin Mary and St. Margaret, Virgin
(now renamed Manor Gatehouse)*

*Reredos of the Martyrs' Altar, Tyburn Convent, Marble Arch, London
Blessed Sebastian Newdigate is third from right, with hands fettered,
next to Our Lady.*

Statue of Our Lady of Walsingham (Marcel Barbeau, 1954; restored by Siegfried Pietzch, 1987), based on the medieval seal of Walsingham Priory.

Sister Elizabeth Exmew and Sister Elizabeth Seygood took refuge in Walsingham after their first expulsion from Dartford Priory.

Prayer for the Beatification of Richard Challoner

Let us pray:

God Almighty and Eternal,
You made your servant Richard
a true and faithful pastor
of your faithful flock in England.
Raise him, we beseech you,
to the altars of your Church
so that we who have been taught
by his word and example
may invoke his name in heaven
for the return of all people to
belief in the gospel
and to the union of all Christians
as the one Church of Christ.
We make this prayer
through the same
Jesus Christ our Lord. Amen.

1741

Cheme But, gray cir. tr 30 ofrmbs 9.
Petersfield. Hant. Perkins. erctr 60. ofrmbs 31. Jun 10. Car. Tabb. 10
Traiford. Suf. Talbot. entr 16. ofrmbs 4. Jun 14.
Cowdry, 300 imp. ops. infantibs. ofrmbs Jun 14. # 114. &12
Buxton Whitenhall. erctr 90. ofrmbs Jan 17 45.
W. Grinsted Houghton. erctr 150. ofrmbs Jun 15. # 41.
Arundel Berc erctr 90. ofrmbs Jun 21 & 22. 20 & 18.
n B. Horsham ő ofrms nc puen spra 7. Arundel
Slindon Norris erctr 90, ofrmbs 67.
Lady Holt & Compton, Brooks 100 erctr. ofrmbs 50 Jun 28.

[Con Perch erctr 30. Cowdry 170. Buxton Grinsted
100. Arundel 50. Slindon 65. Traiford 10. L. Holt &c 64.
Kirkmanvole 80. Briggs 160. Conies 65. Lane 20. Frankland
Tichborn 101. Sherwell 30. Brambridge erctr 100. Winton
Wormansols, Bonner, 78 ofrmbs Jun 20. Sutton 38 £230
Langston Havard &c Briggs 260 ofrmbs Jun 30 & July, 112
Southend Conies 100. ofrmbs 40. Jul 2. Padwell Lane 30.
ofrmbs 11 Jul 3.
Pannington & Avon. Frankland. erctr 200 ofrmbs Jul 5, 7 (18 9)
Sherwell martin 50 ofrmd Jul 9 erctr 23.
Brambridge Langston & da 233. ofrmbs Jul 10. 80 Jul 13. 2.
Twyford Betts needham 32. ofrmbs Jul 11. 19.
Winton Shaw &c 300. ofrmbs erctr 100. Octob 24, 25, 26
Tichburne Fetherstone, 150 ofrmbs Jul 15, 16. 71.
Sutton place 50. ofrmbs Jul 19 26. Anderson.

Kent July 1742. Lodge 80 ofrmbs 25. Nash
Canterbury &c erctr 30. Calehill 39. ofrmbs 12.
Milgate. Chatham, Whetenhall &c 56. ofrmbs 15.
Farnborough & Boxford 13. Westbrook
Horsewell
Scotney &c erctr 40. ofrmbs 16. Battle
erctr 24 ofrmbs 8.
Weston Bucks supra 200. ofrmbs Sept. 5 & 9 61.
Turvey Beds 35. ofrmbs Sept 6. 25
Chauson & Shefford erctr 20. Woborn.
Buckingham & Salton erctr 80.
Brill & Ickford
Bierton 35. ofrmbs Sept 10. 18.
Beverley & Brinkhurst erctr 90 ofrmbs Sept
12, 19

St. Vincent's School, 1876 – 1982. The Chapel can be seen on the right.

St. Vincent's Church (1982)

Playtime at Our Lady's School

St. Anselm's Church, West Hill (1975), newly restored (1998)

St. George's Church, South Darenth (1986)

Interior of St. George's, South Darenth

Catholic Oratory, 22 Copperfields, the Upper Room above the Hair Shop.

Father John Sandom's Ruby Jubilee Mass at St. Anselm's, May 30th, 1998 (L. to R.): Fr. Augustine Oburota, Fr. John Bluett, Fr. Bill Saunders, Deacon Maurice Williams, Fr. Stan Dye, W.F., Fr. John Sandom, W.F., Fr. Tom Rathe, W.F., Fr. Patrick Fitzgerald, W.F., Deacon Vincent Bowgett, Bishop Francis Walmsley, C.B.E.

A mission station was on Sunday last opened at St. Ronan's, Dartford, Father Maurice, a Piedmontese Franciscan monk, is the missioner in charge of this station. The learned follower of St. Francis is now residing at Northfleet, and is engaged upon a Dictionary. The most appropriate site for the re-introduction of the Old Faith would be in Dartford Priory. Some of the ancient structure still remains, and the gateway is a fine specimen of very late perpendicular brick-work. After the surrender of Dartford Priory by the lady abbess to Henry VIII, the monarch made it into one of his palaces. Dartford has been the scene of many stirring events. A royal daughter of England was one of the professed nuns here. Three weeks ago we saw Sister Anne receive the white veil from Bishop Grant, who was assisted on that occasion by Father Maurice. Sister Anne looked particularly lovely in her bridal dress, and quite fitting to be a spouse of heaven.

Opening of the Franciscan Mission.
From an unknown local newspaper, dated 1851.

St. Ronan's in course of demolition in 1938 (Photo: C. E. Francis)

The Gateway, Mill Pond Road, where Mass was said before 1866

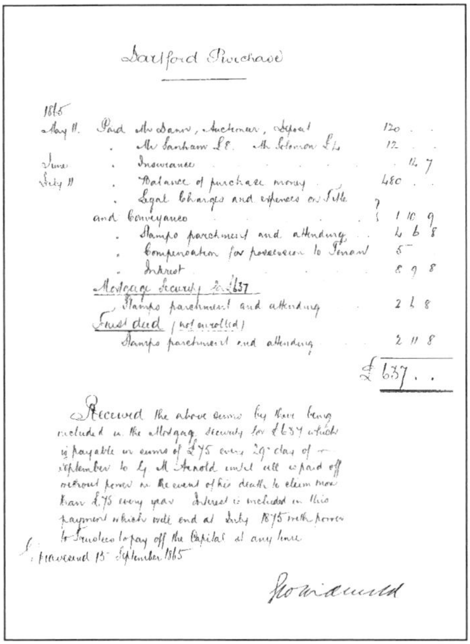

Dartford Purchase

		£ s d
1865		
May 11. Paid Mr Dann, Auctioneer, Deposit		120 . .
" Mr Canham £8. Mr Solomon £4		12 . .
June " Insurance		. 11 7
July 11 " Balance of purchase money		480 . .
" Legal Charges and expences on Title and Conveyance		1 10 9
" Stamps parchment and attending		4 6 8
" Compensation for possession to Tenant		5
" Interest		8 9 8
Mortgage Security for £637		
Stamps parchment and attending		2 6 8
Trust deed (not enrolled)		
Stamps parchment and attending		2 11 8
		£637 . .

Received the above sums by their being included in the Mortgage security for £637 which is payable in sums of £75 every 29th day of September to G. M. Arnold until all is paid off without power in the event of his death to claim more than £75 every year. Interest is included in this payment which will end at July 1875 with power to Trustees to pay off the Capital at any time

Gravesend 15 September 1865

G. M. Arnold

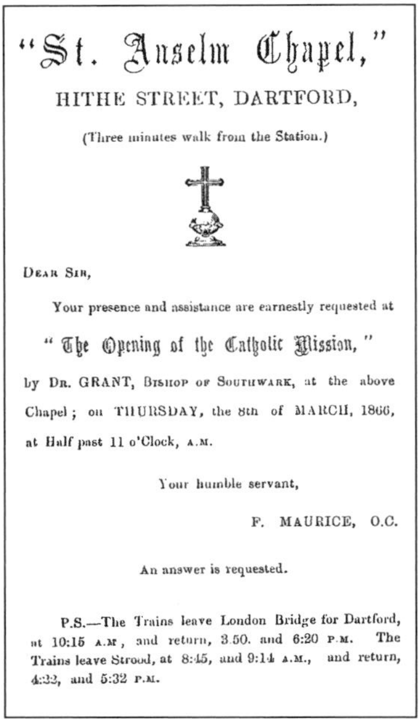

"St. Anselm Chapel,"

HITHE STREET, DARTFORD,

(Three minutes walk from the Station.)

DEAR SIR,

Your presence and assistance are earnestly requested at

" The Opening of the Catholic Mission, "

by DR. GRANT, BISHOP OF SOUTHWARK, at the above Chapel; on THURSDAY, the 8th of MARCH, 1866, at Half past 11 o'Clock, A.M.

Your humble servant,

F. MAURICE, O.C.

An answer is requested.

P.S.—The Trains leave London Bridge for Dartford, at 10:15 A.M., and return, 3.50. and 6:20 P.M. The Trains leave Strood, at 8:45, and 9:14 A.M., and return, 4:32, and 5:32 P.M.

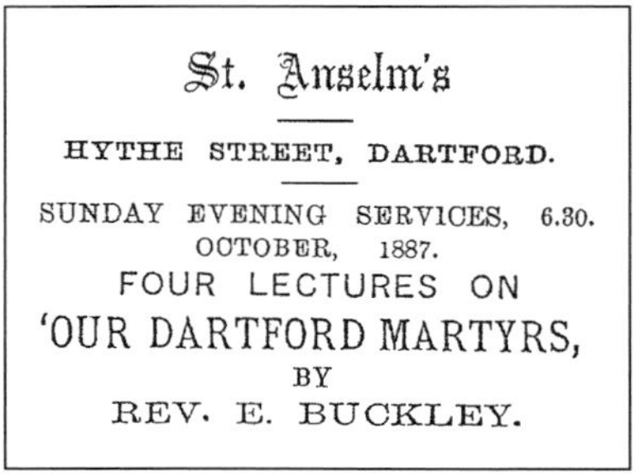

St. Anselm's

HYTHE STREET, DARTFORD.

SUNDAY EVENING SERVICES, 6.30.
OCTOBER, 1887.
FOUR LECTURES ON
'OUR DARTFORD MARTYRS,
BY
REV. E. BUCKLEY.

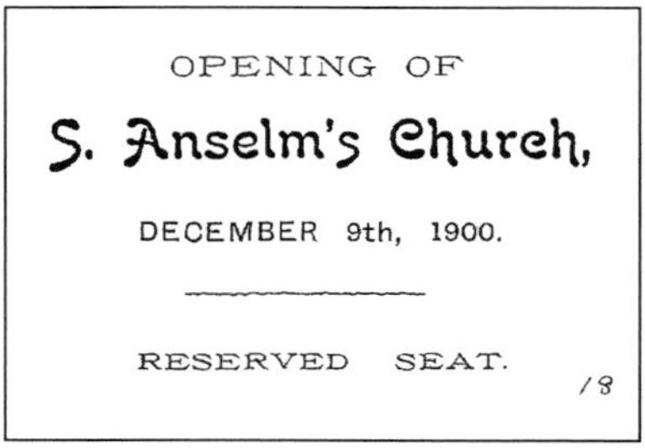

OPENING OF

S. Anselm's Church,

DECEMBER 9th, 1900.

RESERVED SEAT.

18

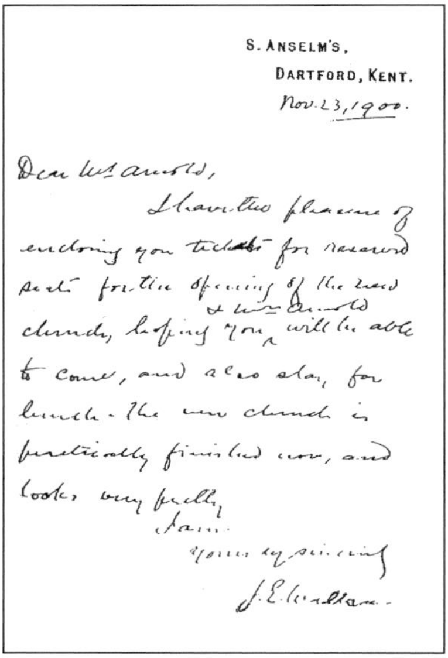

S. ANSELM'S,
DARTFORD, KENT.
Nov. 23, 1900.

Dear Mr Arnold,

I have the pleasure of enclosing you tickets for reserved seats for the opening of the new church, hoping you & Mrs Arnold will be able to come, and also stay for lunch. The new church is practically finished now, and looks very pretty.

I am
Yours very sincerely
[illegible]

Three Churches, 1866 – 1900

*Father Buckley's Church, 1887 (at the end of the pathway),
and the Old School, Hythe Street.*

*St. Anselm's Church, Spital Street
(1900)*

Francis, later Bishop, then Cardinal Bourne, aged eight. He served Mass for Father Maurice.

Bishop Francis Bourne. He laid the foundation stone for the Spital Street Church. In 1974 it was relaid at West Hill by Archbishop Cyril Cowderoy.

Dr. George Winham,
Travelling Missioner

The Travelling Mission: Father Arthur Dudley preparing for the road.

The 'Seven Sentences' of St John Fisher

O blessed Jesu, make me to love thee entirely.
O blessed Jesu I would fain, but without thy help I can not.
O blessed Jesu, let me deeply consider the greatness of thy love toward me.
O blessed Jesu, give unto me grace heartily to thank thee for thy benefits.
O blessed Jesu, give me good will to serve thee and to suffer.
O sweet Jesu, give me a natural remembrance of thy passion.
O sweet Jesu possess my heart, hold and keep it only to thee.

These seven sentences conclude The Ways to Perfect Religion, a little guide to the devout life written in the Tower by St John Fisher for his sister, Elizabeth White, a Dominican nun in Dartford. Each prayer is to be used on successive days of the week.

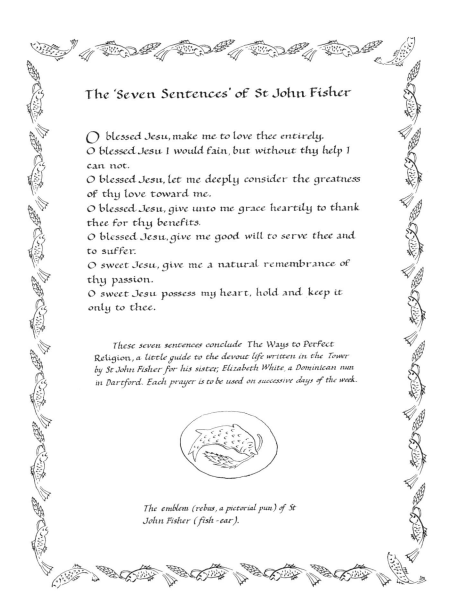

The emblem (rebus, a pictorial pun) of St John Fisher (fish-ear).

The 'Seven Sentences' of St. John Fisher

Chapter 5

St. Anselm's Parish – Father Evans

When Father Evans came to St. Anselm's on July 12th 1923, he was returning to a Mission where he had already spent some years as assistant to Father Mahoney. Now, as Rector, he was at once faced with a crisis. Financial difficulties were forcing the Ursuline Sisters to sell the Convent. Bishop Amigo and Father Evans were anxious not to lose the only Catholic school in Dartford offering a secondary education. The Bishop invited the Sisters of Charity of Our Lady, Mother of Mercy, to take it over, and in January 1924, when the Ursuline Sisters had moved to Sevenoaks, the Convent was able to start the new term as usual but with a new name, St. Mary's, later Our Lady's High School. There were only eight Catholics at that time among the sixty-one pupils.[1]

It was through the Capuchins that the Sisters had first come to Britain. The Congregation is Dutch and had been founded in 1832 by a parish priest, Monsignor Zwijsen, who had drawn together a group of dedicated ladies to care for the sick and needy. The work gathered momentum in a way far beyond his dreams and thus a religious Congregation came into being and was soon firmly established.

In 1852 the Capuchin friars had been offered a church in Pantasaph built by Viscount Feilding and his wife Louisa in thanksgiving for their marriage. (They had originally intended it as an Anglican church but since their wedding they had both become Catholics.) Pantasaph, which became the motherhouse of the Capuchins in Britain, in those early days was a lonely outpost of the Church. Lord Feilding was greatly concerned for the education and care of the poor children of the neighbourhood, a concern he shared with Father Seraphin of

Bruges, the Father Guardian of Pantasaph from 1853 to 1866, who later served in Northfleet and at St. Anselm's. He was a friend of Monsignor Zwijsen and at his invitation a little band of five Sisters of Charity came via Tilbury to Pantasaph, to a cottage that had been got ready for them – their first house in Britain. They arrived there on September 17th 1861, the Feast of the Stigmata of St. Francis.

They immediately set about teaching in three schools built for them by Lord Feilding and they took in orphans. The Sisters endured great poverty as more and more children arrived from the workhouses of Lancashire and they themselves in the early days lived in a cold, draughty, stable and coach-house, which served them as kitchen and refectory. Over the years they built a new convent and orphanage and secondary school in Pantasaph. The Community grew and other houses were opened in the North of England. Dartford was their first house in the South.[2]

Sister Magdalen Fleming, known as Sister Assistant, was appointed Headteacher of St. Mary's High School, a post she held for the next forty years, during which time the school expanded considerably. She and other Sisters and secular staff took the pupils to Tiverton in 1940, just before the Battle of Britain started. After the war places at Our Lady's were in such demand that an annexe was purchased in Heath Close Road to take the secondary classes. The 'daily trek to the heath' continued until 1956 when the new school was built.

So Father Evans' first crisis in 1923 was happily solved and he could look to the Mission. His congregation at St. Anselm's was not wealthy and the collections averaged only £5 a week but fortunately there were two benefactors who came to the rescue, the debt on the presbytery was paid off, and the church redecorated. Once the Mission could be shown to be self-supporting, Bishop Amigo was able to apply for it to be erected as a Parish, and in 1925 Father Evans became the first Parish Priest.

In 1927, there was another crisis when the Kent Education Committee decided to reorganize the Dartford schools. They were 'decapitated' – the children would have to leave at eleven. Dartford West Central Girls' School opened in 1931 to provide secondary education, and the adjacent Boys' School the next year. Bishop Amigo was anxious that the children should not be 'deprived of the Catholic atmosphere'.[3] They met for a time in the morning at St. Anselm's before going to school. Girls were offered places at Our Lady's, which made things easier.

Quiet progress was made in the brief interlude of peace between the two world wars. Prayers were said constantly in those days for the conversion of Russia. One great spiritual landmark in 1935 was the canonisation of St. John Fisher and St. Thomas More.

At that time, the parish included the villages of Sutton-at-Hone, South Darenth and Little Darenth, Horton Kirby, Farningham, and Eynsford, in addition to the Greenhithe district. Bishop Amigo was concerned that in many parts of his diocese there were Catholics living in isolated places far away from any existing church, which was certainly true of the Darent Valley. At the end of 1926, in order to enable these people to attend Mass at least once a quarter, he founded the Southwark Travelling Mission. It had the task of establishing Mass Centres across his diocese, outside the County of London, and covered an area of 3,500 square miles in Kent, Surrey, and Sussex.[4]

Father Arthur Dudley was appointed the first missioner and he started work in January, 1927, single-handed. That year he established five Mass Centres in Kent, four in Surrey, and three in Sussex, as many as one priest could visit quarterly.

On Tuesday, March 15th 1927, after stacking all his equipment into his little car – a portable altar and its furniture, hymn books, vestments, chalice and ciborium, etc. – Father Dudley set off from his temporary base at St. John's Seminary,

Wonersh, on his first visit to South Darenth, arriving at Dartford in the afternoon. Father Dorman, the assistant priest who knew the villages well, had been 'most energetic' in securing the Village Hall at Sutton-at-Hone for daily and Sunday Mass and booking accommodation for him at the village inn at South Darenth, *The Jolly Millers*. The Missioner found it 'most clean and comfortable'. They deposited the altar at the hall and drove to Farningham to visit the Gorman family. Gordon, their son, promised to serve Mass for Father Dudley each day on his way to school. 'Father Dorman,' the missioner writes in his diary, 'has done a great deal to keep the faith alive in these villages, and has an active body of Catechists at work.'

Father Dudley said the first Mass of the mission next morning at 8.30 with only the server present. 'I do hope the Mass said here each morning will stir the waters in this village,' he writes, 'for they badly need it. It is a most depressing and heart-breaking place.' He spent four days visiting all the known Catholics, forty-seven adults and twenty-nine children. There were some families to look up on a caravan encampment near Little Darenth, including a few who were trying to bring up the children in their faith. He called on them all, and told them of the Mass times. He was upset at discovering the conditions in which they were living: there was no Welfare State to ease the Depression between the wars. As he was preparing one of his weekday Masses, a man put his head inside the door of the Village Hall, and looking rather startled asked him if there was something on. 'Yes' replied Father Dudley. 'A service for Roman Catholics.' He disappeared like lightning.

His disappointment was very great when, despite all his efforts, only five adults and three children came to the Sunday Mass. He recommended 'the few' to meet weekly, and recite the rosary 'for the intentions of this place', and spoke of the necessity of family prayers. In the evening he preached at St. Anselm's to an 'excellent congregation' and afterwards spoke to one or two people who were hoping to work as catechists.

The catechists were in fact a godsend. Two or three were at work at South Darenth, visiting families and instructing the children. In May Father Dudley had an interview in Farningham with Miss Garlick, the secretary of the Guild of Our Lady's Catechists. She lived in Bromley, was employed full-time in London for the Catholic Truth Society, and spent her Saturday afternoons and Sundays working as a catechist in the villages and training new volunteers.

'Personal contact' was the watchword of the Mission. Another of Our Lady's Catechists was Monica Byrne, who also worked full-time in London. She and her father had both trained as speakers for the Catholic Evidence Guild and besides this she went out on Saturday afternoons visiting Catholic families; she would sit on the steps of a caravan home instructing the children and with her gift of entertaining and her tireless enthusiasm they loved her.

The work was difficult and the response slow but there were encouraging signs from time to time. Mr. Wicks, the proprietor of *The Jolly Millers*, decided to convert his billiard room into a small hall for meetings. It opened onto the street and Father Dudley thought it would be 'an admirable little place' for Mass, 'just the right size for the congregation'. Mr. Wicks agreed and the hall was hired for future visits.

Attendances had remained heartbreakingly low but at 8 a.m. on Thursday, 12th April, 1928, Maurice Byrne cycled out from Dartford and served the first Mass at *The Jolly Millers*. Father Dudley gave him breakfast before he returned to Dartford: he helped throughout the visit. (Later, like two of his brothers, he became a priest.)

Saturday was 'a red-letter day for South Darenth. The first fruits of the excellent body of catechists here manifested itself, in that about a dozen children from the districts of Farningham, Swanley and South Darenth were brought along by their catechists this afternoon to the temporary chapel at *The Jolly*

Millers.' With the help of the catechists he erected a temporary confessional, using two tables and a curtain – and after giving the children a little instruction and hearing confessions he packed them all into the car and took them home, much to their delight. The catechists had brought flowers for the altar, rugs, and furnishings, 'with a joy and willingness that is truly supernatural', and they inspired him with hope for the future.

Next day, Sunday, 15th April, he writes, 'All my hopes were realized today and there was real resurrection in South Darenth.' The little hall was literally full, with forty-three at Mass, twenty-nine adults and fourteen children, most of whom had been brought by their catechists. As they had come so far, he arranged for cups of hot tea to be served to them before they went home. The day was a wonderful success and created quite an impression in South Darenth, with everyone in very happy spirits. In fact, it created an impression well beyond the village. A French newspaper, *Les Nouvelles Religieuses*, carried an account of 'Le missionnaire en automobile' and the Mass at South Darenth, and the 'clever hands' that had improvised the confessional.

Father Dudley built up the foundations of the work of the Travelling Mission for five years 'with great energy and skill', but sheer exhaustion took toll of his health and forced him to retire in 1931, when Dr. George Winham succeeded him. Father Bayliss assisted Father Dudley and Father Winham for a while before being given charge of a former mission centre.

For their five-day visits the priests were later invited to stay with Mr. and Mrs. Byrne. Monica, sometimes accompanied by her young brother Michael, would go out with the priest on Saturday in his battered old car to visit the Catholics and tell them there would be Mass next day. Postcards were also sent out and posters put up. On the Sunday they would call for people, and take them home after Mass. The good smell of the beer pervading *The Jolly Millers* is still remembered.

In 1930 Monica Byrne left to become a Carmelite nun and without her the impetus petered out and numbers dropped again. The work was still 'heartbreaking'. Father Hayes invited the Sisters at Dartford to help and they later undertook weekly catechism. He organized garden fetes to raise funds to provide a hut and equip it as a chapel. St. Anselm's rallied round and in 1932 a hut was purchased. Scrubbing and polishing, the work of a willing group of parishioners, transformed it and the church at last had a home. One person at Mass said, 'I was rather scared of coming at first, but now that I have seen inside I don't care how often I come.' But the congregation still numbered only twenty-nine. At last, in 1938, there were enough people to justify a weekly Sunday Mass. The 'little church at South Darenth' was by now 'looking very nice'. Father George Stenson proposed that it should be dedicated to St. Therese but Archbishop Amigo, as Bishop Amigo had now become, chose St. George as its patron. It had been blessed and the naming ceremony, at which Dr. Winham preached and his assistant, Father Donnelly, was also present, took place on April 3rd that year, Passion Sunday, in the afternoon.

Later the same year, at Father Stenson's instigation, a choir was started at St. George's, but members were dispersed in the disruption caused by the war.

Meanwhile, at St. Anselm's, Father Evans was establishing a number of confraternities: the Knights and Squires of St. Columba, the Legion of Mary, the Children of Mary, the Guild of St. Agnes and, for the school children, the Guild of St. Philomena. By 1940, there were 168 pupils at Our Lady's High School, of whom only 70 were Catholics, and 85 at St. Anselm's with 75 Catholics.

The church was already much too small, even with the generous provision of Sunday Masses. A replacement was needed and in 1939, with this in mind, Father Evans bought a site at the top of West Hill.

During the Second World War, Dartford was in the front line, both for the Battle of Britain and in the years that followed. The church and schools were fortunate to escape damage. St. Vincent's was evacuated to Kennford and Our Lady's to Tiverton. Three of the nuns remained to look after the children who stayed. They also helped with fire-watching at the King Edward (West Hill) Hospital, which was bombed in September, 1940. Twenty-two patients and two nurses were killed. There have always been large numbers of Catholic nurses, many from Ireland, in the various hospitals in the parish, and they like so many others gave unstinted service during those years when civilian casualties and those brought back from the battlefields across the world arrived in streams that sometimes, particularly after Dunkirk, became a flood. Convalescent members of the forces were offered tea and (wartime!) coffee at St. Anselm's School Hall every weekday by teams of helpers. The church, in the heart of the town, remained open throughout the war and in 1941 Mass Centres were established by Father Evans at Joyce Green and the Southern Hospitals.

In 1950, ill health forced him to retire. It was said that Father Evans paid no regard to his own comfort. The presbytery was unheated and dilapidated, and to have a bath in those days meant a trip round to the public washplace. He made continual sacrifices in order to put money aside for the new church. Although by nature retiring, he had not spared himself in visiting the hospitals; especially during the war his steadiness and commitment must have been a source of strength. After saying farewell to the parish, he returned to his native Ireland, where he died, at Youghal, on February 14th 1953. A Requiem Mass was said for him at St. Anselm's on February 26th and a Foundation Mass is said for him every year on his anniversary. At a distance of nearly half a century, older parishioners still have kindly memories of him.

Chapter 6

Father Coleburt and the Fourth St. Anselm's

The country was still recovering from the war in 1950, when Father Coleburt first came to St. Anselm's. It was a period of austerity, with food and fuel strictly rationed, and the sight of bombed buildings being demolished and of wartime decay (paint had been largely unobtainable for years) gave a forlorn look to victory. The memory of the mushroom cloud over Hiroshima made it also an extremely uneasy peace.

Father Coleburt's first concern was to improve the condition of St. Anselm's. The church and presbytery were redecorated and took on a more cheerful appearance.

He was anxious to find a site in the centre of the town for the new church but planning permission was refused repeatedly. He was more fortunate in obtaining a site for a new primary school on Temple Hill, where farmland was giving way to housing. The new St. Anselm's School opened in 1956, replacing the outworn buildings in Hythe Street. Sister Mary Agnes McAdam (a member of the Community at Our Lady's Convent) soon found herself with twice as many children on her roll.

At about the same time, the Sisters rebuilt Our Lady's High School, with a hall that they offered for parish use when needed. In 1963, however, they could no longer afford to maintain the school and it was handed over to the Diocese to become a primary school for the parish. Six years later the Sisters sold the Convent and moved to their daughter house in Orpington. Some of them continued to teach in the school, which has thus inherited a long tradition, while others were drawn into a variety of new fields of work.

Sister Therese Mary Barnett, who had taught in the High School, was appointed the first Headteacher of Our Lady's

Primary School. She was followed by Sister Dolores Heys, who remained until her retirement in 1975, and still retains a keen interest in the generations of children she taught; she is at the Provincial House in Preston.

The first secular Headteacher, Mr. William Rapley, S.F.O., gave himself devotedly to the school but he took ill and was forced to retire after only two years. Mr. Vivian Pimenta, who came as Deputy Head in 1977, was Acting Head almost immediately and was then appointed Head in 1980. He steered the school through a period of rapid changes in education which included the introduction of local management and the National Curriculum. But, after a long period of ill health, in October 1997 he was forced to retire. Mr. A. McNeillis, the present Head, took up his appointment in January 1998 and was commissioned by Bishop John Jukes on the Feast of the Epiphany at the ten o'clock Mass at St. Anselm's.

Mr. Pimenta died very suddenly on March 13th 1999. People of all ages came to a crowded St. Anselm's for his funeral on March 22nd, many having to stand throughout the Mass. Father William Saunders, concelebrating with four other priests, paid tribute to Mr. Pimenta's gentleness and friendliness and spoke of the part he had played in nourishing the faith of generations of young people in the early stages of their journey through life.

The Sisters of St. Ursula and their successors, the Sisters of Charity of Our Lady of Mercy, helped to lay solid foundations for the parish at both Our Lady's and St. Anselm's Schools, building up a community of faith. Today there is a sense at Our Lady's of continuity with its past. Faithfulness and diligence, the *Fidelitas et diligentia* of the school motto, and kindness and gentleness, outlast the caprices of changing times.

To return to the 1970s and the urgent need to build the new church. It was eventually agreed that the West Hill site would be preferable to any of the alternatives and Ralph Lovegrove was asked to design the fourth St. Anselm's. It is a modern building conceived with a strong sense of tradition and origins, homely, friendly, and inviting, yet dignified in appearance.

It was built to resemble a tent, drawing on the idea of the Israelites camping in the desert. The Ark of the Covenant was kept in a tent – the 'Tent of Meeting' – and there are references throughout Scripture to God pitching his tent among his people. In many ways the building represents the pilgrim Church where the people of the Covenant meet God. The four corners of the Church represent the four points of the compass and signify the power of the Gospel to draw people to Christ from the four corners of the world. The floor dips down towards the sanctuary, following the natural slope of the land, and in the heart of the sanctuary nestles the Blessed Sacrament, enthroned in the tabernacle. Two continuous lines of windows below the pyramid-shaped roof give a feeling of the lightness of a large tent, and the stones encircling the sanctuary catch the play of light. No one is very far from the altar, although the Church seems spacious and about 400 people can be seated.

Archbishop Cyril Cowderoy opened the new church on October 30th 1975, 110 years after Father Maurice had first said Mass in the Hythe Street chapel.

The new church and presbytery are on the site of an old house called *The Homestead*, where Sidney Keyes, the poet of the Second World War, spent the first few weeks of his life. He was killed near Tobruk, at the age of twenty.

St. Vincent's School was greatly developed and modernised after the war. In 1976 the Brothers celebrated their centenary in Dartford, but at about that time custodial sentences for young offenders were restricted to the most serious cases and 'open' premises became unsuitable for the altered needs. The Community Home, as it was now called, closed in July 1982. Some of the Brothers moved to a house on the Brent, at the top of East Hill; all found new apostolates.

They left a generous legacy of land and buildings and of trusting friendship that got the new parish of St. Vincent off to a wonderful start when St. Anselm's parish was divided in 1982. Father Joseph Smith opened a fine new church in the school grounds that was consecrated on May 3rd 1985. The remains of all who had died at the Home, Brothers, Sisters, lay members of staff, and children, were transferred to a cemetery that was prepared beside the Church, where a beautiful garden, lovingly cared for, commemorates them. The school gymnasium was transformed into a Parish Centre, and Hubert House, originally a residential 'unit' of the school, now serves as a meeting place for many voluntary groups and clubs, under the auspices of the Catholic Children's Society. It has the charm of a building made over to a use for which it had not been intended. The rest of St. Vincent's, including the chapel, was demolished, and a housing estate has been built in the grounds.

Since Capuchin times there have nearly always been one or two assistant priests at St. Anselm's. Many later moved to parishes of their own: Canon James Gilvarry is remembered in Easkey in Killala, Father John Wright in Petts Wood, Father Timothy O'Driscoll in Ewell, and Father Brian Leahy in Mortlake. Father Peter Clements, who was Parish Priest first of Our Lady of the Assumption, Tooting, and then for seventeen years of SS. Philip and James, Herne Hill, retired in 1987 to live next door to the presbytery. He continued to say Mass in the parish until three months before his death on August 16th 1999.

Canon Francis O'Sullivan, who was for many years Director of the Southwark Catholic Children's Society, has recently retired from his parish of New Malden to co-ordinate support for marriage and family life in Bishop Tripp's Area of the Diocese. Father John McCormack, Parish Priest first of Wandsworth and then of Mortlake, has retired to a greatly changed Dartford and still helps in St. Vincent's parish.

Father Michael Clifton combines care of the parish of St. Thomas Aquinas, Ham, with his responsibilities as diocesan archivist. He has published a biography of Archbishop Amigo, *Amigo, Friend of the Poor*. Canon Michael Bunce, who in his years at St. Anselm's helped with details of the design of the new church and compiled the first parish history, served as army chaplain before returning to the diocese as Parish Priest first of Sheerness and then of Canterbury. Father (now Canon) James Pannett left us to become Administrator of St. George's Cathedral. On May 28th 1982 he welcomed Pope John Paul II to the Service of the Sick at the Cathedral. In 1986 he was responsible for the re-ordering of St. George's. After sixteen years there he moved in 1998 to St. John the Baptist, Purley, as Parish Priest. Father Josef Doetsch, for many years Parish Priest of Christ the King, Wimbledon, now has care of the parish of St. Aidan, Coulsdon.

Father Maurice Couve de Murville, who came to St. Anselm's as a newly ordained priest, left to become chaplain first at the University of Sussex and later at Cambridge. Only a few months before the papal visit he was chosen to be Archbishop of Birmingham, and he was consecrated by Archbishop Bruno Heim, the Papal Nuncio, on March 25th 1982. One of his first tasks was to organize Pope John Paul's wonderful open-air Mass at Coventry Airport on May 30th. He was leader of the largest diocese in England for seventeen years but in June 1999 he retired because of ill-health. He is at present convalescing after an operation; he hopes to return to pastoral work in a parish.

It has not been possible to find details of all the priests who served here over the years. All in their different ways have brought life to the parish and all have given without counting the cost.

On June 26th 1981 Maurice Williams was ordained by Bishop Jukes at The Friars, Aylesford, to the newly restored permanent diaconate, and on June 17th 1982 Vincent Bowgett was ordained deacon at St. Anselm's. Deacon Maurice served first in Northfleet; when St. Vincent's Church opened Deacon Vincent was appointed there. Since 1988, Maurice (who was privileged to act as Deacon for the Papal Service at St. George's Cathedral) has assisted at St. Anselm's. He is now much involved in services of prayer for the sick. He also assists at the Quiet Room at Bluewater and he is one of twelve part-time chaplains serving in turn in the Faith Zone at the Millennium Dome in Greenwich.

Many of Father Coleburt's old friends came to St. Anselm's on Saturday, 15th June 1985, to join the large congregation for his Golden Jubilee Mass, a very happy concelebration.

In 1986, the hut that had served as a chapel in South Darenth for fifty-four years was replaced by an attractive red-brick church on the opposite side of Devon Road. Father Coleburt was by good fortune able to furnish it with benches from the Convent of Jesus and Mary in Harlesden that were no longer needed by the Sisters. The Stations of the Cross were given to St. George's by Father Eric Mead, Parish Priest of Northfleet. They came from All Saints' Church, Galley Hill, that had been bought from the Church of England as a chapel of ease when Our Lady of Mount Carmel, Greenhithe, was condemned as unsafe and pulled down. The Stations had originally been in the Greenhithe church and are thus a link with the early history of St. Anselm's parish. Plans for converting All Saints' into flats were being made at the time when St. George's was built. Councillor Patrick Melvin asked Father Mead if the Stations could go to the new church, and with Councillor Patrick Coleman arranged for them to be restored; the restoration was generously sponsored by members of St. George's.

St. George's is much loved by its congregation and looked after by them during the week. It has a flourishing music group and there are friendly contacts with neighbouring churches in Darenth and Sutton-at-Hone. It also provides a peaceful setting for day retreats for groups in the parish.

During Father Coleburt's last years, when he suffered much ill health, he was greatly helped by Father Kinnane. Father Kinnane's cheerfulness and sense of humour were infectious; he specially enjoyed working with the young people of the parish. Bank holiday walks and visits to ice rinks are remembered. So, too, are the children's Masses at Our Lady's School. He also showed great patience, kindness and understanding for anyone in difficulties and was tireless, like all our priests, in visiting the sick. He was appointed Parish Priest in Gillingham in February 1988, when Father Coleburt was preparing to retire. He is now very happy as Parish Priest of St. Ethelbert's, Ramsgate.

Father David Gummett, who said his first Mass here on February 2nd 1988, gave his support to Father Coleburt up to his retirement in the spring of that year.

In his thirty-seven years as Parish Priest Father Coleburt had been actively involved in the life of the town, especially in education, in Catholic and non-Catholic fields. He always showed concern for those in the many hospitals served at that time from St. Anselm's, especially for the patients and staff of Darenth Park and Stone House, where he was a welcome visitor and trusted pastor. He had at one time been a Scout and Scouter himself and he always showed a keen interest in the movement, especially in the activities and well-being of the Dartford District Scout Council and St. Anselm's Ninth Dartford Group. Among his many other services to the town, he had for five years been Mayor's Chaplain.

He died on the Feast of the Assumption, August 15th 1993, after a long illness. A local newspaper announced his death with the headline, 'Town's loss is Heaven's gain.'[1] He had become almost a legendary figure, greatly loved in the parish and well known in the town, and his death was felt deeply. His body was received into St. Anselm's on the morning of August 23rd and a Mass of Thanksgiving was celebrated that evening. At the Funeral Mass the next day, Archbishop Michael Bowen presided and Father Michael Bunce gave the homily. People had come from far and wide and Father Coleburt's church was filled to its full capacity with mourning clergy and parishioners.

Chapter 7

Recent Years

Canon George Telford, who succeeded Father Coleburt, said his first Mass at St. Anselm's on May 4th 1988, the Feast of the Beatified English Martyrs. He was both Parish Priest and Dean.

Our Lady's Convent had recently been bought back by the Diocese and it was given to the parish to maintain. It was divided to form a parish centre, which was named after Father Coleburt, and an enterprise centre named the Coldart Business Centre, which now houses several charities, including Life and Cafod, and some small businesses. It was opened by Archbishop Michael Bowen on Wednesday, November 7th 1990. The Coleburt Centre is used by many voluntary organisations and is a favourite meeting place.

In 1991, two priests from the Catholic Missionary Society were invited to preach at a Mission at St. Anselm's, which involved everyone and was in some ways a turning point in the life of the parish. The theme was, 'Come, be my friend.' After the Mission, the church was altered to provide a parish room, which gave much-needed accommodation for the increasing activities which sprang from the week of prayer together. The architect, Judy Brown, later designed an extension to the narthex and made other improvements to the church.

Father Mahoney's organ needed replacement. Canon Telford sought expert advice from the Society of St. Gregory and after much consultation Kenneth Tickell was commissioned to design and build a two-manual and pedal organ.

The empty Hythe Street school on the site of Father Maurice's chapel, with the hall that had been Father Buckley's church, was demolished at this time to make way for Copperfields, a new shopping precinct. Canon Telford secured an upstairs room on the site of the original chapel, which he converted into an oratory. It is rich in Catholic history. He inaugurated a weekly lunchtime Mass there, which was always well attended.

The Canon gave regular support to the Dartford Council of Churches and was several times invited to address ecumenical meetings.

In his short time in Dartford, he quickly got to know everyone, visiting street by street, and he was tireless in caring for the sick. He often preached about self-giving and he showed us what it means.

He left Dartford for Ham in 1992 and his friends at St. Anselm's showed their affection and regard for him when they filled the Church of St. Thomas Aquinas for his Induction on March 15th that year.

Canon Telford died very suddenly on November 6th 1997. At his funeral on November 19th the Archbishop and Canon Beausang both spoke of his refreshing and revitalising influence in the Church, his humility, and his great gift of friendship. The Archbishop spoke also of his work nationally in catechetics and said that it was always Christ that he gave to the world, never merely himself.

At St. Anselm's he had been succeeded by Father Robin Maxted, who was parish priest for the next two years. With Father David Gummett, Father Robin continued the work of fostering lay participation in the liturgy, and both were actively involved in the Dartford Council of Churches. Father David became its first Catholic Chairman but in April 1993 he was appointed to his own parish of The Resurrection of Our Lord, Sydenham Kirkdale, and we said farewell to him on Sunday, April 25th. His Induction Mass on May 28th was attended by many well-wishers from St. Anselm's; through his work for the Handicapped Children's Pilgrimage Trust he still maintains contact with pilgrims to Lourdes from Dartford.

In the summer of 1993, Deacon Vincent Flynn came to assist Father Robin in his final year of preparation for the priesthood.

With only one priest remaining, Mass at the Copperfields Oratory was discontinued, and was replaced by watching before the Blessed Sacrament, which began in Lent, 1994. The little chapel has become an oasis of peace in the heart of the town and a fountain of grace for the parish.

In April 1994 Father Robin told us that after a long struggle with spiritual problems of his own he had decided to leave the priesthood. He had been deeply committed to the Church's ministry of healing; we could only thank God for his years with us and offer him our prayers.

In September 1993, Sister M. Ursula Hyland of the Sisters of Mercy in Gravesend came to St. Anselm's as Parish Sister. Her Convent has a direct link with the Foundress of her Congregation, the Venerable Catherine McAuley, who herself opened the Convent of Mercy in Bermondsey in 1839, her first English foundation. She appointed Sister Mary Clare Moore, one of her earliest companions, to be its Superior and Gravesend was one of eight convents in England opened in turn by Sister Clare, who, in spite of being extremely timid, had much of Catherine McAuley's spirit and vision. (At two days' notice Sister Clare took a group of her Sisters to nurse with Florence Nightingale in the Crimean War and she became her lifelong friend.)

The influence of Catherine McAuley in the nineteenth century was not unlike that of Mother Teresa in our own times. Like Mother Teresa, she had not set out to found an Order. She had been moved by love and pity to open a house in Baggot Street, Dublin, as a school for poor children and a home for destitute women and girls. From this followed her religious vocation. She founded ten Convents in Ireland and two in

England and soon there were Sisters of Mercy in many parts of the English-speaking world. It has been said of her that 'She has thrown a great chain of mercy around the earth.'[1]

The Sisters in Gravesend have opened several new Convents in Kent and they work in many different fields, teaching, nursing, caring for the elderly, and visiting. They have recently founded a refuge for the homeless in their original convent in Edwin Street, Gravesend, which is run by the Presentation Brothers. The Sisters and a group of volunteers, some from Dartford, assist the Brothers in caring for the residents and other parishioners help through sponsorship.

Sister Ursula has revived a link with her Convent first made in 1906 when Greenhithe was served from St. Anselm's; the Greenhithe Convent was a daughter house of Gravesend. She has many different roles to play, in catechesis particularly, but even so she is constantly out visiting parishioners, especially the sick, and she brings a sense of well-being, whatever difficulties people may be encountering.

On April 21st 1994, the Feast of St. Anselm, we welcomed Father William D. Saunders as Parish Priest. He had come to us from St. Thomas More Parish, Dulwich. Father Bill said his first Mass here at twelve noon and afterwards he invited those present to a little celebration in the parish room.

Father Bill, who is now Dean, has for several years past been Director of the annual Southwark Diocesan Pilgrimage to Lourdes for which sick pilgrims from Southwark join forces with groups from the dioceses of East Anglia, Portsmouth, Northampton, and Clifton, and Stonyhurst College. They travel with the help of the Catholic Association, a charity of which Father Bill is also Director. Besides the sick pilgrims, children and youth groups, people of every denomination are invited to take part, drawn together by the same trust and hopes. In 1997, Father Bill was appointed Director of the whole Inter-Diocesan Pilgrimage.

St. Anselm's was well represented at St. Agatha's Church, Kingston-upon-Thames, when on Saturday, June 11th 1994, the Archbishop ordained Deacon Vincent Flynn to the priesthood, and there was another celebration the next day when he returned to say his first Mass here. Father Vincent was then appointed to be our assistant priest.

The new organ arrived in the autumn of 1994. It was blessed by Father Bill and dedicated to Mary, Mother of the Church, at an evening service on December 8th, the Feast of the Immaculate Conception – so recalling Father Wallace's blessing of the Spital Street Church in 1900.

Father Bill's first priority on coming to St. Anselm's was to launch a restoration fund to meet the immediate and longer-term costs of church renovation and maintenance. There was much to be done and work began without delay. In 1997, Christina White described her impressions of the refurbished church in an article in the *Catholic Herald*:[2]

> 'Father Saunders points out pictures of saints, edged in gold, that bring colour to the brick walls of the Sanctuary. They came from the old church, as did a carved oak altar panel . . . To the side a modern pipe organ is decorated with symbols that link the modern parish with the ancient past of Dartford; a lineage of saints and princes.
>
> 'Doves carved in limewood soar high above the organ pipes. On the opposite side is the baptistery with its long windows of blue and green. Candles flicker in the sunlight that casts watery shadows across the polished floor.
>
> 'I liked this church very much. There is a simplicity and honesty in the design, a sense of community and spirit.'

Since Christina White's visit the work of restoration has continued. The roof needed extensive repairs and the windows, lighting, carpet, and kneelers all had to be replaced. Fund-raising in the parish and a legacy of £20,000 from Arthur

McGuiness, who had been a member of St. Anselm's for many years, together cleared the debt. The restoration has transformed the Church.

There have been many comings and goings at St. Anselm's in the past few years. Father Stephen Haylett, who had previously been vicar of All Saints, Foots Cray, was based here while studying at Wonersh after being received into the Catholic Church in 1994. He spent a year as deacon in Addiscombe and was one of a group of five former Anglican priests ordained to the Catholic priesthood on May 11th 1996. He is now assistant priest at Our Lady of Reparation, West Croydon. Father Peter Koszyk, a Polish priest from the diocese of Cracow, spent some months here in 1996 while preparing to go to Musoma, Tanzania. He is now in charge of a remote parish, twenty miles across. There has been a drought and the fear of famine looms; malaria is endemic and there is very great poverty. He has the task of building a new little church and organising the distribution of food and medical aid from Poland, especially for the children.

Deacon John Weatherill assisted in the parish in the summer of 1996 before returning for his final year at the Beda in Rome. He was ordained to the priesthood by Archbishop Michael at St. George's Cathedral on July 13th 1997 and said his first Mass here the following evening. He was appointed assistant priest at St. Paul's, Dover, and in 1999 was made Parish Priest of St. Gertrude's, South Bermondsey. Deacon Philip de Freitas joined us on St. Patrick's Day, 1997. He was ordained to the priesthood by Bishop Charles Henderson on February 2nd 1998, the Feast of the Presentation, and was appointed assistant priest at St. Anselm's, Tooting Bec.

In September 1997 Father Vincent Flynn left us on his appointment as assistant priest at St. Saviour and St. John Baptist and Evangelist, Lewisham. He had served the parish generously for four years, first as deacon and then as priest.

Father Geo' Ben Ezeani, a Nigerian priest from the diocese of Onitsha, was appointed to succeed him here for the following year. He published a novel, *Died in Exile*, while at St. Anselm's and several essays on the African Church and the modern world, which aroused interest in the parish and sympathy for his suffering country. He left us for a course of study at the University of East London. His successor, Father Steven Fisher, a newly ordained priest from St. John's Seminary, Wonersh, was welcomed into the parish for his first Mass here on St. Clare's Day, August 11th 1998.

Two other Polish missionary priests have stayed at St. Anselm's recently while studying English. Father Zbigniew Trata came in 1997 and is now serving in Zambia. Father Andrew Marcin Beltowski was here in 1998 preparing to go to Jamaica. He is living in Maggotty, a small village surrounded by mountains with tropical forest, in the diocese of Mandeville. He writes that his work is 'completely from zero. We will build a parish house, Church and Catholic School. Now there is nothing. Every day we go to the village and speak with people, with children. There are only three Catholic families. Last Sunday was the first public holy Mass in the park. About 30 people went. I think only to see what it is. Every Sunday we will say Mass at the same place and then in the chapel, I hope. The people are really poor, all is expensive in the shops. Many of the people have not a job but they are very friendly and open. I think with God's help we can do good work for the Kingdom of God.'

Father Augustine Oburota, who stayed here during his summer vacation in 1998, spoke movingly at a Cafod service of his experience as a child of being captured in the Nigerian Civil War and living in a camp where the prisoners were entirely dependent on aid from Europe for food and clothing. Father Augustine completed a doctorate in Louvain in 1998 and had been working as administrator of a parish in Namur. He has since returned to Nigeria as Chancellor of the Diocese of Onitsha.

Sometimes it is a little like watching *The Acts of the Apostles* unfold!

Parish life depends on the commitment of parishioners to many ordinary activities, seen or unseen, whether to the Beavers, Cubs, Scouts, Guides, or the Youth Club; or to the Wives' and Mothers' Group, the St. Vincent de Paul Conference, the counting and cleaning teams, the maintenance teams, the Pop-In Parlour, or Cafod. Volunteers working in charitable organisations, teachers, catechists, parents, those who visit the sick and housebound, drivers bringing people to Mass, all play a vital part. Ministers of the Eucharist, sacristans, musicians in the three choirs, and many other helpers, here as in every church give their service.

Father Augustine has sent us this tribute: 'I miss Dartford very much. It is said that a parish is a community of the faithful at prayer. This is quite true of St. Anselm's. I enjoyed the daily prayers, the Tuesday Coleburt Centre lunch, the Wednesday Holy Hour, and Thursday all-day Adoration, the Friday Cafod prayer and lunch, the weekend Masses. It was really lovely being at St. Anselm's. It was another school to me. . . . The involvement of the laity in St. Anselm's in the work of evangelization is quite encouraging.'

Perhaps it is also a tribute to the parish priest who quietly and unobtrusively enables it all to happen and holds it all together, inspiring everyone to greater faith and effort.

On Friday, January 26th 1996, Father Michael Byrne, Parish Priest of Sutton, came on a snowy winter's evening to celebrate Mass for his sister, Sister Monica of Jesus, O.C.D. She had died on the Feast of the Holy Family, December 31st 1995, at Holy Cross Hospital, Haslemere, only twenty days after being brought there by her family from her Monastery at Ware. She was ninety years old when she died and she had been a professed Carmelite nun for sixty-three years.

He told the congregation that at five o'clock on New Year's Eve two young nurses had helped her to bed. As they went off duty, she called out, 'Happy New Year!' 'You're too early,' they replied. 'It's not New Year till tomorrow.' 'I won't be here tomorrow,' she told them. 'I'm going to heaven tonight.' Twenty minutes later she died.

The life and death of Sister Monica remind us of the vital role of prayer in building the Church. From the time of Father Thomas Tilden there has been an unusual number of vocations to the priesthood and religious life among Dartford Catholics. It may not be fanciful to suggest that the prayers of the Dominican Fathers and nuns of the Priory and possibly of an earlier community, and those of the devoted priests and religious Brothers and Sisters who have served here since, have been, and still are, powerful for us all.

In the past few years members of St. Anselm's and St. Vincent's parishes have participated in three great and memorable events in the life of the Church.

The first was the Beatification of Edmund Rice, Founder of the Presentation Brothers and the Christian Brothers, by Pope John Paul II, on October 6th 1996. Father Joe Smith led a group from Gravesend and Dartford that went to Rome for the occasion.

It was a wonderful open-air Mass in St. Peter's Square. Fifteen other great men and women of the nineteenth century were beatified with Edmund Rice: thirteen Polish martyrs, all laymen; the Spanish Foundress of a Franciscan Missionary Order dedicated to the education of poor girls; and the Polish Foundress of the Sisters of the Immaculate, a teaching and nursing Order whose nuns gave protection to Jews in the last war. The Pope spoke of the great witness they had all given to justice and peace. Pilgrims from all over the world were in Rome to honour them.

The second event was the celebration of the fourteenth centenary of the arrival of St. Augustine and his brother monks in Thanet in 597. The Holy Father has written of the importance of this mission as the beginning of the evangelization of the entire Anglo-Saxon world. Archbishop Michael Bowen and his auxiliary bishops and a gathering of about 200 priests, who included ten Benedictine Abbots, concelebrated Mass in the grounds of St. Augustine's Abbey in Canterbury on his feast day, May 27th 1997. There were several thousand people present on the hillside for the Mass, their voices united in praise.

In the afternoon, at the invitation of Dr. George Carey, Archbishop of Canterbury, Benedictine monks and nuns from Britain and France sang the Evening Prayer of the Church in Canterbury Cathedral and heard Cardinal Hume speak of the challenge of the Gospel in our own time, and of the dream of Christian Unity. The great Cathedral could not hold the enormous crowd of people hoping to get in, but for those who were lucky enough it was a beautiful and moving experience.

In August 1997, three young adult members of St. Anselm's representing the parish and the deanery went with Deacon Philip de Freitas on a pilgrimage to France which culminated in World Youth Day in Paris on the 24th. They had first spent a few days in Rouen experiencing the oneness of their faith as they joined with Polish pilgrims and their French hosts in prayer and celebrations of all kinds. The following week they were with young people from 140 countries who had converged on Paris from the parishes across France where they had been entertained. They were greeted first by Cardinal Lustiger and then by Pope John Paul – they write that that was the moment they had all longed for. The Pope asked them to spend their pilgrimage seeking Jesus in the Gospel and in the Sacraments, in preparation for the Sunday Eucharist.

For a few wonderful days Paris was immersed in catechesis, reflection, prayer, and festivals. On the Saturday morning the young people formed a twenty-mile 'chain of brotherhood' round the city. Then half a million pilgrims including Christians of many other churches made their way to the Longchamp Racecourse for an all-night Vigil of Prayer, and eventually over a million, far more than had been expected, flooded to the Sunday Mass. There the Pope, looking frail but immensely inspiring, asked all of them to continue to create a spiritual chain of brotherhood in their own worlds when they returned home – and to meet him again in Rome for the Millennium.

Here in the parish there have also been two memorable celebrations. On May 30th 1998, Father John Sandom of the White Fathers came home to St. Anselm's to celebrate the fortieth anniversary of his ordination to the priesthood with a Mass of Thanksgiving. It was also the forty-fifth anniversary of the ordination of Bishop Francis Walmsley, Bishop of the Forces, who, like Father John, had grown up in Dartford. Father John described him as his mentor at the time when he was considering his vocation.

The evening was fine and sunny and the church, looking very nice after the restoration, was full for the Saturday evening Mass. Concelebrating with Bishop Francis and Father John were three friends from Father John's Order, and Father John Bluett, who had flown over from Ireland, Father Augustine, and Father Bill, who invited everyone to a reception afterwards at the Coleburt Centre. Other priests had hoped to come but had been unable to leave their parishes. Sister Dolores Heys came down from Preston and many other old friends had travelled long distances.

We were all delighted and proud to have two great members of St. Anselm's returning, the priest who has spent the best part of his life in remote and often dangerous mission stations, and the bishop who has served in war and peace in many distant parts of the world. The Mass was inspiring and uplifting, with young and old caught up in the warmth and cordiality of the gathering, and afterwards old friendships were renewed and memories shared in the friendly atmosphere of the Centre.

On Saturday, June 19th 1999, the anniversary of Bl. William Exmew and Bl. Sebastian Newdigate, Father Michael Byrne returned to the parish to celebrate the evening Mass at St. Anselm's in commemoration of the Golden Jubilee of his ordination. Father Michael's role of Founder Chaplain to the Handicapped Children's Pilgrimage Trust is described in the next chapter. For his jubilee many of his friends came from far and wide on pilgrimage to St. Anselm's. Concelebrating with him were Bishop Francis, Father David Gummett, Father Bill, and Father Steven; the folk group led the singing. Everyone was mourning the loss of our greatly loved Cardinal Basil Hume, who had died only two days earlier. But, as the Cardinal would surely have wished, the theme of the Mass was one of Christian hope, joy, and gratitude to God for his blessings. Father Bill presented Father Michael with a chalice, the gift of the parish, engraved with the logo of Jubilee 2000 and its inscription: *Christ yesterday, today, forever.* There was a sense that time past, time present, and time future were indeed 'eternally present' in Christ.

It is strange to reflect that Father Michael, his two brothers – Father John and Canon Maurice – and Sister Monica, their Carmelite sister, have together as a family given the Church more than two centuries of service – a fifth of a millennium. We shall remember June 19th as a day of thanksgiving – our thanksgiving for all those who, as Father Dudley would have said, have 'set the waters all astir' in this parish and far beyond.

And so we come to the Holy Year, Jubilee 2000, the two thousandth anniversary of the Incarnation. For St. Anselm's the year will also embrace the silver jubilee of the opening of our present church.

When Pope Boniface VIII promulgated the Bull granting the first *official* Christian Jubilee Year in February 1300, it was in response to seeing the pilgrims who had been streaming past his residence at the Lateran since Christmas. He learned that they had come to obtain 'The Great Pardon of the Roman Court', of which there was a strong folk memory. He granted an Indulgence to the pilgrims and he was greatly concerned for their welfare, both spiritual and physical – not least for food supplies. About two million pilgrims went to Rome that year, to be cared for – as they were, wonderfully – by the city's 100,000 inhabitants, and the Jubilee brought about 'a great revival of spirituality, of pardon and brotherliness'. As later Jubilee Years came round, every twenty-five years generally, voluntary organisations sprang up in Rome, some becoming permanent, and the city was said to have 'the best caring services in Europe'. The celebrations were halted in the nineteenth century during the political upheavals in Italy.[3]

The Jubilee Year Indulgence has for many years been extended to those unable to visit Rome, who make instead a pilgrimage to a local cathedral during the following year. This year, for the first time, it has also been extended to designated churches in each diocese and to people unable to get to any church who fulfil certain obligations; everyone can participate, and they do so during the Jubilee Year, not afterwards.

St. Anselm's has been designated by the Archbishop as a church for the Indulgence. Instead of the Holy Door at St. Peter's, a Pilgrim Door was prepared and sealed on the first Sunday in Advent. It was solemnly opened at the Midnight Mass of Christmas. New vestments with the beautiful Jubilee logo were another reminder that we belong to a universal church, the five doves around the Cross on the logo symbolising the Holy Spirit given to the five continents. At the start of Mass, Deacon Maurice and the altar servers stood with Father Bill in the narthex as he opened the Pilgrim Door and called on God the Father to 'Help us to open the door of our hearts to your infinite mercy and love', and on 'Christ, the door', to 'Open to us'. A hymn, *Jubilee Praise*, that Father Bill had written for the millennium, was sung by the choir and congregation after Communion.

The hymn had been sung for the first time by the folk group at the Bluewater Shopping Centre on the Sunday before Christmas and it was sung again on New Year's Day at Mass and at an ecumenical service at St. Anselm's that followed the ringing of church bells nationwide at noon. Our one bell, the centenarian from Spital Street, had been hung in the presbytery garden, where everyone took turns to give a resounding welcome to the new millennium.

Pope John Paul II has devoted many years to preparing for Jubilee 2000 and to the work of reconciliation and renewal, especially through his work for Christian Unity. *Churches Together in England* have offered to us six themes for the millennium: respect for the earth, peace for its people, love in our lives, delight in the good, forgiveness of past wrongs, and the grace to make a new start for ourselves and for the world. In the tradition of the ancient Jewish Jubilee, the Churches have placed the remission of debts (now those of Third World countries) high on their agenda for peace and renewal.

So it is in an atmosphere of great hope that we are entering the third Christian millennium.

Jubilee Praise

Words: W. D. Saunders

Music: P. Lloyd, arr. S. M. Whitehead

2. With love and true beauty
   we shine ever bright
   in the Church of God's presence
   who hallows this night.
   In joy unsurpassed
   we sing with accord
   that Mary's Son Jesus
   with faith be adored.

Chorus:

   With Christ as our light . . .

3. Now come, all you peoples,
   in Spirit begin
   to live this New Year
   by banishing sin;
   to live as God's children
   happy and free
   by the light of the Christ child
   who loves you and me.

Chorus:

   With Christ as our light . . .

Chapter 8

'You will be my Witnesses'

As has been mentioned earlier, over the past century St. Anselm's has given a good number of Priests and Religious to the Church. Is this, perhaps, what Father Maurice foresaw when he told Bishop Grant that Dartford would be 'one of the best jewels' in his administrative crown?

Father Thomas Tilden's connection with Dartford is described in Chapter Two. There may have been priests from the parish before 1932 but it has not been possible to trace them. The first names here are taken from a list drawn up from memory by Father Michael Byrne for the 1975 Handbook.

Father Henry Porter, who came from a well-known Dartford family, studied at St. John's Seminary, Wonersh, was ordained in 1932, and was then appointed assistant priest at St. Paul's, Dover. In 1937 he moved to St. Charles Borromeo, Weybridge, where his encouragement of the young people is especially remembered. He adapted a little wooden structure beside the church to create a hall where the children could put on plays and concerts. Archbishop Cowderoy was later to describe Father Porter's work as a curate as 'outstanding'.

In the summer of 1944, which began with flying bombs and ended with rockets, he was made Parish Priest of Our Lady Help of Christians, Mottingham. The little church had been built in 1933 through the generosity of a local benefactor, Mr. Jefferies, who had won the Irish Hospitals Sweepstake. It suffered bomb damage in the war but services were maintained.

Mottingham grew rapidly after the war and Father Harry took up the challenge. The church was repaired and restored – he himself drew up the basic design for the altar – the debts were cleared, and Our Lady's was consecrated in 1952. Next, he built a new primary school, St. Vincent's, which opened in 1953. In 1956 there were four ordinations at Our Lady's; two of the new priests were from Mottingham. But he took ill and in 1957 celebrated both his Silver Jubilee and his return to the parish after five months' absence.

Father Harry was a big man, well-built and with an expansive personality. He was approachable, sociable, lively, kind, cheerful, and resourceful. (With clothing still rationed after the war, he made the May Queen's train from a parachute.) He made light of every difficulty – his laughter is remembered. He loved football and cricket and was a regular Charlton supporter. Equally he enjoyed painting water colours of his churches, and he was practical.

He was kind and welcoming to his young assistant, also from St. Anselm's, taking him on his sometimes hair-raising rounds in his rickety old car. Canon Bogan spoke of him at his Silver Jubilee as a 'solid, four-square character', his good humour unshaken by illness: 'a great priest, a great man and a great friend'. He was only fifty-three when he died on March 12th 1960. Archbishop Cowderoy's tribute continued: 'He was never failing as a parish priest'; he was 'a sincere and true friend' whose life had been 'a dedication to his Church and his flock'. No wonder that he was loved by them.

Father John A. Byrne was born on May 5th 1909. His parents are revered in Dartford for giving three sons and a daughter to the Church. They lived in West View Road in a house no longer standing. John, the first son to become a priest, went from St. Anselm's first to Wonersh. After two years, to the delight of the boys, the Junior Seminary moved to a separate home at Mark Cross. He returned to the Senior Seminary at Wonersh in 1928 and was ordained in 1934.

He was appointed curate at All Saints, Oxted, now in the Diocese of Arundel and Brighton. The parish was widespread and he helped establish the new Mass Centres at Biggin Hill (St. Theresa's) and Edenbridge (St. Lawrence), both of which are now separate parishes in Southwark. As he was saying Mass at all three centres, he was given £5 by his parish priest to buy a car – too little even at pre-war prices. It blew up on Biggin Hill and a modest replacement was obtained. In 1938 he moved to St. Augustine's, Tunbridge Wells, and he was in the pulpit on September 3rd 1939 when the parish priest walked across and told him to finish Mass quickly as war had broken out. The sirens sounded but the all-clear went soon afterwards. The first few months of the war were quiet; later the presbytery was bombed but, fortunately, there were no fatalities. Father John served next at St. John the Baptist, Brighton, and in January 1945, at the height of the V2 rocket attacks on London, he became Parish Priest of St. Benet's, Abbey Wood, where he was extremely happy. Later he moved to Our Lady of Mount Carmel and St. Joseph, Battersea East (now Battersea Park), where, too, he was very happy and much loved. In 1967 he moved again, to St. Boniface, Tooting.

Early one morning Father John was in the sacristy preparing to set off to say Mass at the nearby convent when he was brutally attacked by an intruder. After the attack he was thought to be dead; the police treated it as murder. His injuries were appalling. Shock waves were felt across the whole diocese. He made an almost miraculous physical recovery at Roehampton and then spent a year recuperating at Wonersh, where the students were very kind to him, but the trauma was never healed. Returning to Tooting proved unbearably painful. He was sent to Sanderstead for a short time but eventually he was forced to give in and he retired. He lived at Aylesford for a few years, saying Mass and talking to the pilgrims, and often supplying at Northfleet. He and his two devoted brothers, Father Maurice and Father Michael, spent their days off together. Later he moved to a little house in Sutton in Father

Michael's parish. Here, too, he was happy talking to people while out with his walking stick, and they loved him. When his health deteriorated further, he was looked after by Sisters at St. Michael's, Worcester Park, until it closed, and then, devotedly, by the Little Sisters of the Poor at St. Peter's House, South Lambeth.

He became seriously ill and was taken to St. Thomas's Hospital but the kind Sisters brought him home to nurse and he was looked after with loving care by them and by Father Michael. He died on May 29th 1991. Father Maurice had died the previous year. Archbishop Michael Bowen, Bishop Henderson, and Bishop Tripp all attended his funeral at St. Peter's, then drove down to Sutton where he is buried.

It is difficult to understand why God allows the innocent to suffer. The special power of handicapped children to draw out the best in others is acknowledged by the HCPT. In allowing the attack on Father John, though certainly not willing it, was He once more 'choosing the weak' and 'making him strong in bearing witness to Himself'?

Canon Maurice Byrne was born on January 28th 1912, his parents' sixth child. From St. Anselm's School he went to Dartford Grammar School, and then to St. Joseph's College, Mark Cross, and Wonersh, and he was ordained on May 22nd 1937. He spent three years in Cambridge, graduating in French, and then returned to teach at Mark Cross, where he became Monsignor Edward Corbishley's right hand man. In 1957 he was appointed headmaster and bursar of St. Peter's School, Merrow; the school was greatly developed and extended during his seven years there.

In 1964 Father Maurice was made Parish Priest of St. Paul's, Haywards Heath. The parish, too, developed greatly under his guidance. He oversaw the transition to Voluntary Aided status of St. Joseph's Primary School, which had been built by the Sisters of Mercy, and also the building of St. Paul's Secondary School. He built a small daughter church of the parish, St. Stephen's, Horsted Keynes.

In 1957 Father Maurice and Father John both joined Father Michael, founder chaplain of the HCPT, on its first pilgrimage to Lourdes and he remained a faithful friend of the Trust. His support for the flourishing local Life Group, given wisely and unobtrusively, could also be counted on, and parish premises were always available for Life functions. Towards the end of his years in Haywards Heath he was made an Honorary Canon by Bishop Cormac Murphy-O'Connor, a sign of the high regard in which he held him.

He retired in 1987 after celebrating his Golden Jubilee. He remained in Haywards Heath for a short time, helping when needed. On January 28th 1988 Bishop Cormac wished him a happy birthday and then asked him if he would go as chaplain to the Franciscan Sisters of Littlehampton at their Old People's Home, St. Anne's Convent, in Burgess Heath. On December 26th 1989, St. Stephen's Day, Father John and Father Michael had lunch with him. That night, Canon Maurice had a heart attack and was rushed to Cuckfield Hospital, where he died a month later, on January 29th, aged seventy-seven years and a day. Capable and kind, he is remembered as 'a gentle soul'.

Father Donald Wilkins was born in Woolwich on August 7th 1913 but his parents came to live in Dartford and he grew up here in Highfield Road. He spent five years at Mark Cross and on October 24th 1932 entered the Venerable English College, where his name was duly entered in the *Liber Ruber*. The College, founded in Rome in 1579 by Cardinal Allen (who had earlier founded Douai) to prepare secular priests for the English and Welsh Mission, is renowned for the many canonized and beatified martyrs from among its students. The list in the *Liber Ruber* starts with the College's first student, who was also its first martyr, St. Ralph Sherwin, and comes right up to the present, with the name of every student entering each year.

Father Wilkins was ordained to the priesthood by Archbishop Godfrey on December 24th 1938 in the College Church and on 18th August 1939 he was appointed assistant priest at St. Mary of the Angels, Worthing. It was only a few days before the outbreak of war, which forced the English College to transfer temporarily to Stonyhurst.

Later, he served as assistant priest in Lee, Midhurst, and Chatham; and after a short spell as Parish Priest in Newington, he was appointed Parish Priest of St. Joseph's, Rustington, in 1955. He remained there until 1980 when he retired to become chaplain to the Sisters of Our Lady of Sion at their convent and guesthouse in Findon.

Holy, human, humble, clever, always approachable, the soul of parish events, a great favourite with the children in Rustington and with the guests at Findon – these are the memories people have of his later years. At Rustington, his vision was already affected by cancer and lay readers were encouraged earlier than in most parishes. He sacrificed his own comfort in the presbytery to pay off the parish debt and at the same time was generous and hospitable in the service of his parishioners. On September 6th 1984, Father Wilkins said Mass at the convent, had breakfast with the guests and then died very suddenly in the lane outside on his way to get his motor-cycle. His funeral was at the convent on September 14th. Some of the Sisters had known him from his first days in Worthing and they speak of him with great regard.

Father William Nolan was born in 1917 and grew up in Dartford. His sister Winifred kept up the family home at 36 Wellington Road and was always greatly loved in the parish up to her death on January 4th 1995. Father Michael Byrne took Father

Nolan as his model of what a priest should be when he followed him at the seminary. He studied at Mark Cross and Wonersh, where he was ordained by Archbishop Peter Amigo on May 26th 1945; he then served for a few months in Bermondsey before being transferred to St. Mary Magdalen, Mortlake, in September that year. He remained at St. Mary's for twenty-seven years as assistant to Canon Gibney, who as Vicar General and Protonotary Apostolic had many other responsibilities. The two priests are remembered as 'a great team'; Father Nolan refused several offers of parishes in those years.

In 1945 family life was returning to normal as men came home from the war. Money for holidays was scarce and Father Nolan organised youth camps at Worth Abbey, which over the years became family camps. In the parish he set up family groups, turning out on Sunday nights in all weathers to supervise their work and advise on spiritual matters. 'A great man for visiting the sick', loved for his humility, a friend to young and old alike, he is spoken of in Mortlake today with the highest regard. He left St. Mary's only when Canon Gibney retired in 1972.

He was appointed Rector of St. Patrick's, West Chislehurst, and later Parish Priest. In his short time there, as at Mortlake, he made a deep and lasting impression. His kindness, humour, hospitality, and sheer goodness, his 'profound spirituality', are still remembered. People speak of him as of a friend of long standing, even though he was there for so short a time. On Sunday, November 9th 1975, after the evening Mass, he took ill in the sacristy and he died later that evening. His funeral was at St. Patrick's and he was buried at Kiln Green, Reading. A chalice which had been presented to him by the parishioners of St. Mary Magdalen is still in daily use at St. Patrick's.

He wrote a letter foreseeing his death, which was read at his funeral by Archbishop Cyril Cowderoy. We are grateful to include it here.

> When this reaches your hand, I will have been gathered to my Father's, for I am dying. Do not be grieved; do not weep. Rejoice with me that I have had my call from God, who was never absent from me for a moment in my life. Pray for me if you will.
>
> Death is not a calamity to him who dies, it is only a calamity to those he leaves behind, for death is a deliverance and joy and eternal peace and bliss. The days of man are short and full of trouble. What is there in the world that can offer consolation?
>
> Do not sorrow. I will be with you always and will pray for you, and our parting will be brief.
>
> God be with you, and may he bring you his blessed peace.

Father Michael Byrne, the youngest of the three priest brothers, was greatly influenced in his childhood by his sister Monica and by Dr. George Winham, the priest of the Travelling Mission who became a friend of the family. Father Michael attended St. Anselm's School and St. Joseph's College, Mark Cross, and then studied at Wonersh. He was ordained on June 11th 1949. His first appointment, for September that year, was to Mottingham, as assistant to Father Henry Porter, but before going there he spent the summer supplying for a sick priest at St. Wilfrid's, Burgess Hill, and it was then that he began visiting some Catholic boys at Chailey Heritage, an industrial hospital school founded as a charity by an Anglican lady, Dame Grace Kimmins.

In 1953, on the day after Coronation Day, he returned to Burgess Hill as assistant priest. St. Edward the Confessor, Keymer, St. Luke's, Hurstpierpoint, and St. George's Retreat

House were all served from St. Wilfrid's at that time. Father Michael lived in digs with 'a lovely Catholic family' in Hassocks village.

He returned to Chailey Heritage and struck up a friendship with a young Catholic doctor on the staff, Dr. Michael Strode. Dr. Strode found a room for a chapel, which he furnished at his own expense; his mother made a rug for the sanctuary. Father Michael began saying Mass there once a month. Dr. Strode had the idea of taking the children to Lourdes on a pilgrimage which would also be a holiday. He invited Father Michael to go with him and, along with other helpers, they took four or five boys. They attached themselves to the National Schools Pilgrimage, led by Bishop Humphrey Bright, the Auxiliary Bishop of Birmingham, who is known as the Scouts' Bishop. He came into their carriage on the way home and said, 'Your children have been a focal point for all the others. They went to the Grotto with them. It's a marvellous way of bringing handicapped children to Lourdes – girls as well as boys – an opportunity not to be missed.' He told them to work on the idea. Friends would rally round if Our Lady wanted it.

Out of this conversation the Handicapped Children's Pilgrimage Trust was born. There was a wonderful response to a two-line advertisement that Dr. Strode placed in *The Daily Telegraph* and *The Times* and in 1957 the first formal pilgrimage of the HCPT took place, with forty-three children. Father Michael was Founder Chaplain. Father John Byrne and Father Maurice also became chaplains with the Trust, which now takes more than 2,000 children to Lourdes every Easter week with as many voluntary helpers, who pay their own way. Father Michael, although he has retired from office in the Trust, has not missed one pilgrimage since 1956.

The annual Hosanna House Pilgrimage for older handicapped people is a more recent offshoot of the HCPT. In

1974, a small, newly built hotel (since extended) was acquired in Bartrès, the village where St. Bernadette spent part of her childhood. For the first Hosanna House Pilgrimage, Father Michael enjoyed being both spiritual director and cook. Dr. Michael Strode has now joined the Cistercian (Trappist) Community on Caldey as choir oblate. Brother Michael, OCSO, as he is now, still takes part in the Lourdes pilgrimages. Members of St. Anselm's go regularly on both pilgrimages and some of the folk group provide music for the liturgies.

After four years at St. Wilfrid's Father Michael moved to St. John Fisher, Merton, where he was curate for nine years. In 1966 he became priest in charge at St. Joseph's, Colliers Wood, a new parish, where he stayed for three years.

In 1969 he became Parish Priest of Our Lady of the Rosary, Sutton, where he celebrated his Golden Jubilee on June 11th 1999. His Jubilee Mass at St. Anselm's has already been described. In the autumn, after the Feast of Our Lady of the Rosary, he retired from parish life to realise his dream of becoming resident chaplain at Hosanna House, which is in constant use throughout the pilgrimage season.

The HCPT and Hosanna House Pilgrimages have touched the lives of many thousands of people and have been given sympathetic coverage in the media but Father Michael says he wishes to be remembered for only one thing – that he is a Catholic priest.

Bishop Francis Joseph Walmsley, CBE, was born in Woolwich on November 9th 1926. His family came to Dartford in 1932 when he was six. At first he attended St. Alban's (C of E) Infants' School but he was moved precipitately to St. Anselm's by his conscience-stricken parents when he came home one day and recited the Lord's Prayer adding 'For thine is the kingdom, etc.'

His family was always involved in the life of the parish, his parents in the Guilds of the Blessed Sacrament – men's guild and women's guild – and in fund-raising schemes, garden fetes, concert parties, etc., his sister in the Guild of St. Agnes, himself as an altar server until he went to the Junior Seminary.

His wish to become a priest, an idea first put to him when he was eleven, was discovered by Bishop Peter Amigo in 1940 and he arranged for him to go to St. Joseph's College, Mark Cross, where several boys from Dartford had preceded him.

In 1944 he registered for National Service and in August joined the Merchant Navy as a seaman. He 'celebrated' his eighteenth birthday on board *S.S. Temple Yard*, at sea in an Atlantic Convoy bound for Montreal. Another ship, the *S.S. Fort Thompson*, to which he had been sent but which he had not in fact joined, was torpedoed some 200 miles ahead of *Temple Yard*; so he felt he was very fortunate.

In 1946, now aged twenty, he returned to Mark Cross after two years at sea, and for a year he polished up his English, Latin and French, then in September 1947 went to St. John's Seminary. After 'the usual courses' he was ordained in 1953.

He served at St. Peter's, Woolwich (where his parents had been married in 1925 and where he was baptised in 1926) from 1953 to 1958, and then at St. Peter's, Shoreham-by-Sea, until 1960. In the October of that year, at the request of Bishop Cyril Cowderoy, he joined the Navy as a chaplain.

Subsequently he served at sea in *Ark Royal, Centaur, Victorious, Hermes,* and *Bulwark,* both in the Mediterranean and in the Far East, and ashore at Devonport, Portsmouth, Chatham, and Rosyth; he also served at the Naval Base, Singapore, from 1967 to 1969.

He was appointed Principal Roman Catholic Chaplain to the Royal Navy and named a Prelate of Honour by Pope Paul VI in 1975, and in 1979 he was nominated Titular Bishop of Tamalluma as fourth Bishop of the Forces (RC) and as third Military Vicar by Pope John Paul II. He was consecrated Bishop at the Garrison Church of SS. Michael and George, Aldershot, on February 22nd 1979. In the same year, he was appointed CBE in the Queen's Birthday Honours.

A Bishop of the Forces in peacetime has many civilian roles. Bishop Francis is Spiritual Director of the Catholic Women's League, the Charity that launched Family Fast Day and provided the original impetus for Cafod.

Bishop Francis has remained a loyal friend to all his brother priests from Dartford in good times and bad. There was a very happy evening at St. Anselm's on May 30th 1998 when he concelebrated Mass for the fortieth anniversary of Father John Sandom's ordination, which fortunately coincided with his own forty-fifth anniversary. It was a wonderful reunion appreciated by old and young alike. He returned for Father Michael Byrne's Golden Jubilee Mass in 1999 and we hope to welcome him again on future occasions. One can imagine that the Bishop's simple, straightforward, kindness and sense of humour will themselves have been a peace-keeping force in the Royal Navy wherever he has served.

Father John Sandom was born on September 10th 1930 at 49 Colney Road, Dartford. He was educated at Our Lady's High School here and in Tiverton and at the Salesian Colleges in Burwash and Cowley. It was while on National Service as a medical technician (nurse) in the RAF that he decided to become a missionary. He was ordained as a White Father on May 7th 1958 at Galashiels and flew to Uganda in October that year. In spite of recurring bouts of malaria and dysentery he spent fifteen happy years in the diocese of Mbarara engaged on many kinds of pioneering work in education, administration and development – which included developing literacy, women's clubs and 'bush' schools, building roads and bridges, making fish ponds and planting small forests –all while serving in a 'bush' parish where a sick call could mean trekking for miles.

Everything was shattered by Amin's coup in 1971. Father John survived for six months under the dictator but was then forced to leave. The records and all his things were lost – he had only what he stood up in. After eighteen sad, unhappy, months trying to get back to Uganda, when all hope had faded he was sent to Paris for an intensive course in French, and then to Ouagadougou, the capital of Burkina Faso (Upper Volta), to teach English to seminary students from all over French-speaking West Africa. There were various chaplaincies in the city to care for at weekends: he was officiating military chaplain to two regiments, with a large congregation for their Sunday Mass, and said a 'Sunday House Mass' for the diplomats every Friday evening. He found it all most fulfilling.

A severe attack of hepatitis resulted in home leave to recuperate and then after a year's sabbatical he was asked to start a White Fathers' Community in Queensland. He spent eight wonderful years as Parish Priest of Kangaroo Point. But the need to start Communities in Poland, Mexico, Brazil, India, and the Philippines persuaded the White Fathers to withdraw from Australia and Father John, who had by now been made an Honorary New South Scotsman with Australian citizenship, was called to open a house in Edinburgh. Recently he was posted down to Totteridge, North London, to make weekend appeals, write and translate for the missions, and be general factotum (doing odd repairs and gardening). As he says, 'Never a dull moment!'

Father John's Ruby Jubilee Mass at St. Anselm's on May 30th 1998, which was a wonderful occasion for all those present, has already been described. We hope that he will return for other celebrations now that he is nearer home.

He has written to us, 'We can't be Catholic if we're not missionary – it's a contradiction in terms. Of its essence, a universal church has to be missionary and that right from the start. But missionary in various ways. . . . All of us must be aware of our World Wide Church. The Church of Kitobi,

Ouagadougou, or Kangaroo Point is Catholic only in so far as it represents all the Catholic Churches from all over the world – in so far as it is *the Catholic Church* in that particular spot.'

Father Adrian Walker, who was born on August 6th 1931, is the youngest son of the late Dr. Oliver and Mrs. Sibyl Walker of Shepherds Lane, who were both well-known members of the parish and much involved in its life. He studied at Allen Hall, Old Hall Green, and was ordained at Westminster Cathedral on June 11th 1960. He spent the next four years in Rome working for a Ph.D. and on his return was appointed assistant priest in Edmonton. He was a chaplain to London University from 1971 to 1974 and afterwards joined a team ministry in Bayswater.

In 1976 Father Adrian was made Parish Priest of All Saints, Pin Green, Stevenage, and from 1981 to 1987 he was a founder member of the Stevenage team ministry which jointly serves four parishes. He then went as Parish Priest to Our Lady of the Rosary, Staines, and in 1994 moved to St. Edmund's, Isle of Dogs, which had been without a priest for some months. The church had to be demolished in 1995; Father Adrian says weekend Masses for his parishioners at St. Luke's Anglican Church. He is now engaged in building a new church complex.

Work began in the summer of 1998. On April 23rd 1999, Cardinal Basil Hume, who had told his clergy a week before that he was terminally ill, came to Millwall to bless the foundation stone. Ruth Gledhill wrote of the ceremony in her *At Your Service* series in *The Times* (May 1st 1999), 'Cardinal Hume, probably the country's best-loved spiritual leader, hopes to live long enough to see this church completed in November, as well as to see 2000, deemed a Holy Year by the Pope.

'We all shared an underlying concern for the Cardinal and the only thing that dampened the occasion was the rain. With his characteristic combination of dignity and bonhomie, the Cardinal smiled, joked, and chatted with the parish priest, Fr. Adrian Walker, and his stalwart band of parishioners. . . .

'The Cardinal sprinkled the stone with holy water. "God our Father, we thank you for bringing us together for the blessing of the foundation stone of St. Edmund Rich in Millwall. May this new building always be used for your honour and glory and for the good of the people of this community."

'About £100,000 still needs to be raised by parishioners, but they are determined to see their church rise again.'

Cardinal Hume has not lived to see the opening of the new church. His death on June 17th 1999 has been mourned by the whole nation but we may surely trust that his prayers for St. Edmund's will be even more powerful as he looks down from his 'high place in heaven'.

Father Anthony Porter, who is the nephew of Father Henry Porter, grew up in Dartford, where his parents and sister were all involved in the life of the parish. After studying at Wonersh he was ordained in 1962. He served as assistant priest at Norbury, Tunbridge Wells, and then at St. Joseph's, New Malden. In 1978 he was taken ill and was in intensive care. In his short time at St. Joseph's he had already won the regard of parishioners and made lasting friendships. Since that time he has had an unending struggle with ill-health. He was in turn at the English Martyrs' Church, Streatham, then for a second spell at Norbury, and afterwards at its daughter church of St. Michael, Pollards Hill, where he was appointed Administrator of the new parish. His health forced him to slow down and he moved to St. Edmund of Canterbury, Beckenham, helping the Parish Priest for as long as possible before eventually retiring. Father Anthony still takes a kindly interest in St. Anselm's. He is remembered in the parishes where he has served as a very committed and determined priest.

Father Patrick Cannon was ordained in 1968. Father Paddy has spent nearly twelve years as a missionary in Peru. He went there under the auspices of the Society of St. James the Apostle, a missionary society of diocesan priests in America that was founded by Cardinal Cushing and is run from Boston. Most of his years in Peru were spent in Chimbote, a big fishing port, where he was Parish Priest. The people there depend for their livelihood on anchovy fishing. Recently the fish have been affected by illness and the factories have had to close, causing great poverty of a kind unimaginable in most of Europe. When Father Paddy returned home he assisted in Stockwell at St. Francis of Sales and St. Gertrude for a short time and in 1998 he was appointed Parish Priest of St. Benet's, Abbey Wood.

Father John Peters was born in 1910 and was received into the Catholic Church in 1931. He was very well known in Dartford. He married, very happily, and lived and worked here for many years, eventually becoming manager of the Dartford Cooperative Society. It was after the death of his wife, Evelyn, in 1970 that he was called to the priesthood. He studied at the Beda in Rome and in 1976 became the first priest to be ordained at the new St. Anselm's. He was appointed assistant priest at the Church of the Holy Rosary, Brixton, where he remained for fourteen years. He was tireless in visiting the sick and the elderly and was greatly loved in the parish. In 1990 failing sight and health forced him to retire and he moved to St. Peter's House, in Lambeth. He was cared for devotedly by the Little Sisters of the Poor until he died, on July 26th 1995. Archbishop Michael Bowen, Bishop John Jukes, and many priests of the diocese came to St. Anselm's to concelebrate his funeral Mass on August 3rd. Father John is buried beside his wife in the graveyard of St. Michael's (Anglican) Church in Wilmington. After his death, Elsie, his daughter-in-law, gave his chalice to St. Anselm's. In it is incorporated a gold cross made from his wedding ring. The chalice is a lasting reminder of a priest known as 'a very kindly man, with an uncomplicated faith'.

Father Stephen Haylett was well known in Dartford before he became a Catholic. He served as deacon at St. Alban's Anglican Church while preparing for ordination as an Anglican priest. He gave great support to Life and he was invited to join the Life council; his cheerfulness and optimism and his great kindness are remembered as well as his practical help and advice in organizing an Anglican *Day for Life* at Our Lady's School.

Father Stephen's reception into the Catholic Church and his ordination to the Catholic priesthood in 1996 are recorded in Chapter Seven.

Dom Augustine Holmes, OSB (Stephen Holmes), has chosen the contemplative life. He entered Pluscarden Abbey in 1990, took simple vows in 1992, and was solemnly professed on St. James' Day, July 25th 1995.

He was born on June 10th 1965 at 18 Lonsdale Crescent on the Fleet Estate, and attended Dartford Grammar School. His parents moved to Derwent Close when he was thirteen. He was baptised into the Church of England by Canon Griffin at Holy Trinity while at the Grammar School and as a sixth-former he would often cross the road in the lunch hour to say a prayer at St. Anselm's. He went up to the University of St. Andrew's in 1983 where he read Medieval History, and he was received into the Catholic Church in Folkestone in 1985. Whenever he was at home with his parents he came to Mass at St. Anselm's, during vacations from St. Andrew's, then Cambridge, and later Downside School, where he taught for two years. Dom Augustine writes, 'Visiting the Blessed Sacrament at St. Anselm's did play an important part in my conversion, as did my knowledge of Dartford's Catholic past.'

Pluscarden Abbey, near Elgin in Morayshire, which was originally founded in the thirteenth century, was started again in 1948 by a group of Benedictine monks from Prinknash in Gloucestershire. Since then they have been restoring it to its former beauty – by their physical labours and by their prayers, recreating an atmosphere of quiet reflection and of work dedicated to the glory of God, in the spirit of St. Benedict.

Although a professed monk, Dom Augustine is not at present a priest as ordination is not essential for the monastic life. Pluscarden is the northernmost Benedictine Abbey in Britain and in the world. The monks are hospitable, sharing their Benedictine peace with guests who wish to make a retreat at the Abbey.

Sister Monica of Jesus, OCD (Monica Byrne) who was born on June 18th 1905, was the eldest daughter of Mr. Edward and Mrs. Catherine Byrne and the sister of Father John, Canon Maurice, and Father Michael. When Monica was only six her mother had to explain to her that girls could not be priests but she could be a nun instead. Mrs. Byrne's poor health made her an invalid early on and it was Monica who mothered the youngest children.

She attended the Ursuline Convent and turned down a scholarship to Dartford County School. For ten years after leaving school she worked in Westminster for Mobiloil, helping to support her family. She also wrote stories for the *Catholic Fireside*, which enabled her to join pilgrimages to Rome and Lourdes. Two of her brothers were by now at the Seminary.

In those years, Monica found time, miraculously, to write plays for a youth club, which were put on in St. Alban's (Anglican) Hall, and she also wrote songs which she fitted to well-known tunes. She had a dramatic gift and got the children acting. (Later, in Carmel, she kept this up and wrote plays for the nuns' entertainment, and also hymn words.) She spent spare time every year with Our Lady's Catechists in the hopfields in the Weald of Kent where families from London would camp for the harvest. Capuchin friars from Peckham and Erith came down to offer Sunday Mass and with the catechists prepared the children for the Sacraments. Monica and her father, who was a convert, trained as speakers for the Catholic Evidence Guild under the guidance of Frank Sheed and Maisie Ward and, late on Saturday afternoons, as their turn came up, they addressed the passers-by from a stand in Dartford Market Place, and let themselves be heckled.

Monica's involvement in the work of gathering together the first congregation in South Darenth, with the priests of the Travelling Mission, has been described earlier. There is a sense in which she will always be a patron of St. George's.

It was not until 1930, after the death of her grandmother, who had needed her, that she felt free to become a nun, and it was only after her entry into Carmel that her prayer for a hut in South Darenth to be used as a church was at last answered. She was received as a postulant at the Carmelite Monastery in Hatfield on October 22nd 1930, clothed in 1931, and professed on June 23rd 1932. Her monastery has moved twice in search of greater peace and is now in Ware. The intention in going there was to pray especially for the student priests and the contact is still maintained even though the Seminary is now in Chelsea.

Her knowledge of accounting seemed a godsend to a Community surviving on a shoestring and the nuns recall that everything she touched came to life. Reclaiming rough ground in the garden, keeping up the supply of altar breads, the main source of livelihood for the nuns, or launching the printing of Christmas cards, whatever she was engaged in, Sister Monica's initiative, common sense, attention to detail, and concentration could be relied on. Her kindness and her smile are remembered, the careful tuition in the liturgy she gave to younger nuns, and also her dramatic gifts. Until the final years of aging and infirmity she remembered every detail of the concerns of her visitors and their families. For sixty-five years she remained faithful to the exacting prayer life of her religious community, her peaceful and loving presence reassuring the young nuns as they arrived over the years. The intercessions of Carmelites are far-reaching; we can never measure our debt to contemplative nuns and monks. The story of Sister Monica's serene death on December 31st 1995, the Feast of the Holy Family, has already been told. We may surely trust that like St. Therese of Lisieux she will continue to work hard in heaven doing good for us all here on earth.

Sister Jane Wilkinson, the only daughter of Mr. John and Mrs. Kathleen Wilkinson, grew up with her brother Timothy in the family home in Devonshire Avenue, Dartford. She first thought vaguely of religious life in her last year at Our Lady's High School. She put the idea to the back of her mind for several years at University (Southampton, followed by Reading) but the wish to give her life to God came back during a year she spent working in Israel. Then she came to know the Sisters of the Presentation in Exeter. She lived in a lay community for a year, in a house belonging to the Sisters next door to the Convent; she felt drawn more and more to their way of life and realized that it was in that Congregation that God was calling her to be a Sister. She says that what attracted her first and foremost was their sense of fun and the laughs they had together, and as she learned about the charism of the Congregation her confidence grew and their Foundress, Marie Rivier, became an inspiration and a model. On September 8th 1986 she became a postulant and on November 21st 1987 she began her novitiate. Her first Profession in 1989 was followed by Final Profession on June 24th 1995.

Marie Rivier, who was born at Montpézat at the foot of the Cévennes in 1768, was one of the youngest people ever to become an apostle. She promised Our Lady at the age of five to gather little ones and tell them to love her. When only sixteen months old she had been crippled by a fall and for four years her mother had taken her to pray before a statue of the Pietà.

Marie had pleaded with Our Lady constantly, 'Holy Virgin, cure me and I will gather little ones around you. I'll teach them and show them how to love you dearly.' She began to walk on September 8th 1774, the Feast of the Birthday of the Blessed Virgin Mary, and she kept her promise. When she was eighteen, leaving everything she possessed, with four companions she founded the Institute of the Presentation of Mary. In spite of the ferocious persecution of the Church during the French Revolution, she and her companions secretly summoned people to prayer and devoted themselves to Christian education. They opened forty-six schools in nine years under the threat of the guillotine and by the time of her death in 1838 the number had risen to 141.

Marie Rivier's Sisters now work in nineteen countries. The convent in Exeter, their only foundation in England, opened in 1896. Sisters of the Presentation serve in many fields: adult education, catechetics, missionary, pastoral, and university work. They have opened houses of prayer, dispensaries in mission countries, old people's homes, and student hostels, and they care for children with HIV and Aids.

Sister Jane taught at the Sisters' school until they gave it up a few years ago. She then worked as an occupational therapist in a small community hospital in Exeter , where she was very happy. In 1999 she moved to a convent of her Order in Toulouse, to help at a university hostel and chaplaincy run by the Sisters. She is still a regular visitor at St. Anselm's when she comes home for her holidays.

Father Osmund Lewry, O. P. (Patrick Lewry) was born on May 8th 1929, his parents' only child. They were Anglicans. His mother was a Sunday School teacher; she became a Catholic when her husband, a professional soldier, was away at the war. The family were living in Barnehurst when Father Osmund started at Dartford Grammar School in 1940 but later he is said to have lived on the outskirts of Dartford and Swanley. His connection with St. Anselm's parish is unclear but it is virtually certain that he was one of the Dominican students mentioned in parish records in 1951. He told Sister Immaculate Heart Lawler, O. P., when she was studying at Spode House, that his interest in medieval history, and especially in the local records of Dartford Priory, was a strong influence on his decision to become a Catholic. (She adds that he often spoke warmly of St. Anselm's.) He said he had 'read himself into the Church' between his tenth and twelfth birthdays. Father Osmund used also to speak about the Priory to Father Simon Robson, the friar who cared for him in his last illness, and who tells me that the Priory may claim him too, as it was through Father Osmund's influence that he himself decided to join the Dominican Order.

He spent four years at University College, Leicester (he had had pneumonia just before his finals), and then applied to join the Dominicans. His Latin was not good enough as he had taken the 'Modern Course', for science, at school so he decided to teach himself while doing his National Service. He did well in the army and was offered a commission, which he refused, as he was intent on his vocation. He received the Dominican habit in September 1953, was professed on September 27th 1954, and ordained to the priesthood on September 29th 1959.

He died when he was only fifty-seven. In the last few weeks of his life, at the request of his Order, he wrote an article on the Dominicans who had influenced and sustained his vocation. He called it, *'Surrounded by so great a crowd of witnesses . . .'* It was published in June 1987 in *New Blackfriars*, after his death, instead of the conventional obituary. The following account is based on these few very moving pages and on other information provided by his Dominican friends.

He writes of himself as an eleven year old convert reading the C.T.S. pamphlets that he found at the back of his local church. In them he first met some of the great Dominicans. He was struck particularly by the individuality of Bede Jarrett. As an undergraduate at Leicester, where he studied chemistry and mathematics and was President of the Student Union, he made time for lectures on Dante given by Father Kenelm Foster, O. P., and met other Dominicans. He himself lectured at Vaughan College, the Adult Education Institute in Leicester, and trained as a speaker for the Catholic Evidence Guild. His stand was next to the pungent open-air fish market. He was searching for the truth and he disliked the Sir Arnold Lunn style of anti-evolutionary dialogue which to him seemed 'obscurantism'. He was drawn to the Dominicans at Holy Cross parish, admiring them as people with a breadth of vision and loving the beauty of their liturgy. He decided that to become no more than a chemistry teacher after gaining a glimpse of 'Christ as the unique road of access to the Father's love' would be 'an eleventh-hour idleness of the market-place'.

After finishing his National Service (and having now learned the required Latin), at the age of twenty-four he was able to join the Dominicans. He studied first at Woodchester and later at Hawkesyard. His friends there remember his quiet sense of humour – a little mischievous at times. His ordination, in 1959, was at Blackfriars, Oxford. He spent a year at Manchester studying mathematical logic before returning to teach at Blackfriars. From 1962 to 1967 he was again at Hawkesyard, teaching logic and reading for an S.T.L. He was one of a group of very famous friars there at that time. In 1968 after another year at Oxford he went to Stellenbosch in South Africa to teach theology. He loved the priory and the humanity of the friars there, their brotherliness extending outwards to combat apartheid.

Ten more years at Oxford were devoted to giving innumerable retreats and lectures, writing his first book, *The Theology of History*, teaching at Blackfriars and working for a D.Phil. He was widely sought as a confessor, being known as a man of compassion.

In 1979, now aged fifty, he began a new phase of his life at the Pontifical Institute of Medieval Studies at Toronto, where he soon proceeded from being a Research Associate, to Visiting Professor, Junior Fellow, and finally Senior Fellow. He was teaching, supervising, writing and giving himself as priest. His publications in those years included, *Grammar, Logic and Rhetoric, 1220-1320*, which was a chapter of *The History of the University of Oxford* (1986), *The Rise and Fall of British Logic* (1985) and *On Time and Imagination* (1987). He carried on the prayer group for the undergraduates that his predecessor had started, altering it but retaining the rosary. He was looking forward to continuing the work he had been engaged on in Toronto when he returned to Oxford, but fatal illness intervened. *The Times* said in his obituary that he had died 'at the height of his powers and at the beginning of a richly-promising scholarly career'.

Like Father William Nolan, Father Osmund impressed those who knew him by his serenity in the face of death. He was delighted to be shown a copy of his last book when he was already very ill, and he was working to complete his memoirs until a few days before he died. After quoting from *Hebrews* (4.9): '. . . there remains a sabbath rest for the people of God, for whoever enters God's rest also ceases from his labours as God did from his,' he concludes with the words: 'It is for the joy that is set before me that I endure this cross and despise this shame of a dying witness to Christ crucified and ultimately glorified.'

The official Dominican obituary notice ends with this tribute: 'Osmund, who himself had been so grateful for the witness of older brethren, became himself, in fact claimed to become, a witness for all of us who seek to attain the true Dominican character. He was cared for with love and devotion during those last months by his brethren at Blackfriars, and most especially by Simon Robson. He died on Easter Wednesday, April 23rd 1987, with the community gathered round him singing the *Salve Regina*. He was 57 years old.'

Sister Mary St. Paul (Bridget) Evans is a Canoness of St. Augustine of the Congregation of Our Lady (C.S.A.). I realised very late that she was once a parishioner of St. Anselm's and I am grateful for her generous response to my request for information about her vocation.

She was christened at the Anglican church of St. Peter and St. Paul, Farningham, and has 'lovely memories of the church bells ringing down in the valley and audible on Farningham Hill', where she lived with her family for the first ten years of her life. Her father, Captain Evans who was Anglican, was an engineer with J. and E. Hall. Her mother was a Belfast Unitarian. Sister St. Paul inherited her love of history from them both. The family moved away during the pre-war depression but returned when Captain Evans was appointed Chief Air Raid Precautions Officer to the Borough of Dartford; they lived in a house called Little Trinity in the Hawley Road. As her mother was not supposed to believe in a Trinity the family teased her over this.

Sister St. Paul writes:

'From the autumn of 1938 I was at University and spent only the vacations at Dartford. My father had to work hard to get necessary precautions in place and to get official people to realise how urgent these things were. . . . Although there was no attack by gas, Dartford was pretty hard hit by the bombing, the river making it easy to identify. We knew, of course, that London was getting it far, far harder.

'At Cambridge I was fairly sheltered from the hostilities, though the College took A.R.P. very seriously and a number of students volunteered for fire-watching at key places in the University.

'Now early in 1939 a student friend who was reading English was anxious to go to a Catholic church and be present at Mass, solely because her Supervisor (name for a tutor in Cambridge) said that one could not understand medieval literature unless one had done this. She was scared of going to a Catholic church unaccompanied, so another girl and I volunteered to go with her. The main Catholic church in Cambridge is a huge affair (and also a well-known bus-stop) and not only could we not miss it but once inside we could easily escape notice. We were greatly intrigued by the High Mass. I was a little put off by the Latin 'because they pronounce it all wrong' – I was reading Classics! But on the whole we were all three sufficiently interested to want to go again and again and again. We existed on a diet of C.T.S. pamphlets (twopence in those days, with some fatter ones sixpence or even one shilling). As students will, we argued for long hours at a time; the upshot was, that two of us asked for instruction. Neither of the two was the girl who originally decided to attend Mass.

'Where we were told to go for instruction in the Catholic faith was the house which at that time was serving as the Catholic Chaplaincy for Women Undergraduates – a house of the Canonesses. Why there had to be a Chaplaincy for women was that the University Chaplain refused – albeit with great courtesy – to have women in his Chaplaincy. He was Monsignor Gilbey, a wonderful priest and a fine character; he just had this bee in the bonnet. It wasn't until the early nineteen-sixties that he retired and the Chaplaincy became co-educational.

'Thus I became a Catholic in 1940. By the time I came to leave University, in the summer of 1941, there was a legal requirement to do war-work and I joined the personnel of the Government Code and Cipher H.Q. at Bletchley Park. Like 90% of the employees at B.P., I fulfilled only a lowly role, listing incoming coded messages so that the code experts could work on them. We did have, however, a lively sense of being involved in secret operations of great moment, and there was a very pleasant camaraderie as well.

'I began to think, though, of what I might do when the war was over. It seemed to me that having had the grace of being called into the Catholic Church it was perhaps incumbent on me to do something in exchange; perhaps to try and do something towards cleaning up the world which human beings seemed to have made such a mess of. I knew by that time that nuns were not the unhappy/devious/useless/oppressed women that many people thought they were, and it began to dawn on me that perhaps I could become one of them – though I thought too, that I was much too un-holy to presume to what seemed to me an exalted state. As the idea continued to take shape, I realised that for the time being I should have to wait, owing to the difficulty of freeing myself from my war-working state.

'In the end, however, I managed to extract a letter from Mr. Ernest Bevin, Minister for Labour, permitting me to leave my present employment to become a teacher; and so entered the Canonesses in 1944.'

The Congregation of Our Lady was founded in Lorraine in 1597 by St. Pierre Fourier in co-operation with Blessed Alix Le Clerc for the education of girls, starting in his own parish of Mattaincourt. He was a great saint of the Counter-reformation; working from within, he also reformed the Canons Regular. He was at heart a parish priest but his influence spread far and wide, and Pope Urban VIII said of him: 'I thank God that he has raised up such a saint in the Church during my tenure of the See of Peter.'

The Canonesses have been in England since 1904, when the teaching and nursing Orders were thrown out of France. Sister St. Paul spent many years as Headmistress of their school at Westgate and later was in turn Superior and Warden of Lady Margaret House in Cambridge, Superior of St. Leonard's and Provincial, and Warden and Chaplain of More House (the Chaplaincy for the West London Colleges of London University).

Later, while a Community member at Wandsworth, she greatly enjoyed teaching for two years in the prison until forced to retire because of her age. She is now at Bridlington 'trying to make people welcome', she says, when they come to the convent.

The Canonesses are fewer in number now in Europe than previously but in Vietnam, Brazil, and the Congo vocations are keeping up well. They say that in their history adversity always seems to have led to growth. So Sister St. Paul's dream in the dark days of the war has led her into more than half a century of cheerful and loving service or, as she would say, thanksgiving, to the Church.

Postscript

The details of Father Osmund's life have come to light since the completion of the rest of this chapter. Dartford Priory does not seem to have lost its power to draw people to God.

The English Province of the Second Dominican Order was restored by Father Philip (later Cardinal) Howard in 1661, 76 years after the death of Sister Elizabeth Exmew, the last of the Dartford nuns. Eight years later the new priory moved from its first home in Vilvorde to Brussels. In 1794 it was invaded by French Revolutionary soldiers and the nuns returned to England as refugees. Their life was difficult and precarious until 1866 when they moved to Carisbrooke, to a monastery built for them by Elizabeth, Dowager Countess of Clare. It was in the same year that Bishop Grant opened the first St. Anselm's Chapel in Hythe Street.

St. Dominic's Priory, Carisbrooke, remained a power-house of prayer for nearly 123 years but in 1989 when the Community was reduced to only five members they decided to leave. They were welcomed by their Dominican Sisters to their new home with them at Rosary Priory, Bushey. Sadly, two of the little group have since died. A third was asked to help a comparatively 'young' Dominican monastery in Lisbon, where she has remained. So the life of prayer continues.

St. Dominic's has been purchased by a new Trust set up by the (Anglican) Acorn Christian Healing Trust and is now known as Carisbrooke Priory. Volunteers have given their time to restore the buildings and the garden. There are weekly Open Door services, a group of Christian Listeners offer help to anyone in search of sympathy and kindness, and many activities have been started. There is an art group and there are lectures and exhibitions. Healing of many kinds is thus offered.

For some a visit to the Priory and a walk in the grounds are a healing experience. Several people from Dartford have enrolled as 'Friends'.

At the Installation of the Revd. Chris Lane as Chaplain in Charge of Carisbrooke Priory, on September 7th 1995, the Revd. Russ Parker, Director of the Acorn Christian Healing Trust, said that one reason to hope for a successful future for the Priory was that it was 'holy ground'. There had also been from the beginning a great mutual respect and kindness binding the Sisters who had been there before them with the new community, and a union of prayer. Interest in the Priory on the Isle of Wight is growing.

After being hidden by J. and E. Hall's Engineering Works for several generations, Dartford Priory, as it has been called until the last few years, has become visible again. The building is being cared for. People cherish the memory of their sacred places. Perhaps we may hope that in God's good time our Priory, that was 'holy ground' for so long, will be restored as a house of prayer and healing in the heart of the town.

Our story has a happy epilogue. In June 2000 the Vatican approved a new liturgical calendar of saints' days for England, to be used from the First Sunday of Advent 2000. Three of the changes are of special interest to us.

September 24th, until now the memorial of Our Lady of Ransom, will in future be celebrated as the memorial of Our Lady of Walsingham. The Shrine at Walsingham – the 'little town' where Sister Elizabeth Exmew and Sister Elizabeth Scygood took refuge during the first exile from Dartford Priory – was set up by the then Lady of the Manor of Little Walsingham, Richeldis de Faverches, in 1061. Our Lady had told her in a vision to build a Holy House that was to be a replica of the house at Nazareth – a home for Christ in England – so Walsingham became known as "England's Nazareth'. It was one of the four great shrines of the Middle Ages, with

Jerusalem, Rome, and Santiago de Compostella. It was dedicated to the Annunciation and was the first International Marian Shrine in the Catholic Church. It was suppressed by Henry VIII in 1538.

Catholic pilgrimages to Walsingham, in abeyance for three and a half centuries, were resumed in 1897 through the initiative of the parish priest of King's Lynn and the Founder of the Guild of Our Lady of Ransom. At the Anglican Shrine on the site of the old priory, the vicar of Walsingham began the work of restoration in the 1920s and later the Holy House itself was restored. The Catholic and Anglican Shrines together now attract half a million pilgrims each year and Walsingham has become a wonderful nurturing ground of ecumenism. It has been described by Bishop Alan Clark as 'a beacon of hope and of love and of strength to the Nation'.

Another change in the Calendar of interest to us all is that the forty canonised martyrs will in future be remembered alongside the beatified martyrs of the sixteenth and seventeenth centuries in one Feast of the English Martyrs on May 4th. This will coincide with the Church of England celebration of 'English Saints and Martyrs of the Reformation Era'.

Thirdly, the Feast of St. George, April 23rd, will be raised to the highest rank, to become the only Solemnity in the National Calendar. St. George is, of course, a patron of our diocese and our parish, as well as being since the time of Edward III Patron Saint of England.

Priests in charge of St. Anselm's Mission, Rectors and Parish Priests

Rev. Fr. Peter Maurice of Cossato, OFM Cap. 1851-1869

Rev. Fr. Louis Pellecetti of Castelferretti, OFM Cap. 1869-1872

Rev. Fr. Anthony Sansone of Montelupone, OFM Cap. 1872-1875

Rev. Fr. Liborius Contigiani of Urbisaglia, OFM Cap. 1875-1881

Rev. Fr. Louis Pellecetti, OFM Cap. 1881-1882

Rev. Peter Kernan 1882

Rev. C. De Latte 1882-1884

Rev. Edmund Buckley 1884-1887

Rev. Canon Robert Collinson 1887-1893

Rev. Charles Turner 1893-1897

Rev. John Wallace 1897-1902

Rev. John Moynihan 1902-1904

Rev. William Thompson 1904-1906

Rev. James Mahoney 1906-1916

Rev. Henry Plummer 1916-1923

Rev. John Evans 1923-1950

Rev. Albert Coleburt 1950-1988

Rev. Canon George Telford 1988-1992

Rev. Robin Maxted 1992-1994

Rev. William Saunders 1994-QDS

Assistant Priests

Rev. Fr. William, OFM Cap.

Rev. Fr. Edward, OFM Cap.

Rev. Fr. Thomas, OFM Cap.

Rev. Fr. Winceslaus, OFM Cap.

Rev. Fr. Aloysius Battocletti, OFM Cap.

Rev. Fr. Francis Xavier, OFM Cap.

Rev. Fr. Seraphin, OFM Cap.

Rev. Fr. Bonaventure, OFM Cap.

Rev. Fr. John Paul, OFM Cap.

Rev. Fr. David, OFM Cap.

Rev. Fr. Joachim, OFM Cap.

Rev. Fr. Clement, OFM Cap.

Rev. Fr. Joseph, OFM Cap.

Rev. Fr. Nicholas, OFM Cap.

Rev. Fr. Peter Francis, OFM Cap.

Rev. Fr. Angelo OFM Cap.

Rev. Thomas McMahon

Rev. Michael Cotter

Rev. Anthony Limpens

Rev. Alexander McAuliffe

Rev. Patrick Mackesy

Rev. William Thompson

Rev. Redmond Walsh

Rev. Thomas Fleming

Rev. Herbert Lawrence

Rev. Arthur Mostyn

Rev. Francis Ellis

Rev. L. J. Bourdelot

Rev. John Evans

Rev. Charles McNamara

Rev. Henry Plummer

Rev. Michael Crowley

Rev. Clement Innes-Browne

Rev. Edward Daly

Rev. Joseph Redmond

Rev. Aloysius Phillips

Rev. Gerald Quin

Rev. Desmond Coffey

Rev. Canon Peter Paul King

Rev. William Cashman

Rev. Francis Dorman

Rev. Patrick O'Grady

Rev. Patrick Abbott

Rev. John Forde

Rev. Thomas Hayes

Rev. George Stenson

Rev. Augustine Quealy

Rev. John Bluett

Rev. Francis Callanan

Rev. Patrick McGovern

Rev. Canon James Gilvarry

Rev. Patrick Gallagher

Rev. John Wright

Rev. Timothy O'Driscoll

Rev. Peter Clements

Most Rev. Maurice Couve de Murville

Rev. Brian Leahy

Rev. John Fitzgerald

Rev. Michael Winter

Rev. Michael Lane

Rev. Patrick Fitzsimons

Rev. Edward Adlem

Rev. Canon Francis O'Sullivan

Rev. John McCormack

Rev. Michael Clifton

Rev. Denis Barry

Rev. Myles Kenny, CCSp.

Rev. Edward Crowley, CCSp.

Rev. Gerald Healy

Rev. John Brady

Rev. Carmel Schneider

Rev. Laurance Bishop

Rev. Canon Michael Bunce

Rev. Canon James Pannett

Rev. Joseph Doetsch

Rev. Augustine Kinnane

Rev. David Gummett

Rev. Vincent Flynn

Rev. Geo'Ben Ezeani

Rev. Steven Fisher

Permanent Deacon

Rev. Maurice Williams

Parish Sister

Sister M. Ursula Hyland, RSM

St. Vincent's Parish Priests

Rev. Joseph Smith   Rev. Patrick Zammit

Assistant Priests

Rev. Edward Pereira   Rev. Michael Horkan

Permanent Deacons

Rev. Vincent Bowgett   Rev. Michael Dale

Parishioners ordained to the priesthood from the Parish of St. Anselm, Dartford

Rev. Henry Porter

Rev. John Byrne

Rev. Canon Maurice Byrne

Rev. Donald Wilkins

Rev. William Nolan

Rev. Michael Byrne

Rt. Rev. Francis Walmsley, CBE

Rev. William Hughes

Rev. John Sandom, W F

Rev. Osmund Lewry, O P

Rev. Adrian Walker

Rev. Anthony Porter

Rev. Patrick Cannon

Rev. William Cannon

Rev. Sean Osborne

Rev. Robin Maxted

Rev. John Peters

Rev. Stephen Haylett

Notes

Abbreviations

A   *Archaeologia Cantiana*
C   *Catholic Directory*, or for early years *The Laity's Directory*
D   J. Dunkin, *History and Antiquities of Dartford*, Dartford, 1844
F   S. K. Keyes, *Further Historical Notes*, Dartford
K   S. K. Keyes, *Some Dartford Historical Notes*, Dartford, 1933
L   Dartford Library Local Collection
S   Southwark Diocesan Archive

Chapter 1

1   M. Still, in *Under your feet*, Dartford District Archaeological Group, 1993, p 12
2   M. Leyland, *Interim Report*, A CVII, 1989, p 342
3   St. Bede, *Ecclesiastical History of the English People*, ed. L. Sherley-Price, London, 1990, pp 107-8
4   J. Timbs, *Abbeys, Castles, and Ancient Halls*, 2nd edition, London, 1872, p 312
5   K, pp 35, 40; and D, p 24
6   K, p 20
7   E. E. Reynolds, St. John Fisher, London, 1955, p 65
8   L
9   Bede Jarrett, *The English Dominicans*, London, 1921, p 10
10   Ray Midmer, *English Medieval Monasteries, 1066-1540: A Summary*, London, 1979, p 125
11   E. E. Reynolds, *Saint John Fisher*, p 247
12   Cardinal Gasquet, *Henry VIII and the English Monasteries*, 8th edition, London, 1925, p 183
13   D, p 126
14   Bridgewater, *Concertatio Ecclesiae Cattolicae*, Trier, 1558, Appendix
15   L. E. Whatmore, *The Carthusians under Henry VIII*, in *Analecta Cartusiana*, vol. 109, Salzburg, 1983, pp 108, 133
16   Will of John Roper, in *Archbishop Warham's Letters*, A, II, 1859, p 169
17   Dominican Nuns of Headington, *Dartford Priory*, Oxford, 1947, p 25
18   G. Ambrose Lee, *Blessed Margaret of Salisbury*, London, 1887, pp 45-46
19   L. E. Whatmore, *The Carthusians under Henry VIII*, p 102
20   G. Anderson Miller, *The Noble Martyrs of Kent*, p 21
21   L. E. Whatmore, *Highway to Walsingham*, Walsingham, 1973, p 106

22 Dominican Nuns of Headington, *Dartford Priory*, p 26
23 W. Gumley, *Obituary Notices of the English Dominicans*, Blackfriars, London, 1915, p 191
24 G. Anstruther, *A Hundred Homeless Years*, London, 1958, p 7
25 ibid, pp 7-8
26 ibid, p 14

Chapter 2

1 G. Anstruther, *The Seminary Priests*, Great Wakering, 1975, II p 321
2 E. H. Burton, *The Life and Times of Richard Challoner*, London, 1909, I p 63
3 ibid, I, p 196
4 Eamon Duffy, *Challoner and his Church*, London, 1981, p 22
5 *The Life and Times of Richard Challoner*, II, p 279
6 31 George III cap. 32
7 15 Vic. 15th June, *Proclamation against R.C. Processions*

Chapter 3

Information not otherwise acknowledged about Father Maurice is taken from 9 *Letters from the English Mission* to the Editor of *Annales Franciscaines*, preserved in *Annales Franciscaines*: Year IV pp. 368-375, 457-463, and 540-544; Year V pp. 69-74, 187-190, and 246-250; and Year VI pp. 13-16, 241-247 and 343-348.

1 *Maidstone Journal*, October 22nd 1851
2 L
3 Eric Doyle, *Canterbury and the Franciscans, 1274-1974*, Canterbury, 1974, p 21
4 L
5 L
6 For the information on Father Maurice's life in Italy I am indebted to Bro. Ferruccio Bortolozzo, O.F.M.Cap., Provincial Minister, Frati Minori Cappuccini, Turin
7 Stewart Foster, O.S.M., *Planned Expansion*, in *Mount Carmel*, Carmelite Press, Kensington, Winter 1990, p 197
8 Greenhithe Registers
9 S
10 S
11 L
12 S
13 Information kindly given by Bro. Thomas More Mann, O.F.M.Cap.
14 Ernest Oldmeadow, *Francis Cardinal Bourne*, London, 1940, p 34
15 S
16 D. S. Blake, C.F.C., *A Man for Our Time*, Dublin, 1996
17 *St. Vincent's Community Home Centenary Record, 1876-1976*
18 L

Chapter 4

1 – 3 S

4   L

5   John Burne, *Dartford's Capital River – Paddle Steamers, Personalities and Smallpox Boats*, Buckingham, 1989, pp 23, 45

6 – 11 S

12   St. Anselm's Handbook, 1975

13   Information kindly given by Dr. John Burne

14 – 17 S

Chapter 5

1   Information kindly given by the late Sr. Norah Browne

2   Sr. Dolores Heys, in *The History of the Sisters of Our Lady, Mother of Mercy, in Britain and Ireland, 1861-1982*, pp 1-19

3   S

4f   S

Chapter 6

1   *Dartford Times* (Leader), August 25th, 1993

Chapter 7

1   Sr. M. Angela Bolster, *Catherine McAuley, Venerable for Mercy*, Dublin, 1990, p 115

2   *Catholic Herald*, April 25th, 1997

3   B.C. Foley, Former Bishop of Lancaster, *The Story of the `Jubilee Years later called Holy Years, 1300-1975*, Lancaster Cathedral Bookshop, Cathedral House, Balmoral Road, Lancaster, LA1 3BT, pp. 1, 3, 7, 10, 14, 16, 45, 54-64, 78-9, 85

Chapter 8

I am greatly indebted to the priests, religious, and lay people who have answered my enquiries and provided information for this chapter, not least to Bishop Francis Walmsley, Fr. Michael Byrne, Fr. John Sandom, Fr. Adrian Walker, Fr. Patrick Cannon, and Sr. Jane Wilkinson. Generous help has been given by: Fr. John Weatherill, Fr. John O'Callaghan, Mr. Peter Wingate, Fr. Christian Daw, Fr. Brendan Burke, Fr. Barry Hughes, the Sisters of Our Lady of Sion, Worthing, Mrs. Sandra Jackson, Miss Audrey Butler, Fr. Colin Murphy, Mr. E. McCormack, Mr. W. McArthur, Fr. Augustine Kinnane, Fr. Michael Horkan, Mr. Laurence Burbridge, Canon John Madden, Mrs. Elsie Peters, the Carmelite Nuns of Ware, Fr. Bede Bailey, O.P., Fr. Aidan Nichols, O.P., Sr. Immaculate Heart Lawler, O.P., of the Pius XII Monastery, Fatima, Mrs. Joan Mark, and Dr. D. Lepine.

The Greenhithe Inscription

Father Maurice's Record of the First Baptism and First Mass at Our Lady of Mount Carmel, Greenhithe

The entry in the Greenhithe Register reads:

Ego infrascriptus baptizavi infantulum natum die 27 novembris (1863) ex Joanne Crawley et Maria Gummins, conjugibus et imposui ei nomen Jacobus. Patrini fuere Joannes Butler et Catharina Hurly ambo Catholici

~~Swanscombe Galley Hill~~ 25 Decembris 1863
Greenhithe
f. P. Mauritius O.M.C.

Anno Domini 1863. 25 decembris Natalis Domini prima missa celebrata fuit in Carmelis Domo ~~Gall~~ Greenhithe, in summa aegertate et paupertate . . . . . .
Ego imperscrutabili providentia Dei ad hoc magnum opus vocatus fui et licet indignus Deus non repulit me ut ministerio suo fungerer. Propter quod gratias agens ei qui vilissima utitur ad sublimia humillime subscripsi

f. Petrus Mauritius a Cossato
ordinis capucinorum

In English this reads:

I the undersigned baptised the baby boy born on the 27th day of November (1863) to John Crawley and his wife Mary (née Gummins) and gave him the name James. The sponsors were John Butler and Catherine Hurly, both Catholics.

~~Swanscombe Galley Hill~~ 25 December 1863
Greenhithe
Fr. P. Maurice O.M.C.

In the Year of the Lord 1863, on the 25th December, the first Mass of the Nativity of the Lord was celebrated in the Church of Carmel ~~Gall~~ Greenhithe, in very great sickness and poverty.
I was called to this great work by the inscrutable Providence of God and, unworthy as I am, God did not repulse me from working in his service. Giving thanks for this to him who uses the most worthless for his most sublime purposes, I sign with deep humility,

Fr. Peter Maurice from Cossato
of the Order of Capuchins

(Father Maurice's mistakes reflect his 'very great sickness')

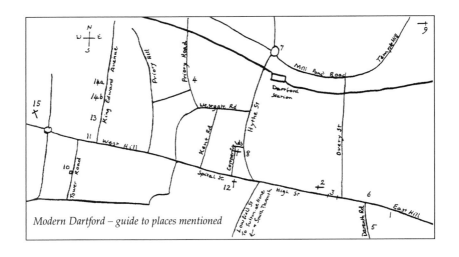

Modern Dartford – guide to places mentioned

KEY TO MAP

1 Roman burial ground
2 Holy Trinity Church
3 The Bridge
4 Dominican Priory
5 Site of St. Ronan's
6 The Martyrs' Memorial
7 Site of Gateway Cottages
8 Catholic Oratory, Copperfields, site of first and second St. Anselm's Churches
9 St. Vincent's Church, site of St. Vincent's School
10 23 Tower Road, site of first Ursuline Convent
11 Site of second Ursuline Convent, later Convent of Our Lady
12 Site of third St. Anselm's (1900)
13 Our Lady's Primary School
14a The Coleburt Centre
14b The Coldart Centre
15 Present St. Anselm's Church (1975)

Artwork and Typesetting by WHM Photosetting   Printed by G. Morbin, Sidcup, England

You, Me, and the Colors of Life

A NOVEL

NOA C. WALKER

Translated by Lisa Reinhardt

Text copyright © 2015 Noa C. Walker
Translation copyright © 2016 Lisa Reinhardt
All rights reserved.

Previously published as *Du, ich und die Farben des Lebens* by Amazon Publishing in Germany in 2015. Translated from German by Lisa Reinhardt. First published in English by AmazonCrossing in 2016.

Published by AmazonCrossing, Seattle

www.apub.com

Amazon, the Amazon logo, and AmazonCrossing are trademarks of Amazon.com, Inc., or its affiliates.

ISBN-13: 9781503940802
ISBN-10: 1503940802

Cover design by Shasti O'Leary Soudant

Printed in the United States of America

You, Me, and the Colors of Life

Janica

By the time I was three years old, I loved all things pink. It just happened. It wasn't like my family had done anything to encourage this—my mother preferred gray, blue, and green to girlie colors. At four, my dream job was princess, all dressed in pink tulle, of course. A year later, I saw a pink-dyed poodle, so from then on I wanted to be a dog groomer. It seemed like fate when, on my first day of school, my teacher wore a pink dress that perfectly matched the pink backpack my mother had grudgingly bought for me. At twelve, my dream job changed to wedding planner, then fashion designer— specializing in wedding gowns, of course. My future seemed all laid out, and my dearest wish was to one day celebrate my own extravagant, romantic white wedding—yes, white, not pink!

Now I'm twenty-four and I just completed my internship as a chimney sweep. I wear mostly black.

Chapter 1

April 27

The huge dark-gray Irish wolfhound trotted alongside the mountain bike, lit by the lightning flashes of its flickering headlight. Ears pricked and fur ruffled by the strong wind, he seemed to be enjoying himself immensely.

Janica pedaled faster, climbed the slight incline to the bridge, then coasted across. The bike's deep-treaded tires hummed over the asphalt, cutting through the distorted reflection of the crescent moon in puddles left from the last rain shower. Millions of sparkling silver stars danced on the river's surface. Somewhere, a church bell sounded four times, followed by eleven deep, resonant strokes that echoed through the muggy night. A solitary car approached from the opposite bank, turned onto the bridge, and headed toward Janica. Squinting against the glaring headlights, she thought she saw something move up ahead. Panicked, she slammed on the brakes.

Unprepared for the sudden stop, Balou dragged her several yards before scrambling to a halt and turning to give her a questioning look. The car crossed the bridge and disappeared between the rows of houses, the sound of its engine dying away. Janica peered at the nearest pillar and gave a start. A tall, broad-shouldered figure was standing on the gleaming metal railing, one arm flung around the pillar. The wolfhound caught the scent and wagged his tail eagerly, squirming like a puppy with a new toy.

"Lie down," Janica ordered.

Without taking her eyes off the black silhouette against the starry sky, she set down her bicycle on the sidewalk. Hesitantly, she took a few steps toward the man. Fragments of thoughts whirled through her head like bats, appearing out of nowhere and vanishing again. Had he noticed her? It was probably a good idea to avoid startling him. Why was he standing up there? Did he want to jump? Or was he just admiring the skyline?

"Pardon me," she ventured softly.

The man gave a start. Janica leapt toward the steel railing, but the man didn't slip—just turned his head robotically. His eyes were startlingly empty.

"Go away!" he barked and turned back to the river, seemingly fascinated by the black waves with their silver caps.

Janica swallowed hard. It was obvious that the man was not well. Was he actually going to jump? She leaned over the railing and looked down. This part of the river was shallow, and the rocks just below the surface would surely be fatal from this height.

She straightened up and looked around. The structure of cold stone and shimmering-blue steel lay deserted in the pale moonlight. There wasn't a soul around. No one to help her.

"I'm not going anywhere until you climb down from there," she replied in a shaking voice.

"Please leave me alone."

Janica frowned. Was it a good sign that he'd said "please"?

She noticed Balou creeping closer on his tummy, but she couldn't pay attention to the dog just then. Her heart was in her throat. Should she call the police? Or should she stay with the man, let him know he wasn't alone?

"I live just across the river. Would you care for a drink? It's lovely out on the balcony this time of night."

Janica rolled her eyes at her choice of words. She didn't want to give the wrong impression, but something told her that the chances of her offer being accepted were minimal.

"You shouldn't invite strange men to your apartment!" he scolded, giving her a reproachful look.

Janica suppressed a smile of relief. If he was still capable of worrying about the well-being of a stranger, he wouldn't jump, would he?

"I've got an excellent bodyguard," she said, trying to keep the conversation flowing.

She gestured to Balou, who took the opportunity to express his enthusiasm for the stranger with a furiously wagging tail, panting tongue, and tilted head.

"You mean this teddy bear?"

Was there a hint of amusement in his voice? What exactly was going on here? Janica felt like she was on dangerously thin ice. She was afraid she might lose her footing—or, worse, that he might.

Balou, on the other hand, jumped up and placed his front legs over the top rail, and nudged his new playmate with a wet nose.

The man blinked several times, then unclenched his fist and stroked the dog under his chin.

For a split second, Janica considered taking advantage of the distraction to drag the man off the railing but decided against it in light of his muscular build. She might cause the exact opposite of what she meant to do.

"His name is Balou," she said instead, noticing with relief how the man's angular, clean-shaven face softened. "And mine is Janica. What's yours?"

"Steffen," he said distractedly. "I've got a little dog. Moppel. A mix of everything and nothing."

He paused, and Janica felt a lump form in her throat as she watched despair return to his face. His gaze turned hollow, deep furrows formed on his forehead, and the corners of his mouth dropped.

"I had a little dog," he whispered before turning back to stare at the wide black ribbon dividing the city in half.

"What happened to him?" Janica pressed.

"My wife—ex-wife—kept him. For our daughter's sake. She's very attached to him."

"It's so nice for children to grow up with a pet," Janica said emphatically, thinking of the loyal Icelandic pony that had comforted her for so many years.

She guessed the man must be around thirty and wondered why he was already divorced at such a young age. Was that why he was thinking about ending things?

Janica took a deep breath and asked that terrible question out loud. But he just shook his head, then shrugged.

"My parents' accident, the divorce, the child's death . . ."

"You lost your child?"

Janica closed her eyes with pity. Was there anything worse than having to bury your own son or daughter? A small, innocent creature, their whole life ahead of them. Children should always outlive their parents.

"Not mine, but . . ."

The man shook his head and clenched his hand again. Displeased, Balou edged closer, still on his hind legs, and began licking the fist.

Headlights approached on the road along the river. The roaring engine suggested a heavy vehicle, but it turned down another street before reaching the bridge. Janica wasn't sure whether she was relieved or disappointed. The main road was humming in the distance, but not loudly enough to drown out the chirping crickets or the wind in the birches, willows, and beech trees. Here and there, a window was dimly lit, others flickered with the bluish light of a TV.

"I killed him."

A choking sound escaped Janica's throat. Maybe she should get out of here. His warning about strange men echoed in her mind.

Chapter 2

Janica's white T-shirt rustled softly in the breeze and a shiver ran down her spine. She tried to look relaxed as she leaned her head against the metal railing and stretched out her legs. She'd felt hot while riding, but now she was glad for her long jeans—it was cold on the bridge, and the sidewalk here wasn't particularly clean.

"We're commonly known as a task force, but that reminds people of the Nazis, so our official name is Special Forces Unit, or SFU for short. One week ago, we were called to a hostage situation at a single-family house. A distant relative was holding the wife and three children hostage. It was a confusing situation, especially since our negotiators were never able to make contact. We had no idea why the man was holding the family captive in their own home. The hours passed . . . until suddenly we heard gunfire."

Steffen paused and looked up at the starry sky. His posture suggested calm, but the erratic way he stroked Balou, who'd trustingly placed his head on the man's thigh, showed how troubled he was. The dog whimpered.

"The husband—the father—was going crazy."

"Understandably," Janica whispered.

"Yes, absolutely. I've got a family." Steffen ran his fingers through his short blond hair. "If anyone hurt my Marie—"

He broke off and buried his face in his hands, his broad shoulders trembling. Janica tensed up, realizing where this story was going.

"Are you sure you want to hear this?" Steffen asked, looking at her intently.

Janica smiled in spite of herself.

This man, who belonged to some sort of elite unit of the German police, was hurting so badly that he'd been ready to jump off a bridge—and now he was worried about her?

"Don't worry, I can take it."

If he only knew. She pushed aside the memories of her own past.

"We almost never need to use firearms. Shooting at a person happens once every eight to ten years, maybe. But that day, we found ourselves in a dangerous and chaotic situation. We feared for the hostages' lives and had to act. I had a clear shot at the man as he walked past a window, and I aimed for his thigh. The moment I pulled the trigger, my colleagues stormed the house."

Steffen paused to suck in air. It was as if an invisible force was pulling him to the bottom of a deep lake, and it took him several agonizing minutes to reemerge.

"And then that child, out of nowhere . . ."

Steffen's voice failed him. He pushed Balou aside, pulled up his legs, and wrapped his arms around them, wedging his head between his knees.

His words were muffled. "The little boy fought for his life, but today I got the phone call."

Janica pressed her lips together. Tears welled up in her eyes. She longed to put her hand on Steffen's shoulder, but she stopped herself. His body shook from the guilt and despair. All of a sudden, he sat up with a jerk, making her jump.

"If only I hadn't tried to spare that guy's life!" he shouted into the night, raging at himself and the whole world.

For a few seconds, the wind, the leaves in the trees, the waves, and even the distant traffic noise seemed to fall silent, as if the world was holding its breath in the face of so much pain.

"If I'd aimed higher, the family would still be together. I destroyed them."

"Steffen—"

"I destroyed my family, too!" he snarled at her. "My constant absence, my stubbornness, the obligation to secrecy—work always came between me and my wife. She asked me a hundred times to change divisions, but I didn't want to. It's tough getting into the SFU, and I didn't want to throw away all that training. I felt like I was doing something important!" Steffen paused to collect himself. "I guess I destroyed Marie's life, too. Children should grow up with both their parents."

Janica didn't reply. She had no idea what she should or shouldn't say. A child's death was always terrible, unnecessary, and unfair. Steffen knew as well as she did that he never meant to hurt the boy. But this gave him no consolation, didn't ease the pain in his heart and soul.

Janica wrung her hands. She'd never dealt with a suicidal man pouring his heart out to her on a sidewalk in the middle of the night.

Should she ask him to go see her father? He lived outside of town, but Steffen needed someone to talk to—someone trained in these things.

Silence descended over the two of them and the dog. The traffic noise seemed to pick up again, mixing with the rustling of leaves. Despite their proximity to the city center, the deep, plaintive hoot of an owlet came from somewhere nearby.

"It's late. I've kept you long enough," Steffen suddenly said in a sober tone.

"I don't mind. I've got tomorrow off."

"I don't even know what you do for a living."

9

"It doesn't matter."

"Save people who climb bridge railings?" he asked.

"Not every day."

"You're a good team, you and your dog."

Janica smiled and got up. She brushed the dirt off her jeans with both hands. Balou hopped up and stretched, yawning.

"Where do you live? I'd like to walk you home."

Steffen gave her a long look before replying, "There's no need."

"But I'd like to."

"Don't worry. Tonight . . ." He trailed off, suddenly seeming strangely weak and exhausted.

Janica eyed the changes in his face and posture with renewed suspicion. "Please, Steffen. I feel responsible for you now."

He gave her another one of those thoughtful looks, half closing his left eye while studying her. Janica expected a comment along the lines of "I can look after myself," but he just nodded and picked up Balou's leash. As he leaned down, Janica caught a glimpse of scar tissue from a bad burn.

He must have noticed her looking, because he straightened up and pulled down the collar of his dark T-shirt, revealing more scarred skin.

"I tried to save my parents from a car fire," he explained quietly, letting go of his shirt collar and nodding toward her bike.

Janica picked up the bike in a daze, thoughts whirling through her head like a storm. This man had watched his own parents burn to death. And now, the boy's death had been too much for him. She shook her head. On the surface, Steffen seemed tough and fit, but his soul must have been suffering for a long time, and his love for life had shrunk to the size of a tiny seed. But Janica knew that, with enough love and care, even the tiniest seed could grow into a strong tree.

Chapter 3

Thomas, dressed in nothing but pajama pants, his brown hair tousled by sleep, opened the door. Frowning, he looked at Steffen, whose eyes twitched nervously as he stared vacantly past him. Without a word, Steffen staggered down the dark hallway and disappeared into the spare bedroom. Thomas thought his elder brother looked like he'd taken some kind of drugs. He'd assumed Steffen was in his room, but now he realized he should have known better. Since the accident with the child, Steffen had spent every night pacing for hours on end, or else tossing and turning in the creaking guest bed, noisily muttering to himself. Tonight, however, the apartment had been quiet, so Thomas figured exhaustion had finally caught up with his brother. The poor guy had to sleep at some point, after all. And so did he! The sleep deprivation was already messing with him. Just that day, he'd done hall duty during recess—just like every Friday—not stopping to wonder why a different teacher than usual relieved him. After recess, he headed to the teachers' lounge—just like every Friday—to enjoy a coffee during his free period. Half an hour later, one of his students knocked on the door and asked why he wasn't coming. When Thomas asked with surprise whether he was supposed to fill in for someone, the student grinned and replied, "No, it's your math class! Same time every Thursday!"

Thomas's tired thoughts were interrupted by a female voice wishing him a good night. Confused, he looked up and saw a tall young woman, her unruly red hair tied up in a tight ponytail that seemed to glow in the light from a nearby streetlamp. The bright turquoise of her jeans leapt out at him, as did the neon-green laces of her sneakers.

Surprised that Steffen had brought a woman home—and annoyed at him for leaving her standing on the doorstep—Thomas stepped aside.

"I'm sorry, I didn't see you there."

"How could you? You're still asleep," she replied with a soft chuckle that made him grin.

"Please come in," he heard himself say, even though entertaining a visitor was the last thing he wanted to do at this hour.

The redhead's eyebrows shot up. She obviously hadn't expected the man who'd picked her up to be living with another man. She didn't look like a streetwalker, though.

"Thanks, but I'm headed home. I was just on escort duty."

"Escort duty?"

Thomas was wide awake now. Was this one of those mysterious female agents from the Special Forces Unit? No one really knew anything about them.

"Well," she stalled, turning like she was about to make a run for it.

She reminded him of a student who'd forgotten her physics homework at home.

"You can tell him, Janica, I'm going to bed," Steffen called before slamming the door to the guest room he'd been staying in for the past year or so.

Thomas was anxious to get back to bed, too, especially since the next day wasn't Saturday like he'd hoped, but Friday *again*. He crossed his arms over his bare chest and leaned against the doorframe. At least the nosy neighbor woman was asleep, so he was only embarrassing himself in pajama pants in front of *one* woman.

"When I met Steffen, he was on the bridge railing," Janica began, then shrugged helplessly.

Thomas understood immediately. The past year had been disastrous for Steffen, who had always been so resilient. His wife had kicked him out for good, and he hardly saw his daughter anymore. One of his best friends, the only one he'd had outside the Special Forces Unit, got in a climbing accident, went missing for a long time, and was eventually found dead. Then last week, the hostage drama and the ill-fated shot. The child had been the same age as Marie. Steffen had been sent to a police psychologist, but he didn't like how tough she was or her impatience with his customary chivalry. And on top of everything else, the first hearing about last week's terrible incident was scheduled for tomorrow. *Today,* Thomas corrected himself with a glance at the church clock.

"We talked for quite a while. About his divorce, the SFU, and the child, but I'm sure you know more than I do."

Thomas nodded, casting a glance down the dark hallway. Steffen had told a perfect stranger about his job? He'd never been this careless before. It was important for members of the Special Forces Unit to remain anonymous, for their own safety and that of their families. He must have completely lost it. Ready to jump off a bridge? Well, at least it would simplify some things.

Thomas cleared his throat.

"Your friend needs help," she said tentatively.

"He's my brother," Thomas clarified, turning his eyes back to the woman who'd saved his brother's life. He shook her hand and said, "I'm Thomas, and I'm sorry you got dragged into—"

"I'm not sorry!" she declared. "I don't know if your brother would really have jumped, but I'm still glad I happened to be there."

"Me, too. I'm so grateful for what you did. You're right: Steffen needs help. He saw a psychologist through work, but . . ." It was

Thomas's turn to shrug. Why was he opening up to a stranger this way? Is that how Steffen had felt, too? Had he also felt oddly comfortable with her, attracted to her attentive kindness?

"Perhaps it might be a good idea for him to speak to someone outside the police force?" Janica suggested.

Thomas leaned against the doorframe again. The woman could have just dropped Steffen off and left. She didn't even have to walk him home—in fact, she could have just pretended not to see him on the bridge.

"It's not that easy," Thomas muttered, lowering his gaze, suddenly conscious that he'd been staring at her. "He travels a lot for work. Then there's the secrecy and all the training. He has hardly any friends or social life. On top of that, his superiors would drop him the second they caught wind of any psychological stuff. With a job like that, he needs to be 100 percent reliable."

Janica rubbed her neck and stared past him down the hall. She seemed to be mulling something over.

"I know someone . . ." She trailed off, suddenly shy.

He gave her an encouraging nod. Any help for Steffen was worth considering. He felt his stomach cramping at the thought of Steffen actually trying to take his life. The familiar old pain coupled with the equally familiar fear of loss suddenly engulfed him. It took all his strength to turn his attention back to the extraordinary apparition standing on his doorstep.

Janica continued. "He studied psychology and theology and has a lot of experience with people in extreme situations—but he lives on an old farmstead more than thirty miles from here." She paused again and tilted her head to one side in a silent question.

Thomas shifted from one foot to the other, the chill of the night air creeping into his bones.

"Well, Steffen's on leave right now. Though there are hearings he has to attend. How do you know this person?"

"He's my father."

Thomas rubbed his cheek as he thought it over.

"Why don't you give me your phone number?" she said. "I'll give you a call in the morning once I've spoken to my parents."

Thomas nodded and disappeared into the house. He hesitated as he reached for a notepad. *Is she just trying to recruit a client for her father?* he wondered, but then shook his head. No one spends half their night helping a suicidal person and then tries to weasel money out of them. He scribbled his landline and cell numbers on the pink notepaper and went back to the door.

Janica accepted the little square of paper with a smile. "Red-currant-jam-cooking pink." She folded the note several times and stuck it in the back pocket of her unusual jeans.

Peculiar as the naming was, he had to agree with her: The color really did remind him of the foam on a pot of currants—and by turn, his mother.

"I better get going."

"Thanks again for your help."

"It was a shock to see Steffen up there on the railing. I'm glad he doesn't live alone." She hesitated a moment, then raised her hand in farewell and hurried across the stone tiles, finally disappearing behind the boxwood hedge.

Thomas heard a metallic scraping as she picked up her bike from the sidewalk, then a hushed command that sounded like it was meant for a dog. She rode off toward the river so she didn't need to pass by the gate again, which meant he couldn't catch one last glimpse of her. He sighed heavily. He should have offered to take her home. But she probably would have said no. No woman in her right mind got in a stranger's car. And she probably wouldn't want him to leave Steffen.

Thomas looked up at the starry sky. With the woman gone, the reality of what had happened hit him with full force. Steffen had tried to take his own life. If Janica hadn't happened to be cycling past at that late hour, his brother's body would probably be drifting downriver right now. Thomas closed his eyes. Steffen was the only family he had left. Didn't he realize how badly Thomas needed him? His strong, athletic big brother had always been his hero—always there for him, full of exciting ideas and a wonderful sense of humor. Thomas had always been the serious one, the one who color-coded his life, while Steffen happily mixed and matched.

Thomas also loved his sister-in-law and his niece. The two of them had meant family and home to him, but that safe haven had fallen apart like an abandoned house. Overwhelmed by grief, Thomas put his back against the door, slid down, and slumped onto the wide stoop. Leaning his head back, he stared into the vast endlessness of the black sky.

Steffen's inimitable sense of humor and his strong will to live, which had been especially evident following the death of their parents and his long hospital stay, had given way to a quiet, melancholic silence in the last few months. Thomas had noticed the change but taken it for a normal reaction to all the heavy blows his brother had been dealt. But clearly, his personality change had been more than a regular grieving process or a healthy period of reorientation. Pain had eaten its way deep into his brother's soul. Should Thomas have seen it? Done something?

A sigh rose up from deep inside him. At least it wasn't too late, thanks to a perfect stranger. At that moment, he wouldn't have been surprised if Janica had been dressed in a white robe instead of her white T-shirt and those Day-Glo jeans. To come riding onto the bridge at just the right time—at such a *strange* time! And to have found just the right things to say. She was like a guardian angel. Steffen's guardian angel.

Chapter 4

April 28

Janica lugged the black mountain bike up the shaking metal staircase, past the two other apartments, all the way up to her attic apartment. She set it down on the rickety landing and whistled for Balou, who hated both the steep climb and the metal grating. One time, Janica had stumbled over the dog and fallen, and ever since, he'd had to wait at the bottom of the steps until she whistled.

She opened the cherry-red-painted door, stripped off her gloves, and threw her keys into the hanging basket before closing the door behind Balou. Mechanically, she filled his water dish and prepared his dinner, which he wolfed down with great enthusiasm—it being much later than usual—while Janica headed into her blue-tiled bathroom to take a shower.

Her hair dripping, Janica sat down at the old, scratched oak table, which was as long as the entire kitchen and living area and had therefore been pushed against the wall, and poured herself a large glass of water from a bottle on the table. She gulped it down, poured herself another, and stared into the liquid, lost in thought as she made the water slosh from side to side.

"That was close," she muttered.

Balou looked at her with his head cocked to one side, then rested it back on his front legs.

Again and again, she went over the events of the last two hours. She shuddered at the thought of the young life that had nearly been extinguished—a life that still held as much depth and color as a rainbow. Drained, she leaned back, watching the play of light on water as she considered how to ask her parents to take in a very special guest. She didn't doubt for a second that they'd do anything they could to help, but they needed to be careful how much they took upon themselves. Her father had already burned out once.

Her thoughts turned back to Steffen. Hopefully, he wouldn't try to finish what she'd interrupted. Had he already made up his mind? Was his inner turmoil forcing him back outside—tonight, even? Tomorrow was the hearing, after all. Was he afraid of being indicted? Of a court case, a guilty sentence? Was the voice in his head pronouncing him guilty already? Did he believe his death would pay for the boy's life?

Of course, he'd just wanted to help that poor family. And yet, there would be a formal investigation. It was probably standard protocol. Still, it must be so awful for Steffen to have to explain what shouldn't have happened—what had neither been planned nor wanted and yet still happened—and to repeatedly relive that brief, fateful instant. He shared the parents' and siblings' pain. Would the officials at the hearing get that? Did the boy's relatives have any idea how much their son's killer was grieving his death? Or were they intending to press charges?

Brooding about it wouldn't get her anywhere. Tired, Janica struggled to her feet, left the water on the table, and went into her tiny bedroom decorated in warm pastels. She sank into her pillow and lay there for a long time, wrapped up in her thoughts. She hadn't crossed that particular bridge at that particular moment by chance. She had been destined to find Steffen. Their paths had crossed for a reason. She was as sure of it as she was that, in just an hour or two, a new day would dawn.

Chapter 5

The golden reflections on the water were blinding as the sun came out from behind a cloud. Janica grabbed the sunglasses off the top of her head. A gust of wind blew corkscrew curls into her face, so she gathered her hair with both hands and plaited it with nimble fingers. The wine-red patio umbrella above her billowed and creaked in protest. As usual, Balou had his back paws on a piece of wood, front paws flung over the railing, which spared him from standing on the metal grate. He'd been watching the cyclists and pedestrians along the river for over an hour. Having finally seen enough, he jumped down and disappeared into the cool apartment.

A short while later, booming footsteps on the metal staircase announced someone's arrival. Janica put her novel down on her stomach and listened, her feet braced against one of the lower rails. The footsteps paused briefly by the first door, then continued along the landing and up the next set of stairs. They stopped again briefly by the second door, then continued. Janica pushed her sunglasses back and waited until she saw a dark head of hair and a broad back: Thomas. His face was as earnest as it had been last night, and he seemed deeply troubled.

"Hello again, Ms., uh—"

"Janica's fine."

She looked at her visitor expectantly. She'd called early that morning to give him her father's number and the news that he'd agreed to meet Steffen.

"Steffen decided to meet your father," Thomas explained, sounding depressed.

Something must have happened, she thought.

"I took him to the hearing and picked him up afterward. But now he's locked himself in his room and won't talk to me."

Janica jumped to her feet. Her book hit the grate with a dull thud. "Is he—?"

"I don't think he's going to hurt himself. Before I came here, he was yelling and screaming at me to leave him alone. I'm sorry about just showing up like this, but I have no idea what to do. I don't want to call the police psychologist. I've got the feeling the two of them aren't going to get anywhere."

Thomas put his hands in his pockets helplessly.

"I don't know what to do in situations like this, either," Janica said, picking up her book.

"You did pretty well last night," he countered, obviously uncomfortable coming out and asking her for help.

"Out of necessity," she explained with a halfhearted smile.

"I know I'm asking a lot, especially since you don't even know us—but do you think you could come and talk to him? It might help. He's very much the protective type and would never hurt a woman or do anything that would make her feel uncomfortable."

"You do realize I can't be on call for him?"

"Of course! You've already done so much," Thomas replied, visibly embarrassed, shifting his weight from one foot to another.

Janica found his stiffness and his reluctance to ask her for help worrisome rather than annoying. If she had to rate Thomas on a color scale, he wouldn't make it past a boring gray or conservative brown.

"I—I'm just asking you to help me take him to see your father. Then you'll never have to see us again."

Janica folded up her deck chair with the book inside and leaned it against the gray-and-white plaster wall.

"Did you come by car?"

"It's in the no-parking zone."

"I'll be right there. Do you mind if my dog comes?"

He hesitated, then shook it off. "Not at all."

"I'll see you downstairs."

Thomas tried to hide his embarrassment behind a grateful nod and hurried down the stairs, which swayed from side to side. Janica pulled the protective cover over the umbrella and went inside. She pulled on a light sundress that she called her After Eight dress on account of its mint-green color and dark-brown piping, slipped into black linen shoes, and reached for her handbag.

Balou, who'd been sleeping on her bed—which he knew wasn't allowed and which explained why he hadn't rushed out to meet the visitor—followed her excitedly.

She paused at her door while Balou tackled the tricky staircase. Second thoughts filled her mind. Was she doing the right thing, getting into a car with these men she barely knew? She had Balou, who, despite his puppylike demeanor, did watch over her. Still, she didn't feel entirely comfortable, so she called her parents to let them know where she was going to be and with whom, then stowed her phone close at hand in a pocket rather than her handbag.

She climbed down the stairs and placed a hand on Balou's shaggy head. He followed her to the front of the complex, where an old, dark-blue Opel was idling. Before Thomas had a chance to get out, Janica opened the back door and signaled for Balou to jump in. Thomas winced as the dog greeted him enthusiastically, wagging his tail so hard that the car pitched from side to side. Janica heard a muffled cry as she headed around to the passenger door.

"You said dog, not bear." Thomas's voice was strained with ill-concealed reproach.

"Sorry. I always forget how big he must seem to strangers."

She clicked her tongue to stop Balou from giving the young man's face a full wash.

"Lie down," she commanded, and almost laughed at the relief on Thomas's face when the dog obeyed. She clearly didn't have anything to fear from this nervous young man, and Steffen must be too wrapped up in his own problems to pose a threat.

Thomas, who'd been wondering how on earth his brother was going to find room in the car, listened to Steffen and Janica's negotiation over the front seat. Clearly, his brother's chivalry was so deep seated that it functioned even now, in spite of him being a mess. In the end, Steffen won and squeezed in back with the dog, who placed his big head trustingly in the man's lap. Despite Steffen's halfhearted protests, Janica moved her seat as far forward as it would go.

"But you let me know before your legs fall off."

"I'm fine," Steffen insisted.

As he steered the car toward the main road, Thomas glanced in the rearview mirror and saw that bear of a dog closing its eyes with relish at his brother's vigorous petting. He thought how Steffen had always had a soft spot for dogs, while he himself tended to treat them with suspicion. His relationship with man's supposed best friend had a rather poor start when he was six. A German shepherd had jumped up on him, and, unprepared for the dog's considerable weight, little Thomas had lost his balance. He could still remember the fear as he fell backward into the lake. He'd even struggled with the comparatively small dog Steffen and his wife had gotten three years ago. Mostly, he'd tried to ignore the animal. Lost in thought, Thomas tapped a finger against the steering wheel. In addition to his wife and Marie, Steffen was probably missing the little ball of fluff, too.

His ambitious, successful, popular brother's life had been completely turned upside down these last few months. Bad luck had attached itself to him like a leech, and Steffen couldn't seem to handle the additional ballast. Now it threatened to drag him down a dark, bottomless whirlpool. Though Thomas didn't know Janica's father, he focused all his hope on the man. If he was anything like his daughter . . . radiating life, knowing all the right things to say.

He cast another glance in the mirror. Somehow, Janica had managed to coax Steffen out of his cave and maneuver him into the car. Or perhaps credit belonged to Janica's four-legged friend, aptly named after the happy-go-lucky bear from *The Jungle Book*. He wondered whether Steffen had taken the back out of courtesy or to be with Balou—a creature that wouldn't ask difficult questions, wouldn't make demands, wouldn't disappoint him like people did.

"Would you prefer to take the highway or country roads?"

Lost in thought, Thomas blinked several times at Janica's question. The young woman didn't seem to mind his rudeness. "Highway," he replied, wondering how anyone could prefer the slow, winding road through the backcountry to the highway, which wouldn't even be particularly busy this time of day.

Janica nodded, but he sensed her disappointment. She turned in her seat and smiled at the peaceful scene in the backseat.

"How was the hearing? Or would you rather not talk about it?"

Thomas cringed. Steffen had stormed out of the hearing and then locked himself up in his room the moment they got home. *How could she ask that?* The ordeal had obviously been extremely upsetting, which Janica should have known, especially given Steffen's state when she arrived.

"Not really," Steffen replied, cool but not impolite. He seemed to have a firm grip on himself in Janica's presence.

"Maybe later, when you've had time to digest everything," Janica replied easily, and turned back.

Steffen grunted his agreement. Silence set in again, interrupted only by the revving of the engine and the occasional clicking of the blinkers.

Finally, Thomas turned onto the highway on-ramp and stepped on the gas. He couldn't wait for this trip to be over and done with. He wasn't the type to make friends or go on adventures. His brother had always been the go-getter, but Thomas preferred his life organized and predictable. For her part, easygoing Janica didn't seem to mind changing her plans from one second to the next. Thomas found her warmth admirable and enviable on the one hand, but on the other, he worried that she might turn out to be an overly familiar nuisance. Who knew how clingy and pushy she could be? She was obviously a person of extremes, as evidenced by the size of her dog and the garish colors of her clothing.

Another half an hour passed in silence, each of them lost in thoughts that seemed to build up in the car like a cloud.

Thomas would have liked to know what it looked like, this fog of thoughts and emotions. Murky and dull from Steffen, worried and helpless from him, and spiked with Janica's peculiar insouciance and lightness? He gave a start when Janica told him to take the next exit, embarrassed by his absurd reveries.

They followed the road through rural hill country for a good fifteen minutes—passing through a handful of tiny villages sleeping in the summer sun, going around several lakes, and eventually turning off the main road into a dense forest. The narrow road wound its way uphill until the majestic spruce trees abruptly gave way to a view that made Thomas think they'd just driven into an oil painting. They were surrounded by sun-dappled green meadows and brown-and-yellow fields dotted with old farmhouses. Janica directed him down a dirt path, and he frowned. Any minute now, they'd probably reach the signpost marking the middle of nowhere.

After a good two hundred yards, the bumpy back road lined with dark trees ended in front of an extensive compound that—with its old stables, barns, and sheds—must once have been a working farm. The shutters and front door, as well as the huge barn doors, had been painted a cheerful red. Thomas saw white and gray geese waddling freely around the yard, and chickens were pecking excitedly under an archway by the stables. He climbed out in a daze and leaned his crossed arms on the roof of the car. Opposite the house, just beyond where he'd parked, a meadow covered in wildflowers cascaded down a steep slope. A murmuring creek snaked down the hillside. On the next rise, several horses were grazing in a paddock enclosed by a log fence. Thomas took in the forest around them—the grove of white birches, the weeping willows swaying in the wind along the creek—and thought he must be in paradise.

He inhaled the warm air greedily, taking in the smells of soil and forest, and felt a sudden, almost painful, longing for freedom and fulfillment. *What a perfect place to bring Steffen,* he thought, feeling infinitely grateful to Janica.

The frantic barking of the wolfhound charging past directed his attention to the neat farmhouse. One of the huge red barn doors had opened, and an elderly man with gray hair and a fuzzy beard, very similar in color to the dog's coat, stepped outside and was promptly pinned against the second door by an exuberant Balou. The fact that Janica wasn't calling off her dog told him that Balou's latest victim didn't mind the boisterous greeting.

The chickens cackled in protest as a chubby woman came rushing through the archway, her red curls giving her away as Janica's mother. She hurried toward her daughter, flowery skirt billowing around her legs like a field of wildflowers in the wind. The woman wrapped her arms around Janica.

To his annoyance, Thomas felt a tiny jab in his heart. He was a grown man, almost thirty, but he still missed his mother's embrace. This reunion looked deeply heartfelt, even though the two women probably saw each other regularly. The mother seemed so relieved to find her daughter alive and well that you'd think Janica was just back from three years in a war zone.

Then Balou and Janica swapped positions as if they'd done it a hundred times before. Janica's father held her just as tightly as her mother had, but the dog behaved quite differently. He approached the woman with a wagging tail, pressed himself against her legs, and held still while being patted like a carpet in need of cleaning. Balou clearly knew that Janica's mother didn't want one of his full-body hugs.

Steffen, who'd been waiting by the car with his brother, began walking toward Janica's father. His confident stride irritated Thomas, though he also couldn't help admiring how Steffen had gotten a grip on himself.

But Janica's father frowned. He didn't seem deceived by the young man's feigned normality. "You must be Steffen Hejduk? I'm glad you decided to come."

Thomas didn't catch Steffen's reply, as he found himself being greeted by Janica's mother. She gave him a warm, sincere smile and invited him into the barn for coffee. Surprised, he followed the two women through the red door. The former barn had been lovingly converted to a kind of cafeteria, with the old wooden beams now serving as rustic decoration. A counter ran down one side of the room, holding a chilled display cabinet containing three different cakes, a fully automatic coffeemaker, and a basket of savory baked goods. In front of the bar stood two long picnic tables, one of them set for five people.

"You made me cheesecake?" Janica exclaimed, helping herself to a large piece. "And without wrinkly brown raisins!"

Thomas grinned to himself. It took so little to make Janica happy. A drive through the country rather than along the boring highway, no raisins in a cake, and she beamed like she'd just won the lottery.

Thomas sat down next to Steffen, who was also looking around the room with admiration.

"Do you board backpackers here?" Steffen asked.

"Yes, and our guests."

Janica's father pointed to a steep staircase leading up to the former hayloft. At the top was a landing with a banister running the length of four rooms. The red sign on a fifth door directed guests to the laundry and bathroom.

"Since this place is built into a hill, we even have wheelchair access to one of the rooms," the man explained, visibly proud.

Thomas, who already felt like an intruder or a supplicant, was a little embarrassed when Janica's mother served him some cake like a waitress.

Her father declared in his pleasant resonant voice, "We don't care much for formalities, so we'll use first names if you don't mind. My wife is Heidi, and I'm Peter. Yes, like the kids' book—but, no, we don't raise goats or wear long braids."

Chapter 6

A red hawk circled high in the deep-blue afternoon sky, and from time to time, its hoarse cries could be heard on the ground. Balou raced down the well-trodden path to the creek and hurled himself into the water, while Janica and Thomas trailed behind. The gurgling water, the crickets, the birdsong, and the horses, who snorted and shook off the summer's first horseflies, all contributed to Janica's beloved melody of peace, life, and home. As she'd expected, introducing the Hejduk brothers to her parents had gone well. Her parents made a good team. Over coffee, they'd described their life on this farm. Janica had watched as the young men relaxed—first, Steffen, and eventually, Thomas, too.

"Your parents are great," Thomas said as he followed her across the creek, hopping from rock to rock.

They walked over to the wooden fence, where Janica placed her arms on the sun-warmed top rail and rested her chin. The horses on the other side continued to graze, unperturbed by their visitors.

"They have a good instinct for people," Janica said. "Maybe because of how much they've been through themselves. Until recently, Dad worked as pastor for a large parish, but they didn't understand or appreciate him. He eventually collapsed under the workload and pressure.

We didn't hear him laugh for weeks, and he's normally such a cheerful person."

"Like Steffen."

Janica nodded in silence. She had no trouble imagining Steffen as an open and social person. She could tell those qualities were still there, deep inside him, buried beneath layers of heavy burdens. It was up to Steffen to take down the walls he'd built to protect himself. But he couldn't do it on his own, just like her father hadn't.

"My father helps people from firsthand experience. These days, he doesn't put much stock in what he studied. The theories they teach in psych and theology classes might apply to a certain percentage of the population, but it's not 'one size fits all.' His strength lies in the time he takes to get to know each person and their circumstances."

"That sounds good. I want my brother back the way he was before."

Janica gave a laugh. "That's impossible!"

"What do you mean? He'll never be the same?"

"No, he won't. Profound events like the one your brother's going through change people. They leave a mark. Sensitive people who have experiences that try to drag their soul down a dark hole never come back the way they were before—but they do have a chance to come back even better."

"Like your father?"

"Like my father. Just look around." Janica's arm swept through the air. "My father lived in the city all his life. He worked himself half to death. Now he's out here. He works part time for a nearby parish doing emergency pastoral care, and looks after the guests in my mother's B&B. He slowed down and simplified his life."

"Semiretirement isn't an option for Steffen."

"Maybe not." Janica laughed again. "What's important is that he realizes life is worth living. Problems, pain, and suffering are all part of the human condition. Not only so we know what happiness is, but also because they build character, change us, teach us."

"That's a bold theory."

"You think?"

Janica looked sidelong at Thomas. He avoided her eyes and watched the horses, frowning and silent, but Janica had a decent idea what he was thinking. He was probably wondering how someone so young could make such grand pronouncements. What could she know about suffering, her father's burnout aside? He couldn't see any point in his brother's suffering. He wanted a quick fix that would bring his strong, brave brother back as if nothing had happened.

Wasn't that the problem? With all the advances in medicine, with powerful anesthetics at their disposal, people didn't take pain seriously anymore, just suppressed it with drugs. A blessing, but also a curse, because pain could be a warning sign—a symptom of greater physical or mental problems. And what happened when it could no longer be suppressed?

And woe to him who dared fall seriously ill. How quickly the fabric of society ripped, failed them. People's hearts were sick in this regard, having been lulled into believing that everyone must be fit, beautiful, and perfectly healthy at all times.

Janica was about to share these thoughts when Balou decided he'd had enough of playing in the water. He scampered toward them and shook off, the wet air shimmering in all the colors of the rainbow. The drenched young man cried out in protest while Janica laughed heartily, which earned her an indignant glare. She ignored it and clapped her hands encouragingly. Balou practically exploded. He squeezed through the gate into the horse paddock and barked for Janica to follow. She climbed in and chased the dog, who ran ahead at first, but then turned so suddenly that his mighty paws sent dirt flying through the air. The colorful mix of Haflingers, Iceland ponies, and Fjord horses eyed him restlessly. After a few minutes, Janica was winded. Disappointed that the chase was already over, Balou jumped up on the fence in front of Thomas, who stepped back and frowned with disapproval.

Janica was sorry to see it. Obviously, Steffen was the one in dire straits, which wasn't surprising considering what he was going through, but his younger brother wasn't exactly full of life. He seemed serious and very proper, boring and uptight. He probably had his life perfectly under control—but what kind of life was that?

"Leave him, Balou. Thomas is a guest, not your playmate."

She laughed and felt the sun shining right into her heart. She loved being at the farm. It felt so good to laugh out loud.

"Go on, Balou, run! Get those lazy, fat ponies!" she cheered.

He didn't need to be told twice. Barking excitedly, he flew toward the seven horses. Clearly familiar with this game, they bolted, bucking and kicking with exuberance. The thunder of hooves filled the air and the soft ground vibrated as they galloped past. Their manes and tails waved like flags in the wind and their bodies gleamed in the sun.

"Isn't it a majestic sight?" Janica called without taking her eyes off the horses.

"Yeah," Thomas replied without conviction. "Aren't the manes of those light-brown horses usually kept short? So you can see the dark stripe inside?"

"The Fjord horses? We prefer to let their manes grow. But you're right, most of these ponies wear their hair buzzed like Steffen's."

This time she at least got a hint of a grin, confirming her suspicion that, somewhere deep inside, Thomas shared his brother's sense of humor. When had he buried it? At his parents' funeral?

A movement caught Thomas's eye, and he turned to see two men walking across a little bridge and continuing on toward the forest. He shaded his eyes with his hand and asked, "Is that Steffen and your father? Are they finally talking?"

"Either that or singing."

Thomas rested his arms on the fence and gave Janica a piercing look. "I thought you understood how serious the situation is. But I guess he's my brother, not yours. You don't have to care."

Janica took a deep breath as she watched the horses coming toward her. They turned sharply just before reaching her and galloped along the fence. The sharp reply on the tip of her tongue vanished. She smiled and climbed up onto the fence, perching beside Thomas's arms, still watching the horses and the dog.

"For your information: My father enjoys singing. Yes, I was joking, and yes, I know you don't feel like joking right now. You're worried about your brother and you have every right to be. But it doesn't help Steffen for you to fall into the same dark hole. What my father needed most when he was depressed was a family who was there for him, who kept life going, and who dared to crack a joke from time to time. I may not be a trained psychologist, but I know that laughter is the best medicine. It opens the heart and lets you see the good things in life. And there are good things in life, even in among all the dark and difficult places, even if they are hard for Steffen to find right now. And we're not helping him find those moments of happiness by banishing them completely. That's what I think, anyway. But like I said: I'm not trained in such things. My father is, though."

Janica turned toward Thomas, balancing carefully.

"Maybe Steffen is already talking about his problems. But maybe they're talking about the landscape, soccer, or the last trip they took. You told me Steffen didn't get along with the psychologist assigned through work—well, maybe that wasn't about her abilities, but the circumstances that brought them together. They'd never met before, knew nothing about each other, couldn't relate. My father would never offer advice before getting to know his patient. He's not under the same time pressure as Steffen's psychologist, and I bet she wishes she weren't, either. By the way, I wouldn't be surprised if my father asks Steffen to stay here for a few days."

"I see," Thomas muttered, and ran his hand through his hair with embarrassment. The gesture was almost identical to Steffen's. "Forgive me. I didn't mean to be rude."

"You're worried and impatient, and I upset you. Perfectly normal."

She winked at him, jumped off the fence, and whistled for Balou. The dog immediately started running toward her, but not without glancing back at the horses several times along the way. It was obvious how much he would have liked to continue the game. He squeezed back through the fence and ran right into the creek, drinking thirstily. Thomas watched the animal closely, and when Balou came out of the water this time, Thomas stepped aside so only Janica got showered.

Chapter 7

April 29

The streetlamps in the small villages had long been switched off, and merciful darkness blanketed all the pain and joy, the hope and seemingly unfixable troubles of their inhabitants.

Black night had descended over the hill country. As black as Steffen's life? Thomas sighed loudly in the quiet car. Only yesterday, Thomas's world had been perfectly fine. Well, apart from worrying about Steffen. And then, out of nowhere, a red-haired woman appeared outside his door and told Thomas something impossible: Steffen had tried to take his own life. Steffen, his big brother! Steffen, the funny guy, the charmer, the sports fan, the strong one, the model policeman in the Special Forces Unit, the popular golden boy, had tripped over the cruelty of life and didn't want to get back up? If anyone knew pain and despair, it was Steffen. It was he who'd tried to save their mother from the burning wreck, he who kept a level head in hostage situations and bank robberies, found the right words, remained calm and collected.

Thomas switched on the radio. Loud music with a thumping bass boomed from the speakers but didn't manage to drown out the voice in his head. It kept asking what he'd done wrong, told him to help his brother. But how? How could he help?

His thoughts returned to Janica. He was glad she and her family had taken Steffen in. Perhaps he'd manage to get some sleep out in that peaceful paradise. There was no one to disturb him, nothing to remind him of his former life and the blows he'd had to take. The hill on which the farmstead sat seemed out of this world, as if it were hovering in a cloud, far above death, pain, grief, and fear.

Also, for a few nights at least, Thomas wouldn't have to listen anxiously for his brother getting out of bed. He didn't have to sleep with one eye open, on guard in case his brother tried to harm himself again.

Dinner with the Meiers had been pleasant. Even Steffen had joined in the conversation from time to time, letting his wry sense of humor shine through—which hadn't bothered anyone except Thomas. How could Steffen stand on a bridge railing, intending to end his life, and then—barely twenty-four hours later—joke around as if nothing had happened? How serious had he been about jumping? Had Janica misread the situation? And had Steffen let her? Why? Had he been attracted to Janica from the beginning? Steffen had always been a bit of a womanizer.

But Thomas knew better. He'd seen Steffen after the hearing—his body a ball of tension and gloom, a deep furrow of disapproval and anger between his brows. Then, the moment he climbed into the car, he'd gone limp—frighteningly feeble. Steffen had trembled as if it were freezing cold, barely managed a coherent sentence, and locked himself in his room as soon as they got home, ignoring Thomas's pleas to open the door.

That was when Thomas thought of asking Janica for help. He shook his head at himself. What had he expected from the woman? She'd admitted she had no experience with suicidal people. She'd probably never even been depressed. And yet she'd instinctively said and done all the right things.

Thomas noticed with irritation that he was creeping along the highway at under sixty miles an hour. He squeezed the gas pedal until the marker posts on the side of the road flashed past like ghosts. Ghosts of terrible memories, ghosts of unfulfilled desires, ghosts of fear . . . Thomas wondered what it would be like to drive his car into the pillar of the bridge up ahead. How quickly would it be over? Would it hurt? And then what?

He thundered underneath the bridge. He'd never be able to do anything like that. And there was no reason to. He liked his job, despite the heavy workload, the occasionally difficult colleagues, and the, at times, ridiculous demands from the Department of Education and parents. He had one or two friends and was sure he'd find a wife at some point. His life might not be the most original, but it wasn't bad, either. At least he hadn't shot a child!

Thomas knew he'd never fully understand the tornado of pain raging inside Steffen, but he did understand that it drove his every thought and action. He knew how Steffen tortured himself with what-ifs and the impossible wish to turn back time. Everything dear to Steffen, everything that had made him who he was, had turned to rubble. It wasn't hard to understand why Steffen wanted to leave this chaos behind, forget it all.

Was Janica the only good and beautiful thing Steffen saw in life at the moment? Thomas slowed down, pulled into his driveway, and stopped outside the closed garage door. He switched off the engine, leaned back, and felt the silence of night descending on him like a lead weight. A longing flared up inside him, like an ember fanned by a sudden gust of wind. He ached to turn around and drive back to the farm. Back to his brother's side. Back to Janica, who was like a ray of sunshine breaking through dark clouds. Back to her parents, who'd welcomed him and Steffen like family. He wanted to go back to the magical, remote place.

"Cut the crap," Thomas grumbled to himself and briskly unbuckled his seatbelt.

The only plans he had for the next two days were to grade a pile of math tests, which he *could* do at the farm. But no, it was ridiculous to even consider going back there in the middle of the night. Tomorrow. Tomorrow was soon enough! He needed to get a grip on this strange yearning in his heart.

Thomas got out of the car and opened the front door of his row house. The silence and emptiness inside nearly knocked him off his feet. His brother's peculiarities had annoyed him since he moved in—just for a couple weeks, Steffen had assured him back then—but without him around, the house seemed somehow . . . dead.

Stop being a fool, Thomas thought. After all, Steffen hadn't even been there all the time. He'd left for training excursions and operations, gone to Italy for three weeks, spent nights out with friends. Most of the time, Steffen was good company. He was easy and cheerful, unless he was coming from seeing Marie—until last Friday, of course.

Steffen had fought hard to hold it together after the shooting, but when he got to his brother's place, something broke inside him. He staggered in at the crack of dawn like he was drunk. Halfway to his room, he collapsed on the floor with a feral scream that still echoed through Thomas's mind. That one scream made it out, but the rest of the grief was still trapped inside, devouring Steffen's joy, his openness, his will to fight, his strength—and his soul.

Thomas sank into a light-brown leather chair. It felt cold against his skin, like it didn't want to hold him, like it was telling him to get up and leave. And go where? To Janica, her parents, and Steffen?

Angry at his own confusing thoughts, he clenched his fists and closed his eyes. Suddenly, he was overcome by fear. Steffen was the only guest staying in the old barn. Nobody would hear if he got up, if he hung himself from one of the rafters or ran off into the forest to jump off a cliff.

Thomas chewed his lip nervously. The last time he'd prayed was more than ten years ago, after Steffen had dragged him to safety before running back to the burning car, desperately calling for their mother. Not for their father, as there was no chance he'd still be alive. The driver's side was nothing but a mass of bent-and-twisted metal. Thomas had prayed with all his might for his mother's life and his brother's safety . . . but God seemed to have been deaf that day. Or too busy with other people's problems, or . . .

"Please," was all he managed.

Chapter 8

At Janica's command, the dark Icelandic gelding with his flowing, almost-white mane broke into a canter, speeding along the forest track and out into the hills bathed in sunshine. The blue of the sky, the green of the forest, and the colorful dots on the meadows seemed to burst with intensity that morning. Horse and rider startled a small herd of red deer that had been grazing by the edge of the forest. The graceful animals leapt back into the shadows of the trees as Janica whistled back Balou, whose hunting instinct they'd awakened. Yellow brimstone butterflies danced erratically above the low rye. Bright-red field poppies and violet-blue cornflowers lined the fields that Janica and Cesar the gelding whooshed past before slowing down for the next incline.

At the top of the hill, Janica stopped the horse, who snapped playfully at the barking, wound-up dog. Below her, she could see the horse paddocks and her parents' home, nestled in the green hills. She shaded her eyes and spotted Steffen and her father. They were sitting on a bench by one of the old outbuildings, seemingly lost in conversation. Janica smiled at the peaceful sight. Her father was good for Steffen, and Steffen was good for her father. Peter had chosen to slow down, but that didn't mean he'd lost his skills or his love for people, and certainly not his desire to help them. He needed the stimulating conversation, the challenge, the approval their guests offered. They had several regulars who came to stay at the farm, to drink in the magnificent surroundings, the cheerful company of her parents, and, most of all, the nurturing and profound conversations with Peter. Recognizing people's needs was his forte. Accepting them the way they were, loving them enough to invest his time and energy. Society didn't value those skills anymore. You had to show results, put on events, get noticed by the media, prove your impact with numbers. Building relationships wasn't measurable, couldn't be quantified. But that investment formed the foundation of mutual trust that enabled healing conversations. Her father had often been accused of wasting time when all he was doing was giving as much strength, attention, and love as was needed to help someone. In Peter's view, that was his most important task as a man of God.

Hearing Balou begin to bark, Janica stood up in her stirrups and Cesar turned his head toward the narrow access road. A blue Opel was slowly approaching the farmstead. Janica's eyebrows shot up. Thomas was back surprisingly early. She hadn't expected him before late afternoon, and then just to drop off some personal belongings for Steffen. Thomas had seemed distinctly uncomfortable the day before. Only during dinner had he finally loosened up a little. Noting the man's exhaustion, her mother had tried to convince him to stay the night, but Thomas had declined and driven home late. Had he even slept, or had he lain awake worrying about his brother?

Janica spurred on her horse, and the two of them shot down the gravel road. They burst into the courtyard just as Thomas was getting out of his car, and the young man flattened himself against the vehicle in fear. Hooves clattering and mane, tail, and Janica's red curls flying, they pulled up beside him. Balou threw himself on the visitor, and Janica pretended to be too busy dismounting to notice.

"Janica!"

Thomas's indignant, pleading cry forced her to giggle and look up.

Balou had his paws on either side of Thomas's head, pinning the man to his car. The dog was panting right in his poor victim's face.

"He likes you." Janica laughed, which earned her an angry glare.

"Janica, please!"

"Balou, shame on you!"

Balou dropped to the ground and buried his nose under his right paw.

"Very funny," Thomas muttered and backed away from the dog, only to receive a curious nudge from Cesar.

"Did you train all your animals to do this?"

"No, it must be your charm."

"If I didn't know from yesterday that your dog obeys you so well, I'd have had a heart attack!"

"You're scared of dogs?"

"Not scared, really. Let's say I treat them with a healthy dose of respect." Thomas gave a lopsided smile and shrugged, stepping backward as the horse swung its big head toward him again.

"Then you must forgive me," she said. Janica saw Thomas's look of surprise, and also the way he stared at her. She pretended not to notice, undoing the girth and pulling the saddle and blanket off the horse's back.

She carried the saddle to the stable, where she placed it on the rack and her helmet on its hook. On her way out, she paused in the doorway. Balou had disappeared, probably off to find Peter and Steffen. Thomas was looking a little lost standing between his car and the hitched pony. Finally, he dared to take a step toward the animal. He reached out and placed his hand on its neck. The gentle gelding merely twitched his ears. He was wonderful with children and novices.

As Janica walked toward the pair, Thomas jerked his hand back as if he'd been caught out. Janica lowered her head to hide a smile. She untied the reins, led the horse alongside the hitching rail, and used it to hoist herself onto the horse's bare back.

"I'm taking Cesar to his paddock. Want to come?" She held out her hand invitingly.

"On the horse? Down that hill?" Thomas was staring at her as if she'd gone mad.

"No, I'll be taking the road and the bridge. Cesar doesn't like to jump."

Janica leaned down and grabbed his hand, leaving him no choice but to brace his leg against the rail and let her pull him up. When the animal took its first step, Thomas quickly clasped her waist with his arms.

"Aren't we too heavy?" he asked quietly, then quickly added: "I mean, you're not very heavy, of course, but—"

"Cesar is pretty tough, and we're not going real far."

Janica let Cesar set a slow pace, sensing the nervous beginner on his back. When the animal's hooves clattered on the bridge, Thomas, who'd just started to relax a little, tensed up again and tightened his grip on Janica. At the gate, she asked him to simply slide down the horse's rear, which he did obediently. Hitting the ground, he backed away anxiously. Janica swung her leg over the animal's neck and landed elegantly in the tall grass. Pollen enveloped her like a cloud. She studied the fine mist intently and concluded: "vanilla-custard yellow."

Neighing happily, the other horses came to the fence to welcome Cesar back. Janica took off his bridle, lowered the top rail, and watched as the gelding jumped over the bottom one, bucking with joy.

"I thought you said he doesn't like to jump," Thomas said.

"And it's true, with two exceptions: when he returns to his family in the paddock, and when it's time to go back to the stable in the evening."

"I see."

Janica pushed the rail back into the metal bracket and began walking along the fence, planning on taking the shortcut across the hill on their way back. She'd given the bit a rinse in the creek, and now the bridle was hanging over her shoulder, dripping onto her gray-and-red polka-dot T-shirt and blue riding pants.

Thomas caught up in a few long strides, and followed her along the narrow trail lined with tall grass, bushes, and yellow buttercups.

"I hadn't expected you back this early. Did you get any sleep?"

"I dozed off in a chair and woke up early with a stiff neck. I couldn't get back to sleep, so I came here."

"Have you had breakfast?"

"Coffee from McDonald's."

"I haven't eaten yet, either. Mom will be delighted when she finds out there's an extra mouth to feed. She loves it!"

"Your parents are very selfless people."

"They are." Janica stopped and turned to Thomas. "Why didn't you accept their invitation last night?"

"It had nothing to do with you or your parents."

"You just didn't want to impose?"

"Well, your father already had to lend Steffen some PJs, and your mom had to sacrifice a brand-new toothbrush from her stash, and—"

Janica waved dismissively. "That's no trouble at all."

"I'm just not used to that sort of thing," Thomas replied with a smile that made him look vulnerable.

"You're not used to people helping each other out?"

"I mean, I am. Steffen helped me after our parents—" He broke off and pushed past her.

Janica quickly caught up. "Would you at least consider staying until tomorrow? I suppose you've got to go to work on Monday. I do, too, by the way."

"Need a ride?"

Janica shook her head impatiently. No, she didn't want a chauffeur. But Thomas looked like he badly needed company, cheering up, fresh air, and a decent night's sleep.

She told him as much, and then Thomas was silent for a long time. After they'd crossed the creek and were following the trail up the hill, he eventually asked, "Is there anyone you wouldn't take under your wing?"

"No idea. I don't go looking for my victims, after all. I just stumble across them."

Thomas grabbed her arm, forcing her to stop. He seemed restless, as if bothered by a thought too embarrassing or inappropriate to say out loud.

Janica waved away a fly in front of her face and took a step back, forcing Thomas to let go of her. Softly, without meeting her eyes, he asked, "You are real, aren't you?"

Janica stopped short, raised her eyebrows, and finally broke out in roaring laughter. She laughed so hard that her stomach began to ache and she tumbled into the tall grass. Another cloud of pollen rose up and was carried away by the soft breeze. Tears were rolling down Janica's face now, and she didn't bother wiping them away. She was delighted to see Thomas's mouth twitch as he struggled to suppress the laughter rising up.

Gasping for air, she asked, "How on earth did you get the idea I might not be?"

"Well, you turned up on the right bridge at just the right time—an unusual time. You knew what to say to Steffen, you have this amazing place, and then, this morning, I drove past the turnoff four times and swear it wasn't there! I started to believe you had to be in my car for the road to appear, and then I turned around one more time and suddenly there it was."

Janica felt exhilaration sparking up inside her again like fireworks, and fell back in another fit of laughter. Thomas sat down in the grass beside her, pulled out a few blades of grass, and tied them in knots, waiting patiently. Finally, she sat up, nudged his shoulder with hers, and explained.

"There are two practically identical corners on that part of the road, and our turnoff is around one of them, but there's nothing around the other. That solves your mystery."

"I'll have to think about whether I believe you or not, all right?"

"You do that!" Janica giggled, happy to see the conspiratorial sparkle in his eyes.

Obviously, Thomas wasn't the empty suit she'd feared him to be. What he needed was a task that could help him find purpose in life, and to learn that thankfulness can bring great joy.

Chapter 9

Heidi placed the last bowl into the dishwasher, filled the detergent holder with powder, closed the little flap, then the door, and, without looking at it, pushed the "Start" button. Her eyes were resting on Janica, who sat sideways on the corner bench, staring out the window. Heidi helped herself to a second cup of coffee and sat down beside her daughter.

"What do you see?"

"Two brothers who couldn't be more different."

"What else?"

"One man with a crushing sense of responsibly and the heart of a fighter, which is currently trying to catch up with his soul, and a second man who approaches life with a great deal of fear."

"Fear?"

"Well, caution, maybe sadness. Like he's seen how fleeting life can be."

"We're all different. Not everyone can laugh in the face of pain."

"I know, Mom," Janica whispered with a smile.

"Your dad is looking after the fighter. They're getting along well. He found out that, on Thursday, Steffen took some prescription pills for the first time. Maybe the dosage was off or his body just had a bad reaction. It could explain the sudden exhaustion, the behavior on the bridge. Poor Steffen's heart is broken. He's suffering, but your dad thinks he wouldn't really throw it all away. He has a daughter, after all. Thomas, on the other hand—"

"Yeah, I mean, who looks after Thomas?"

"Does he need looking after? He seems to have an independent, orderly life."

Janica shrugged, and Heidi grinned. To her daughter, orderly meant boring, and independent equaled loneliness. That's just how she was: Plain wasn't good enough, everything always had to be more. To her, buttercups weren't just yellow, they were "sunshine-on-a-hazy-day" yellow. The leaf of a birch tree was "green as verdigris on Grandpa's coin collection." A butterfly wasn't colorful, but a "galaxy of brilliant hues." And who could begrudge her that exuberance—especially with her past?

Heidi finished her coffee and gave her daughter a kiss on the cheek. Janica was unusually still, not taking her eyes off the two brothers. After a while, Heidi got up and went to feed the chickens and geese. She could hear laughter and Balou's excited barking coming from the horse stable. The village girls must have arrived to ride the horses. The dog was a lot like his mistress, and no one had been surprised when she brought the shaggy wolfhound home from the shelter. Both were constantly on the move, not willing to waste a second. They were cheerful by nature, loved unconditionally, and always found time to stop and smell the roses.

Heidi picked up a bucket and filled it with feed. While the grain flowed from the sack into the steel bucket with a soft noise, dust dancing slowly in the rays of sunlight, Peter came into the stable.

"Trying to fatten up your chickens?" He pointed at the overflowing bucket. "What are you thinking about?"

"About our daughters. Jenni is so different from Janica, isn't she? Stunningly beautiful and successful, adored by men, countless friends—although I honestly wouldn't know how many of them would stick around if Jenni ever lost her glitz and glamour."

Peter raised his eyebrows, signaling that he was all ears.

"I was just thinking. When Steffen needed someone to lean on after the divorce and his best friend's accident, no one was there. I wonder what it would be like for Jenni. On the one hand, of course, I hope her friendships will never be tested like that, but on the other, it would be good to know if there's someone she can rely on. You and I won't be around forever, and Janica . . . ?"

Peter took the bucket from his wife's hand and pulled her into his arms.

"You're worrying about extreme scenarios that might never happen. Isn't it our job to focus on the here and now? And here and now we have a deeply hurt man who is tearing himself to pieces, plus his melancholy brother."

"Melancholy?" Heidi smiled up at Peter. "Janica, of course, interpreted it as sad!"

"Of course she did." Peter laughed.

Heidi leaned against him, but her thoughts remained with Janica, who'd learned at a young age to make the most of each day.

Chapter 10

May 1

Thomas broke off midsentence and turned from the blackboard to see his students busily packing up their pencils. Class must nearly be over. He sighed. Lots of his physics students had great potential, but it was often limited by their laziness.

"That's right, go ahead and pack up. I guess you don't need to write down your homework assignments to remember them. A different one for each of you, of course."

The class gave a collective groan.

"Why can't you cut us a break?" the class clown grumbled, loud enough for Thomas to hear.

"Your own fault. Why did you choose to study physics?"

"We couldn't have known you practically live at school!" the young man replied. "I for one have a girl waiting for me, and my stomach's grumbling."

"I was wondering what all that noise was. And I've got a reliable source that says your 'girl' got detention today."

The students giggled and suddenly didn't seem to mind sitting still for a few more minutes.

But then the bell rang and triggered another wave of shuffling and fidgeting. Thomas, struggling to keep track of which topic he was assigning to which student for homework, tried to revive his ballpoint pen with some frantic scribbling, but it appeared to have gone on strike.

"You win! Off you go!" Thomas said with a grin, and closed his book with a thud.

The room was empty within seconds. Thomas packed his things, fetched his jacket from the teachers' lounge, and headed home. On the way, he stopped at a stationery shop.

As he pushed open the shop door, a tinkling of bells tore Thomas from thoughts of his lazy class. He turned around and studied the bronze-colored bells that still swayed gently. How long had the chimes been hanging there? Forever? He'd been a customer at this paper and craft supplies store since he was a little boy. He looked around, and, hoping no one was watching, grasped the door handle and opened the door again. The bells rang again.

"Hardly anyone notices that old thing anymore," the shop owner's voice boomed from behind him, and Thomas winced in embarrassment.

He smiled helplessly at the stout elderly man.

"I don't even hear it anymore. It's . . ." The old man cleared his throat. "I got so used to that little song over the years. It's a shame, really, because my wife used to like it so much. I hung those bells on our twentieth wedding anniversary. Now she's been dead for ten years, and I don't even hear her melody anymore."

The man shook his head and shuffled away.

Thomas's eyes followed him, and he became aware of a strange feeling in his chest. The shopkeeper had noticed the melody that day—just like him! Thoughtful, he looked at his hands. They were still covered in painful blisters from his day with the Meiers. Janica had made him muck out the stable with her for over an hour. Wearing her father's gum boots, he'd carted the dirty, steaming straw to the dunghill in a wheelbarrow. To his surprise, he hadn't found the pungent and sweet odor repulsive, but somehow comforting and homely. Janica had pointed out an unusual array of knotholes in the stable wall, through which rays of sunlight were falling, painting patterns on the ground. Thomas had been amused by her childlike enthusiasm, but also felt a little wistful. When had he lost that lightness of heart? The sparkle in the eyes, the enjoyment of simple things? And why had Janica been allowed to keep it?

He eyed the little bells suspiciously. Janica would probably like the tune, and she would still notice it after thirty years' time.

He shook his head and headed for the ballpoint-pen refills. Deep in thought, he grabbed a basket along the way and tossed in two glue sticks and a bulky folder. He studied the refill cartridges, annoyed that someone had mixed them all up again. Twice before, he'd bought cartridges, only to get home and find they were the wrong ones. He started sorting the cartridges back into the right boxes. His thoughts, which seemed to do as they pleased, returned to the farm.

Thomas had been genuinely shocked when he'd learned that Janica was a chimney sweep. He'd imagined her as a loving kindergarten teacher, or an artist, wildly throwing colors about. But chimney sweep? Over Janica's laughing protest, Heidi had told him about her daughter's pink phase, the girl's high-flying ideas about becoming a wedding planner, and about her great wish to celebrate her own extravagant wedding in a white princess dress. But event planning required more attention to detail than Janica could muster, and her dreams of fashion design were doomed from the start by her lack of drawing and sewing skills. Then, a close friend of the family with a chimney-sweeping business was desperately looking for an intern, and her father kept joking that Janica was just like the chimney sweep in *Mary Poppins*, a character who always knew how to find joy in any situation. For some reason, Thomas suddenly found her choice of profession rather fitting.

Why couldn't he get the farm and its inhabitants out of his mind? Was it the fact that they seemed to have found the secret to a happy, fulfilled life? Wasn't that what the whole of humankind was after?

"Can I help you?"

Thomas gave a start as a female voice tore him from his thoughts. The young cashier was looking up at him eagerly with a big smile that revealed strikingly white teeth.

"Thank you, but I shop here almost daily. I can find my way around."

"I know how often you shop here," she declared, not leaving his side.

The thud of a shopping basket on the counter told the shop assistant she was needed elsewhere. Thomas breathed a sigh of relief when she turned to leave, a disappointed look on her face. Steffen would have been ready with a witty reply to such an awkward attempt at flirtation, but Thomas just felt extremely uncomfortable.

He frowned when he heard a familiar voice. He stood on his toes to peer over the shelves. Standing at the counter was Janica.

She was wearing black pants, a short black jacket, and, for a dash of color, a white scarf with red, orange, and purple horses. She must have been at work. But what was she doing in this part of town? Could this really be a coincidence?

Thomas was too far away to catch what the shop assistant was saying to Janica, but her buoyant laughter filled the shop. Did she ever have bad days? Days when she didn't feel like laughing? Did she know sadness, worries, fear, or illness, or did she simply laugh it all away? He rolled his eyes at his own thoughts, and a second time when he saw what the shop assistant was wrapping up for Janica. It was an assortment of beads that made Thomas suspect Heidi had been wrong about Janica's pink phase being over. The beads ranged from a soft piglet pink to purple, mixed with a few glimmering golds and silvers.

"Enjoy!" the shop assistant called after her.

A moment later, the bells rang out.

Thomas did something he'd never done before: He dropped the shopping basket and ran outside. Janica was just getting on a bus, so he quickly climbed into his car. He pulled out and followed the bus from stop to stop, until it halted outside a two-story building by the edge of the forest, in a part of town Thomas had never been before. Janica was one of the few people getting off here, so Thomas started looking for a place to park. The bus turned around and headed back the way it had come: last stop on this line.

He reversed into a small parking space, straightened the car until the front wheel scraped the curb with an awful noise, and got out. Gray and speckled pigeons scattered in all directions when he crossed the small alleyway and turned down the long side street that led back to the bus stop and the building Janica had entered.

Then he stopped, suddenly overcome by doubts. What was he doing here? If he wanted to talk to her, he could call or visit her at home. It was ridiculous to stalk a woman halfway across the city just because she bought some tacky beads! The house looked a little like a kindergarten or a small school. It was probably just another building where she worked as a chimney sweep, and the beads were probably a birthday present for the daughter of a friend.

Thomas ran his fingers through his hair. This wasn't about the beads or the fact that he suddenly noticed things he wouldn't have just a few days ago. This was about Janica. She fascinated him. To his surprise, he realized he wanted to learn more about her, to belong to her circle of friends. And not just as the younger brother of the man she had rescued. She was good for him. Life was easier, happier, and more colorful when she was around.

He ran his hand through his hair again. Did that mean his life was hard, sad, and gray? Possibly. He didn't really have a circle of friends, never went anywhere apart from his perfectly planned summer vacations, and couldn't boast of any hobbies or club memberships. But did that mean he was leading an unhappy life? He shook his head decidedly. He was lucky, happy.

"Can I help you?"

Not only did the question interrupt his train of thought, but it also annoyed him greatly. This was the second time today he'd heard it—did he really look that lost? Did he look like he needed help, and if so, with what?

"I . . ." He shrugged helplessly.

The woman with short gray hair and a slim figure smiled at him expectantly. Was he mistaken, or was there an amused glint in the small brown eyes behind her glasses, almost as if she habitually found lost men standing in this spot? Were there others like him, washing up on this sidewalk like beached whales, asking themselves questions about life?

Thomas made himself stop acting like a student caught texting during class. "Pardon me. I saw a friend of mine, but she disappeared into this building before I could call out."

The woman glanced at her slender gold watch and nodded. "The bus must have just passed by. Janica usually comes at this time."

"That's right, Janica Meier," Thomas confirmed, abandoning the idea she'd come here for work.

"Follow me, I'll take you to her."

"Oh, no, thanks. I don't want to be a bother." Thomas waved dismissively and felt his face grow hot. The situation was getting awkward. How would Janica react to his unexpected arrival? The only way he could know she was here was if he'd followed her—which was embarrassingly true.

"You're not a bother. Janica has brought friends along in the past, hoping they'd help out a bit. But most of them never come back."

The woman took his arm in a trusting, but at the same time unyielding, gesture, like a wise aunt determined to guide him in the right direction. With energetic steps, she dragged him up a winding path to the front door. Without giving him time to change his mind, she pulled him inside, and he wondered if he'd better put up a fight. What was he getting himself into?

A wide corridor with a deserted reception desk on the left and coat hooks on the right led them to a glass door that opened automatically. The roof of the circular room was made of glass and came to a point in the center, letting in plenty of sunlight. Two twelve-year-old girls in wheelchairs were sitting at a table, playing The Settlers of Catan. A type of reclining wheelchair sat in the middle of the room, holding a boy of roughly the same age, his back bent, but delight on his pale face. A young woman, presumably his mother, was sitting in another armchair, reading to him. A middle-aged man pushing an IV pole came through a door opposite Thomas and disappeared down another corridor. Scribbled letters on his neon-yellow T-shirt said his name was Werner.

Then Thomas spotted Janica. She was sitting at a table with her back to him, playing with a little girl in a pretty yellow dress. The child didn't have any hair, and she had a huge bandage around her head. Thomas swallowed hard at the sight of her dark eyes. They held a lifetime's worth of pain and knowing, despite her young age. Beside them sat a woman in another one of the armchairs that were scattered all around, each upholstered with a different fabric. The woman was wearing a long black dress and a cleverly knotted white headscarf, which she was busy rearranging. The mother, probably younger than Janica, looked haggard and spent. When Janica addressed her, a smile crossed her face, wiping away the pain for a moment and turning her into an exotic beauty.

Thomas was relieved when the gray-haired woman placed her warm hand on his arm. At least he wasn't facing this depressing scene alone.

"We're a hospice for children and teenagers," she explained, sensing his discomfort. "We house children and families that don't know how many tomorrows they have left. The children find some peace here, and the families find time to recharge before facing their lives outside. Some are cancer patients, others have genetic diseases as diverse as the children's personalities. Some of them are here because their families can't care for them at home any longer, but don't want them to spend their last days in a hospital. We're there for them every step of the way. Sometimes it's only a short path, and other times we walk a long way with them. Janica is one of our volunteers. One day she just blew in like a whirlwind, completely unexpected. She's a real blessing for the children and their families. She has the gift of giving hope, even where there's none left."

"We call her our angel," a male voice said behind him.

Thomas jumped. Either the man had been a cat in a previous life or Thomas had shut out everything but the woman's voice and the shocking scene in front of him.

One of the girls at the table turned toward them, squeaked with excitement, and sprang to her feet. Although it was obvious that she wanted to run into her father's arms, she could only manage one painfully slow step after another, until she finally collapsed against his chest, exhausted but happy.

"Hello, little Rat. Are you cheating again?" the man asked, picking up the frightfully skinny girl and carrying her back to her friend.

He leaned down to give the second girl a kiss on the top of her head, then sat in one of the armchairs, his daughter on his lap.

"Over time, our guests become one big family. They need the support of others going through similar things. Of course, there are those who prefer privacy and solitude. We respect both, and our facilities are designed accordingly."

Thomas nodded. He suddenly felt empty, drained, as if the children's pain was sucking all the energy from his body. Unable to think of anything else to say, he asked, "Why did that man call his daughter Rat? That's an odd term of endearment."

The woman giggled. "She likes butterflies. So, a few years ago, Janica said that she was like a caterpillar who'd someday turn into a beautiful butterfly. But her brother laughed and said, with her pointy face and her constant cheating, his little sister was more like a rat. The name stuck."

Thomas nodded and frowned, wondering if it was appropriate for him to ask what illness Rat was suffering from, and whether she would live. He decided against it, worried he might sound voyeuristic.

The door across the room suddenly flew open and a girl came storming into the round room. She had short black hair that looked like she'd cut it herself without using a mirror. Three colorful bead necklaces were jingling around her neck, a little like the bells in the shop. She looked around searchingly, and when she spotted Janica, let out a wild scream that was taken up by the boy in the wheelchair. His mother laughed and closed the book.

"Janni, Janni!" the girl cheered and ran across the room.

Janica jumped to her feet, caught the girl in her arms, and spun her around.

The boy's mother turned the wheelchair so he could watch, and Rat's father and the two young teenagers turned to look, too. The girl in Janica's arms, who looked like a ruffled baby bird fallen from its nest, had managed to turn the tranquil, cozy scene into happy chaos within seconds.

"Look!" the child said the moment Janica set her down, spinning around herself.

Her wide skirt, a shimmering-purple fabric with layers of light-pink tulle on top, billowed around her legs. The girl staggered, but Janica caught her.

"Ohhh, everything's spinning," the little girl said, then laughed cheerfully.

"Happy fifth birthday, Annabelle."

"You're saying it wrong again! You're doing it on purpose! I'm six!" the girl whooped, giving Janica a playful push.

"Oh, forgive me. You're a big girl now!"

"Yes, I'm starting school this year!"

"Then the fun and games are all over! Serious life is starting now."

"That's what Dad always says, too. But Mom says he's teasing me."

"Your mom is a very clever mom."

"And beautiful! And she bought me this skirt for my birthday. Isn't it magical?"

"Very magical! Perfect for a princess!"

"And so the circle is complete," Thomas muttered under his breath.

A puzzled look from the gray-haired woman told him he knew things about Janica's life that no one here did.

As if she'd heard his words, Janica turned around. A mischievous smile spread across her face. "Looks like someone smelled the birthday cake."

Embarrassed, Thomas stuck his hands in the pockets of his jeans as far as they would go. He wished the ground would open up and swallow him, especially as the whole room turned to look. When had he missed his chance to leave? When he realized these were seriously ill children? Or when the Muslim girl had captivated him with those dark eyes that held the pain and understanding of an entire world? When a cheerful little girl with beads around her neck burst in, and, despite her sickness, radiated more joy than he had ever felt?

"Who is that? Is that your boyfriend, Janni?" Annabelle demanded, skipping toward Thomas.

She scrutinized him with big blue eyes that reminded him of the Caribbean Sea around Costa Rica, then held out her dainty hand.

"Hello, my name is Annabelle. Today's my sixth birthday. It's an important day because I'm not a little kid anymore, and I'm gonna go to school. You look nice. Almost like an actor from Hollywood. But not as nice as my dad. He's from Belgium and he visits on weekends. My mom is German. And she's the most beautiful woman on earth. Dad says I'll be beautiful, too, when I grow up. What's your name? Where do you live? How do you know Janni?"

Thomas, who'd almost had a panic attack when everyone turned to stare at him, suddenly felt a broad grin spread across his face. He had no idea how it got there. He crouched down, took the small hand into his large one, and replied, "Congratulations on your big day, Annabelle. And I think your parents are right—you're going to be a very beautiful woman one day. My name is Thomas, I live in town, and I met Janica a few days ago outside my front door."

"Finally, someone who remembers all my questions!" Annabelle declared, causing the room to erupt in laughter.

"There were only three."

"Dad says I talk too much and I ask too many questions."

"If you don't ask questions, you won't learn."

"Yeah! I'll tell him that."

Thomas made a silly face, drawing giggles from the audience. "Well, you tell him I know because I'm a teacher."

"Wow!"

Thomas basked in her admiring gaze and wished his students would show half that reverence.

"I want to be a teacher, too," Annabelle declared.

He nodded enthusiastically, but suspected the idea had only just popped into her head, and she would probably want to become a whole lot of different things by the time she grew up. Looking up into everyone's smiling faces, he suddenly remembered where he was. The pain that shot through him was like a thorn in his heart. When he looked to Janica for help, she winked and tilted her head toward an open door, behind which Thomas could see tables, chairs, and a huge pink cake that looked better suited for a wedding than a child's birthday.

He gave Janica a grateful smile and turned back to the little girl, whose hand he was still holding.

"So where is that birthday cake of yours now? I could smell it all the way across town. It led me here!"

Annabelle burst out laughing, leaned in, and whispered, "That's a pretty silly excuse, Thomas. And believe me: Janni isn't stupid. She knows you're here 'cause of her. But I'll play along, if you want."

Know-it-all, Thomas thought. But then he looked into the eyes of the Muslim girl again. He revised his judgment: *Seen it all.*

Chapter 11

Janica felt warmth spreading inside her as Annabelle examined one small box of beads after the other, turning them this way and that to make them glitter. Petra, her mother, dabbed a tear from the corner of her eye and smiled at Janica. Tears were part of everyday life at this place, just like laughter, and no one tried to hide one or the other.

Derja, the Turkish girl, was leaning over the table—practically lying on it—carefully watching every glimmer of the polished beads.

"Janni?" Annabelle's voice sounded reproachful.

Janica turned to the birthday girl, who was sitting between Jessika and Sven, both of whom were staying here for the first time.

"You bought the gold beads with the glitter twice!"

"Oh, did I?" Janica raised her eyebrows, although she knew what a poor actress she was.

"I think . . ." Annabelle started, paused, gave Janica a thoughtful look, then turned to Derja. "Would you like these?"

The girl's black eyes lit up like stars at night. She gave her mother a timid and questioning look. Selina looked at Janica. They smiled at each other in silent understanding, and Selina gave her daughter a nod.

"Yes, please," Derja whispered, watching in disbelief as Annabelle slid the small plastic container across the table to her.

"Thank you very much," the girl said—a little louder now, but well mannered as usual.

Enraptured, she raised the little box in the air and watched it sparkle while Annabelle picked up the next present.

"This one is from Dad," Petra said, brushing a strand of hair out of Annabelle's face.

"But the cake is from him!" Annabelle laughed.

"He wanted to give you something else as well," her mother replied.

Janica noticed the sadness in her eyes. Petra clearly wished her husband had come rather than staying at work in Belgium.

Annabelle ripped open the blue wrapping paper with pink flowers and pulled out a plush elephant. The birthday girl inspected it carefully from all angles before putting it down beside the beads, the new shoes, and the still-deflated bouncy ball, whose reddish pink reminded Janica of Hubba-Bubba chewing gum. Like all the plush animals Annabelle's father gave her, the elephant had a "Steiff" button in its ear—it was designer, expensive. Every night, Annabelle decided which of the animals piling up in her room to sleep with. She always fell asleep cradling one in her arms, and Janica knew she'd happily give them all up if she could only spend more time cradled in her father's.

Pierre was a sporty man in his midthirties, extremely ambitious and successful, but he had no idea how to deal with his daughter's leukemia. Annabelle was their only child, a wanted, planned child following several miscarriages, and the diagnosis had completely thrown him off balance. He loved his wife and Annabelle, but was spending more and more time in Belgium.

Janica couldn't blame him. Watching your child suffer was sometimes more than a parent could handle. But Petra and Annabelle really needed him—now more than ever. Still, Janica couldn't judge Pierre. No one could ever know how they'd react in a situation like that. Maybe it was better for Annabelle not to see her father very often if the alternative was to watch her illness turn him into a wreck. Janica held out hope that Annabelle would win the fight against this malicious disease—and it was looking good for her at the moment—so her father wouldn't have to torture himself for not making the most of their time as a family.

Janica's gaze turned to the new visitor. Thomas had seemed lost when he first arrived, and she'd worried he might bolt. But Sven, the only boy in the house apart from Florian, the boy with Duchenne muscular dystrophy in the reclining wheelchair, wouldn't let him leave. Sven's parents worked hard to feed their family of eight, so, some days, he didn't have any visitors. He hadn't fared well in the children's hospital, despite the psychologists, the social workers, and the dedicated staff. But since a generous sponsor had helped bring him to the hospice, he'd blossomed. He had two weeks left here before he'd get to return home.

Now, Sven and Thomas were deep in discussion about model railroads, and the thirteen-year-old boy was bursting with joy to be sitting next to someone who knew something about the subject.

"I'm going to cut the cake now!" Annabelle the whirlwind yelled, interrupting the animated conversations all around her.

She picked up the—in her hands—enormous knife, and walked to the magnificent, three-tiered cake. It was covered in pink frosting and decorated with marzipan princesses, horses, dogs, and even a carriage.

Annabelle was a generous girl who'd learned to take pleasure in other people's joy, and the pieces of cake she cut were accordingly large.

Janica suppressed laughter as she watched painfully polite Thomas allow Annabelle to serve him a laughably massive slice. While the other adults shared a piece among three or four of them, she watched as he struggled valiantly to consume the monstrosity. After a few minutes, she felt so sorry for Thomas that she walked over and placed a hand on his shoulder. Close up, he looked even more miserable than he had from the other end of the table. A dollop of sickeningly sweet frosting was stuck to his mouth.

"Annabelle is a child, even if she's a very clever one. She won't notice if you don't eat all this pink atrociousness. And even if she does—how many times, do you think, has she left food on her plate?"

"Save me, Janica, I'm gonna be sick," he whispered in return, infinitely grateful when she took away his plate.

She returned with a pretzel—no butter, as Thomas had consumed enough butter for twenty pretzels.

She leaned down again, whispering as she placed the pretzel next to his coffee cup. "Drink your coffee—you might just get lucky and not turn pink!"

Sven, who was devouring his pink mess with relish, laughed. Janica crouched down and tugged at the sleeve of his well-worn shirt.

"Look after Thomas for me, Sven. He's new here."

"Me, too."

"But you've probably already noticed how complicated grown-ups can be, haven't you?"

"I sure have!" Sven agreed emphatically.

"From time to time, we need someone young like you to show us how to live life the *easy* way."

"All right, I'll look after him."

"You two do realize I can hear you?" Thomas grumbled from the left.

Sven broke out in laughter again and Janica stood up, whispering quietly into Thomas's ear, "Sven's lonely. He could use a friend."

She didn't wait for a reply, just strolled off like she was headed to the restroom. She didn't stop there, though, but left the building and took the next bus. Thomas had found his way here, he could find his way out again. She hoped his first visit to the hospice wouldn't be his last, as it had been with many of her friends in the past.

Janica

I knew it the moment I saw Thomas at the hospice. It was a fleeting moment, no longer than the flap of a sparrow's wing. In that brief moment, I realized it wasn't Steffen I'd found, but Thomas. He was the one who needed me. Steffen was my parents' task, and they took him in like the son they never had.

Annabelle and Derja, Sven and Florian, Jessika and Rat were all doing surprisingly well that day. Only Merle, the three-year-old who'd never had a chance, was lying in her pretty room, cared for by the doctor, the staff, and her single mother, waiting for the end. The end of this life, which she'd entered with a poor genetic start. But that wasn't anything I couldn't handle. One life was ending—one of many. Where little Merle was going could only be better than where she'd been.

Since his surprise visit two weeks ago, Thomas returned to the hospice five times. I never asked him how he had turned up there in the first place, because I didn't want to embarrass him.

The very next day, he'd returned carrying a faded wooden crate that smelled awfully of damp basement and contained the remnants of his old model train, which was now rattling along the round walls of the common room—transporting pills, syringes, chocolates, and messages. The two *tinkerers had even built sturdy bridges over the track for the wheelchairs, beds, and trolleys.*

He and Sven had gotten close, and Thomas had even promised to visit him at home. It probably wasn't Sven's last stay at the hospice, but going home was still cause for celebration. Thomas, on the other hand, was celebrating his start at the hospice, even if he wasn't aware of it. His life had finally begun the day he followed me into this beautiful building.

And then, from one hour to the next, the intoxicating contentment inside me vanished. Flew away like wild geese in fall.

Chapter 12

May 14

Janica was in the middle of reheating some leftovers when her mother called, uncharacteristically hysterical. They couldn't find Steffen. Janica had to come immediately and bring Thomas to help with the search. And switch on the radio in the car. Flustered, Janica turned off the stove and dropped the pot of pale-yellow pasta and tomato-red sauce on the counter.

She reached Thomas on his cell phone on a break between two classes. Shortly thereafter, his car brakes squealed outside. Balou tumbled down the stairs as fast as his fear allowed, and Janica followed at a much slower pace. She had no idea how she was supposed to react, what she could say or do. She knew her way around ill children, but not healthy young men who wanted to end their life prematurely. It stood in an unreal contrast to the children she cared for. They grabbed life with both hands, but all too often, didn't have the strength to hold on.

"Have you heard the news? Have you heard? How could this happen? Those idiots!"

Janica opened the door for Balou. Frightened by the man's angry outburst, the dog flattened himself on the floor of the backseat, looking confused.

As soon as she'd climbed in and shut her door, the Opel sped off.

"Hey, there's a speed limit for a reason. Do you want to run over a child or an old person?" Janica shouted.

He immediately slowed down and muttered an apology.

She put on her seatbelt and studied Thomas, who was watching the traffic grimly. The dark strands of hair falling over his face made him look a little bold, dashing. As he changed gears with hard, mechanical movements, every muscle in his face fluttered, revealing his inner turmoil.

"What happened?"

"The Special Forces Unit is deployed much more frequently than the public knows, because many of their operations don't get released to the media. Not just to protect the victims, but also the members of the unit."

Janica nodded. Thomas had pulled himself together, at least enough to explain.

"Somehow, the media got wind of what happened three weeks ago." Thomas spat out the word "media" like it was a hot tomato burning his mouth. "Of course, now the story is getting blown out of all proportion. Even the tiniest radio station has picked it up, the TV stations will be next, and then every sensationalist rag!"

"What happened?" Janica asked again. "Did they get Steffen's name?"

"No, thank goodness! Are you on Facebook?"

"Sure."

"Just look!"

Janica didn't understand, but she opened the app on her phone. "Now what?"

"Start scrolling."

Janica scanned the newsfeed and, indeed, it wasn't long before she found a post about the "child shooter":

> *Why do they always have to shoot right away? Isn't there another way? Those poor parents!*

Janica remembered what Steffen had told her about how rarely firearms were used. Clearly, she wasn't the only one who knew very little about the Special Forces Unit.

She kept scrolling and found another post one of her acquaintances had "liked":

> *Think first, then shoot! Of course, those steroid-junkie cops probably don't even have a brain under their black helmets.*

Janica gasped. The comments all seemed to be in agreement:

> *He should be put against a wall—Adrenalin-fueled?— Three weeks ago already? They were trying to hush it up. I bet they won't even release a name!*

The comments went on and on. Only one man, elderly, judging by his profile picture, wrote:

> *What if he didn't see another way? I hear there were more children in the house. And he probably wasn't aiming for the kid.*

Janica looked out the window in silence, watched the trees and road markers speed by, and noticed how terribly fast Thomas was racing along the busy highway.

"People want safe roads. They want to be able to go to the bank without getting robbed. They want to walk the streets at night without fear of being beaten up or raped. They want . . . dammit!" Thomas banged the steering wheel with his hand. "But God forbid a policeman asks for their ID. God forbid they get a speeding ticket. God forbid they go to a protest and there are policemen there to protect buildings or other demonstrators or whatever. Don't those idiots realize that they're throwing rocks at people who are just doing their job, who are there to protect them, who might even agree with them and be standing on their side if they didn't happen to be on duty? And God forbid a policeman makes a mistake! Then they attack like rabid dogs."

Janica wanted to ask Thomas to slow down a little, but he was already talking again, agitated, angry, and desperate—out of fear for his brother.

"Of course, operations have gone wrong in the past, and there probably have been times when they used more force than necessary. But the men and women in the police force have feelings, too. They're not robots. There have been changes, improvements, a lot of training. I bet you a million dollars: If Steffen hadn't taken that shot—with his boss's OK, by the way—and the hostage taker had killed the family, these same idiots would be asking why taxpayers have to finance a Special Forces Unit if it just stands by while a family is being murdered. They'd be saying you can't count on the police!"

"Thomas?"

"Hmm?"

"Please slow down."

Thomas looked at her for a dangerously long moment. Then he slowed down for the second time in fifteen minutes.

"I'm sorry."

"Getting into an accident isn't going to help Steffen."

"I know, but—"

"You want to start looking for him as soon as you can, I know."

Thomas nodded and tightened his grip on the steering wheel. His knuckles were white and Janica resisted putting her hand on his. Affectionate gestures toward men were difficult, unless the man had been a friend for many years and you could be sure it wouldn't be misinterpreted.

Thomas remained silent and focused all his attention on driving, so Janica leaned back and prayed silently. She opened her eyes again when they turned off the highway, and a few minutes later, she pointed out her parents' elusive turnoff.

Two saddled-up Icelandic ponies turned their heads when Thomas roared up outside the farmhouse. He jumped out of the car and hurried toward Peter, who threw Janica's riding pants to her across the car roof. She changed in the passenger seat while her father tried to reassure Thomas. A few moments later, Heidi came out of the house wearing her hiking boots, and—with Thomas in tow—headed off on foot.

"Let's go," Janica's father called, and she jumped in the saddle of the gray, brown, and white pinto mare.

Balou ran circles around the horses, barking excitedly. Janica sent the dog back to the house.

"How could this happen?" she asked as her father led them toward the eastern part of the woods.

"No idea. The radio was on in the stable, like usual. Your mother wasn't even listening until Steffen stormed past her, cursing. Only then did she realize what the report was about."

"Do you have any idea where Steffen might be?"

"We've been going for a lot of walks lately."

Janica took that as a "no" and frowned. Should they focus on places that were good for jumping off? Her stomach cramped painfully, and she felt nausea welling up. She forced back her fear and focused on the fast gallop they had broken into on the open track. When they entered the shadows of the forest again, Janica's father slowed down.

"He hasn't been well since yesterday," Peter explained when Janica rode up beside him. "Your mother took him to another hearing. He didn't say much, only that the internal investigators were doubting his side of the story."

"How the—" Janica pressed her lips together before asking more calmly: "What are these people imagining? That Steffen was aiming for the child?"

"No, God, of course not. It's about shooting techniques, and about certain protocols for situations like those."

"I know I'm not a police officer, but I'd like to know how many hostage dramas follow a predictable pattern, especially since Steffen said the situation was extremely messy and dangerous."

"You're not the only one," Peter muttered and stopped at a fork in the road. He pulled his ancient cell phone from his vest pocket and dialed a number. "Which way did you go, Karl?" he asked.

Janica gasped. Her father had brought in the local cop. He'd have to report the incident, which probably wouldn't look good for Steffen's psych eval. But was that important right now? Maybe it would be better for him to leave the SFU anyway, despite his passion for the job. How would Steffen handle it if he was dismissed? Would it drive the nail even deeper into his aching heart? Janica wiped her hand over her sweaty face. Questions were whirling around her mind, doubts and fears tugging at her like a howling gale tearing out the leaves of an exposed tree. How could they both protect Steffen and help him? She needed time to think. But first they had to find him—alive.

The rays of sunlight painted golden lines and dots on the soft forest carpet of moss and pine needles. Tiny pale-blue flowers craned their little necks toward the light. The damp smell of dirt mingled with the tangy odor of spruce and broadleaves. Thomas was looking frantically this way and that, his heart hammering in his chest as if it wanted to leap out and help search for his only remaining family member. He could hear small twigs and dry pinecones snapping underneath his and Heidi's shoes, and the vociferous concert of the birds in the treetops. Everything around him was pulsating with life, but his insides were being shredded by a storm. He felt as though someone was twisting his soul with both hands, trying to squeeze out every bit of hope and ounce of happiness he'd accumulated these last few days. Grief rolled through him. During the last two weeks, he'd felt alive and appreciated for the first time since his parents died, even though that seemed crazy in view of his brother's troubles. But wasn't this crisis an opportunity for Thomas to give Steffen some of what his big brother had been giving him for years? Attention, a helping hand, the feeling he wasn't all alone in this world?

Now it was Thomas's turn to be the strong one, to take the lead and support his brother. Had he been doing enough? Should he have come to see Steffen more rather than spending time with Sven? But his brother had seemed fine, almost happy. And Peter had far more life experience, more wisdom, a trained eye for Steffen's needs. Thomas had always been the little brother under Steffen's wing. Could they really just swap places? Nothing had prepared him for this. Had he failed?

How stable was Steffen now? The radio this morning, the leak, all those accusatory questions must have knocked the wind right back out of him. Was it bad enough for him to want to finish what he had started on the bridge?

"Thomas?" Heidi asked breathlessly.

Her voice tore him out of the dark waters he'd almost drowned in. He practically gasped, filling his lungs with the damp, sap-scented air before turning to Janica's mother.

"I can't keep up with you."

"Should we split up?" he asked, eager to cover as much ground as possible.

"You're not familiar with this area. And I don't want to leave you, upset as you are."

Thomas took another deep breath and exhaled slowly. Janica's family could be awfully blunt. He found Heidi's concern for his state of mind during the search for Steffen a little annoying. However, he knew that, if the situation wasn't so fraught, her thoughtfulness would make him feel all warm and fuzzy.

"Fifteen men are out here looking. We will find him!" Heidi declared.

Thomas nodded, resigned. Yes, they would find him. Just like the search party found Steffen's friend. Too late.

"We will find him alive and well!" Heidi added and clasped his hand.

Her hand felt like his mother's. Gentle, yet strong. Warm and hopeful. At least that's what he imagined as he returned her squeeze.

Together they marched along the uneven path covered with roots, shaded by trees, lined by flowers and ferns, which ran only yards from a sheer cliff.

"Did Steffen tell you that, the day before yesterday, he got a phone call from the father of the child who died?"

Thomas stopped abruptly. "What? No!"

"Steffen's lawyer facilitated the call at the father's request. He said it would be better to show a willingness to cooperate rather than rile the man up even more against Steffen. He strictly forbade Steffen to apologize in any way, however, since that would be the same as an admission of guilt."

"The man's pressing charges?"

"I don't know. Steffen didn't tell us anything about the conversation, but he was very upset afterward. Perhaps because he would have liked to tell the man how sorry he was about everything, but couldn't."

Thomas looked at Janica's mother with a clenched jaw. Didn't that man realize what the alternative to Steffen's shot could have been: all three children and his wife dead?

Heidi raised her hand and gently brushed Thomas's cheek. His mother used to do the same thing when he was sad or hurt. Did all mothers instinctively know this comforting gesture, which conveyed with such amazing clarity that you weren't alone?

"Steffen went outside after the call and sat on a bench behind the house until dark. He cried for a long time. Tears cleanse the soul. That's why I don't believe that he's going to hurt himself today. This situation is terrible, but he's carrying a glimmer of hope in his heart—like a tiny light in the dark of night."

Thomas nodded even though he couldn't share her optimism. She didn't know Steffen like he did. His brother didn't do things by halves. His unfinished business on the bridge was an exception, probably because Janica had interrupted him, together with her bear of a dog. But maybe, just maybe, he didn't know his brother as well as he thought? Hope rose like a balloon toward the specks of blue sky among the treetops. People changed, after all, learned from difficult situations and marched on with renewed energy. Because they had to? Because they'd been taught to? Because it was instinct? Steffen had done the impossible before, after the accident. Thomas had, too—survived it, moved on—but his last memory of real, carefree happiness was the hours immediately before the accident, when the Hejduks had spent the day out together for the first time in a long time. He, his parents, and Steffen, shortly before Thomas's seventeenth birthday.

Thomas stared into the increasingly dark green between the unmoving tree trunks. If his capacity for joy and contentment, and his ability to see the good and beautiful in life, had nearly died along with his parents, then what would happen if they found Steffen dead today? What else would he lose?

The sun moved mercilessly across the sky, showing how quickly the day was passing. Heidi's cell phone remained silent, no other search party reporting Steffen's safe return. With each yard Thomas covered, each branch breaking under his step, and each insect he wiped off his sweaty face, he imagined a part of his heart turning to stone, then falling off and landing painfully in his stomach.

A nasty voice in his head hissed that he might as well turn around, that it was already too late. He tried to block it out by repeating Heidi's words of encouragement, but when the sun disappeared behind a mountain ridge, the hissing grew into deafening screams.

Bright red-and-purple streaks on the horizon announced nightfall and intensified the storm of despair and anger raging inside Thomas. He started when Heidi grabbed his arm.

"There!" she gasped.

Thomas raised his head. In front of them, the hill made a half circle, and at its outmost point, a sandstone-colored bluff towered above the green valley. A man was standing close to the edge, gazing out at the sky's bracing display of colors. The wind was pulling at his tight T-shirt, causing tiny ripples to dance over it, and his shorts were flapping. The man swayed, but took another step forward. He was only inches from the edge, and the idyllic view seemed to laugh in Thomas's face.

"No!" Thomas yelled and started to run.

Branches slapped his face and grabbed at his clothes as if trying to hold him back. He desperately fought his way through the trees, stumbling over a root and grazing his knees and hands, but he jumped back up. At the edge of the forest, the soft ground changed to hard, light-colored rock. He was only five yards from Steffen. Blood rushed in Thomas's ears, his heart pounded against his chest.

Then Steffen moved. Thomas screamed in horror.

Chapter 13

Steffen turned around and looked at Thomas with surprise. "What are you doing here? You scared me half to death."

Thomas shook his head in bewilderment. His brother sounded so calm. Was he sure of his decision this time? Had he come to terms with it?

"Get away from there," Thomas replied. His voice sounded like fingernails on a chalkboard. It didn't seem to belong to him.

"You know I'm not afraid of heights."

"I beg your pardon?"

Steffen ran his fingers through his hair. Suddenly, he broke into a smile. "Did you think I was going to jump?"

"Are you surprised?" Thomas snarled. He clenched his fists, feeling like an idiot. Unfazed by the sheer drop to his left and right, Steffen walked toward him. Thomas resisted punching his brother in the face. Steffen would easily deflect the blow, and Thomas wanted to avoid further humiliation.

"I'm sorry I scared you."

"Do you realize there are twenty people out looking for you?"

Steffen looked confused for a moment. Then he turned and gazed at the colorful sunset. "What time is it?"

"Nearly ten."

"Damn. I lost track of time. Did Heidi and Peter get worried and call you?"

"Gee, you think?"

"Come with me," Steffen replied, and stepped to the edge of the bluff again.

Thomas looked back. Heidi was sitting on a log, half hidden behind bushes, talking on her phone. Keeping a close eye on the sheer cliffs, he followed his brother out onto the precipice and crouched down for safety.

"Just look at it," Steffen said.

Below them, green meadows lined the valley floor. Two silver ribbons, lively rivers that joined up at the end of the valley, divided the rolling hills. Bright flowers shone up at them despite the fading light, like dashes of paint dabbed here and there with a playful brush, and a barley field was turned into an ocean of gold by the setting sun. The surrounding hills were covered in a mixture of birch, willow, pine, oak, beech, and spruce trees swaying in the wind. Behind them, the dark, forested mountains towered above like watchmen.

Crickets were chirping and a few birds were singing good-night songs as the colorful watercolor in the sky slowly faded.

"I've been standing here for hours. I had a lot to think about after talking to the child's father and hearing the radio this morning."

"Steffen . . ."

"It's all right, little brother. I didn't come here to kill myself, just to think. I need to come clean with myself. If the boy's father can fight the urge to make accusations . . ." Steffen swallowed hard and crouched beside Thomas, who finally relaxed a little.

"I wouldn't have jumped off the bridge, either," Steffen admitted. "At least, that's what I suspect now. Janica arrived so fast. I couldn't have been on the railing for more than a few seconds. I suppose I lost control, especially since the dosage was wrong on my drugs."

Thomas nodded and felt his panic dissolve. But wariness remained.

"I don't know why all this happened. I don't understand it. But I have to accept that there are things I can't change. I'm the one who killed somebody, not the hostage taker. But I realized today: The evil in that situation didn't come from me."

"You were trying to help."

"Yes. I wanted to protect the woman and her children. I wanted to return them safely to the man outside the police tape who was going crazy with desperation. Because I know what it means to lose the people you love. Unfortunately, I couldn't give him back all of them, but three, at least."

"That's a lot better than none."

"I wish that lunatic had never gone into that house! I wish I'd seen the boy in time or aimed higher! I wish he'd pulled through—" Steffen closed his eyes for a moment, then continued, his voice calm again. "But men are fallible. Perfection only exists in what we call heaven. The hostage situation wasn't resolved the way I wish, but it could have ended worse."

"Much worse," Thomas sighed with relief. He might not lose his brother after all, not to quietly beckoning depression or to furiously shouting death.

Perhaps the coming weeks and months would bring further blows from within and without. Perhaps the suffering Steffen had caused would come crashing down on him like storm-whipped waves. For the first time, though, Steffen seemed ready to keep his head above water.

"Let's get back to the farm," Steffen said. He got up, held out his hand for Thomas, and helped him to his feet. The brothers stood face-to-face, fighting a common enemy for the second time in their lives. Thomas gave Steffen a tight hug. It was their first embrace in a long time, and they grinned sheepishly at one another as they let go.

When had they grown apart? Not while Steffen was married and Thomas a regular visitor at their place. In the past year? When Steffen lost his family, his home, his best friend? When he needed Thomas the most?

Thomas gazed at the mountains stretching out in shades of blue and gradually disappearing behind a milky haze. He narrowed his eyes as he realized how far out of his depth he had been these past months. Steffen's suffering had shown him that the safe, orderly world he'd been trying to create didn't exist, not even for his tough big brother. His distance from Steffen turned out to be not politeness, but helplessness—fear of saying the wrong thing, doing the wrong thing. He was determined to do better from now on. But how?

"Shall we, boys?" Heidi's voice rang out.

An affectionate smile spread across Steffen's face at the sound of her voice. Thomas felt a little envious of Steffen for having found a home for his heart and soul, but pushed the notion aside immediately. Steffen needed it. It was his world that had been turned upside down, after all, not Thomas's. But a question flashed through his mind: Hadn't his own world been upside down for years?

Chapter 14

July 4

Dark clouds were piling up beyond the roofs of the city. They seemed to suck the light from the atmosphere until all that was left was a dirty, yellow-green glow. A few swallows shot past Janica's head as she studied the riotous sky. Her dark-blue T-shirt clung to her body in the muggy air. Rain would be welcome, but the clouds brewing on the horizon heralded more than a regular summer storm. A gust of hot wind bent the birch trees, their trunks starkly white in the murky light, their leaves shaking so hard their silver undersides flashed like lightning. Thunder rolled angrily in the distance.

The next wild gust of wind blew Janica through the hospice door. Helga was sitting at the front desk with her glasses low on her nose, typing away with a pinched expression. Janica knew something was wrong. The usually sunny woman wasn't smiling, and she wasn't wearing any makeup. Janica knew Helga mourned each time a child died, and when she saw it coming, she'd take off her mascara before it could leave ugly black streaks on her face.

Janica approached the huge, curved reception desk with heavy steps and dropped her strawberry-red handbag on the ground. The bag was covered with the signatures of children, most of them long gone. She rested her forearms on the smooth counter.

"Who?"

Helga leaned forward and clasped Janica's hands in hers. "Rat."

Janica closed her eyes. Tears formed in the corners, let go, and left a glittering trace on her flushed face.

"Her father had to take her to hospital last week. They couldn't get her back on her feet." Helga sniffed and her grip on Janica's fingers tightened. "She's been here since yesterday. It's going very fast."

As Helga patted her hand, Janica forced herself to open her eyes. They'd seen each other cry many times. There was no need for shyness.

"But Rat was determined to wait for you."

"Why didn't you—?"

"We tried. It kept going straight to voicemail."

Janica nodded and tried to catch her breath. She'd noticed earlier that her phone battery was dead.

A flash of lightning lit up the corridor, dispelling for a moment the dark cloud that had formed around the two women.

"She was getting sicker by the minute. Her breathing—"

Janica needed no further explanation.

"Who's with her?"

"Her father and older brother."

"Did they say anything?"

"You can go in."

Now it was Janica's turn to sniff loudly. She pulled her hands from Helga's and turned mechanically toward the round room.

No happy greetings awaited her, no beaming smile, no cheeky remark. Children and parents sat huddled together, clinging to the life they were given, knowing too well that each one of them would face the end sooner or later.

Jessika, her sister, and her mother were back. She was noticeably chubbier than during her first, brief stay at the hospice, and her coloring was better. Derja wasn't there—Janica knew she was home with her family until the next round of treatment, after which she'd be back to recover. Annabelle was home, too. She was doing well and couldn't wait for school to start in fall.

Two new children were eyeing Janica curiously. Their parents and siblings seemed distraught, helpless at being in such proximity to death. They would learn to deal with the constant tumult of hope and despair. Their children's illnesses would give them no choice.

Janica nodded warmly, but only Jessika reacted—she raised her hand and waved, but the gesture came out desperate, morbid.

Janica walked down the corridor that led to Rat's room. The door was closed—an unusual sight, as the social child loved nothing more than talking and playing with others.

Trembling, Janica reached for the handle. The metal felt ice cold. Suddenly, she felt as if the ground had opened up beneath her feet. She braced herself against the doorframe and waited for the world to stop spinning. Heat shot through her body. She couldn't fend it off. The hall started to spin again, and she had to lean her forehead against the door to hold herself up.

When the tornado died down at last, Janica looked up. She hadn't drunk enough water today, she scolded herself. A dull and strangely empty feeling in her head made her wait a little longer. She couldn't walk into the room in this state. She needed a clear head—for Rat, her father, her seventeen-year-old brother—and for herself.

The seconds turned into minutes. No sound came from the other side of the door. Everything was quiet. Quiet as death.

Finally, Janica squared her shoulders and pushed down the handle. The door opened into the room quietly, smoothly, unobtrusively, like a gentle passing from this world into the next.

An IV pole was standing uselessly to one side, and the oxygen tank hissed horribly, as if it wanted to make sure everybody knew how bad things were. Janica only knew Rat as pitifully skinny and haggard, a weak and awkward teenager—a faint echo of the formerly rosy-cheeked, suntanned girl. Janica was all too familiar with dying children, but her heart still cramped painfully when her eyes fell on the bed. A thin, pointy face was sticking out from the colorful bedding, her body barely raising the blanket off the mattress. The eyelids, blue with tiny veins, were closed, and short dark hair stuck out from her head in all directions. The burrowing cancer had turned her young body into a fragile wreck no longer able to function.

Even though Rat had only just gotten back, the walls were covered in photos and drawings, and her huge collection of board games sat on the shelves. Her father must have known his daughter would never open them again, never move the pieces across the boards or hold the cards in her hands. He'd brought them to comfort her, to create familiar surroundings now that, thanks to the drugs, she wasn't feeling any more pain.

Janica loved this man for his brave dedication, his self-sacrifice, and his positive attitude. The painful good-bye ahead wasn't his first. He'd lost his wife seven years ago, also to cancer. Now he was sitting by the bed like a tower of strength, holding his daughter's limp, white hand, whispering into her ear.

Janica's eyes turned to Rat's brother, Karsten. The tall, dark-haired teenager looked the same as always: handsome and relaxed. But his clenched fists and his rigid stare fixed on the well-worn board game boxes revealed his pain and fury.

Janica closed the door softly. She walked to the other side of the bed, sat down, and picked up the child's cold hand.

"Hello, Rat," she said with a smile, leaned forward, and kissed her cheek.

A thunderclap rattled the windowpanes like it was showing off all the strength that Rat lacked. An instant later, heavy raindrops began to beat against the glass like the drumming of nervous fingers. Janica pushed aside the idea that death was knocking at the window, demanding they finally hand over this little life.

"I'm sorry I couldn't get here sooner. I wasn't expecting you back so soon."

Karsten snorted angrily. Janica ignored him. Nothing and no one could interrupt this moment between her and Rat—not the thunder and lightning, the noisy rain, or the grieving brother.

"But you've always had a mind of your own," she added and stroked Rat's fuzzy hair.

Tears streamed down her face, leaving dark marks on the yellow sheets. Janica took a deep breath. How many times had she played The Settlers of Catan, Sevens, Carcassonne, and UNO with this girl over the years? How many butterflies had they attempted to draw and ended up laughing at the resulting giraffes and UFOs? One time, after Rat had a huge growth spurt, they'd gone shopping together. Later that day, they'd turned the round room into a fashion show, and the then ten-year-old girl had shown off her new jeans, trendy tops, and most of all, the many colorful scarves she had *needed* to buy.

Janica looked at Karsten. He was wearing the turquoise scarf with the dark-blue stars—Rat's favorite. The turquoise was the color of a high-country lake bathed in sunshine, and the blue stars reminded her of the last minutes between dusk and darkness. Gottlieb, Rat's father, had donned the moss-green scarf that gradually faded into a gentle lily-yellow. The two would probably wear those scarves until they were threadbare rags, and then display them lovingly in their apartment.

With a sigh, she turned back to the pointy face with the translucent skin. Rat wasn't really with them anymore. The morphine was to make dying easier for her, take away her pain and fear and spare her having to feel the horror of the last, choking breaths. But it also prevented Janica from saying good-bye properly, thanking the girl for all the joy she'd brought to her life.

Janica raised her head when Gottlieb cleared his throat.

"Before Rat let Dr. Kraus administer the drugs, she told me she had a message for you."

Janica swallowed hard and winced when a lightning flash lit up the room, followed by a thunderclap she feared would tear down the walls. The rain turned to deafening hail, and Gottlieb was forced to raise his voice so Janica could hear him.

"She said she didn't want to wait any longer. Not because of the pain, but because—while she was napping—a voice told her it was time. I don't know if she meant the voice was saying it was time no matter what, or if it meant *Rat* was really ready."

"I think both are right."

Gottlieb nodded and wiped away a tear, and Karsten snorted again.

"Rat said she was never any good at school, but she remembered everything you told her about heaven since she first came here four years ago. She said she'd go there now and find out if you were fibbing. Then she smiled." Gottlieb exhaled loudly and waited for the strength to continue. "She smiled and said: Because you never used to suspect when she cheated at a game, she assumed you were telling the truth about heaven. Apparently, you've never been a good liar, at least not good enough for her."

Janica couldn't manage more than a nod. At games that required bluffing and trickery, Rat won even without cheating.

"She would like you to have *The Swarm of Butterflies* painting. The one with the turtles. She said you'd know which one."

Janica nodded. The old painting was meant to be of turtles, but thanks to their crummy drawing skills, it came out looking more like butterflies. It had been a running joke for years whenever Janica had tried to cheer up the girl after rounds of chemotherapy and radiation.

She'd never be able to draw butterflies or turtles with another child without thinking of Rat. But that was OK—it was right. She'd tell the sick child about a cheerful girl who'd been brave even in the face of death, and the story would help them find hope and courage. Just another way Rat's life and death would have meaning.

"She also asked me to give you one of her scarves. The awful yellow one with the silly tassels."

Janica laughed softly as her tears flowed faster. Rat knew her so well.

"When we went shopping for those scarves, Rat said we had to buy at least one that was totally ridiculous and ugly, because she'd never be able to do it again. It was her one chance in life to waste money on something silly! It actually took us most of the afternoon to find something ugly enough. When we finally found it, we laughed and laughed."

Janica couldn't hold back any longer. She pressed one hand to her mouth and sobbed, her head sinking into the sheet.

Gottlieb placed his heavy hand on Janica's hair, silently thanking her for the hours of happiness she'd given his daughter amid all the suffering, the countless treatments.

His voice trembled and barely managed to rise above the merciless hail. "She asked you to give Balou a big kiss from her. And she said to tell you how much she loved you."

"Enough of this shit," Karsten growled, slamming the door as he bolted.

Gottlieb winced and jumped up to follow.

"Stay with Rat," Janica said and got to her feet.

Another wave of dizziness swept over her, a reminder that she still hadn't drunk any water.

"He's so angry," Gottlieb said.

"Of course he is. He loves Rat, and she's the second important person cancer is stealing from him. I'd be worried if he wasn't angry."

Janica

The rain helped, though neither the icy pellets nor the gentle drops afterward could wash away the grief and heaviness in my heart. It was as if even the sky was crying for the loss of a child. But wasn't our loss heaven's gain?

A few minutes after Karsten and I returned from a long conversation and an even longer silence, Rat died. How like her to wait until we were by her side before slipping away.

And now it was back with a vengeance, the merciless emptiness that always followed the loss of a loved one, the grief that tore a hole in my soul. No, I wasn't drawn to these children because I was seeking pain and suffering, but because I needed the love and the laughter of their little hearts. Like a sponge, I soaked up their courage, their will to fight, and their strength. They know what it means to live fully, because they're in a staring match with death. It's because they know hardship, loneliness, and pain that they can feel joy so deeply—at least most of them. There are always exceptions: Usually older children who have let go of their innocence, who are too far removed from the gift of wonder we're all born with.

Chapter 15

July 7

It hadn't stopped raining for days, almost as if the sky couldn't rein in the clouds anymore, as if the natural order was out of whack. But today, the summer sun finally chased the gray clouds away, dried the roads, and turned wet meadows and fields into steaming cauldrons of mist. It changed color in the shifting sunshine, morphing from grape-gray to pale gold.

The day the storm broke had been Thomas's last day of school. It was late afternoon, and he was on his way home from the farm. He'd picked up Steffen there in the morning and taken him to an appointment with the police psychologist and then to visit his daughter. On the drive back to the Meiers' place, Steffen had been sullen and withdrawn. He finally told Thomas that Marie had been raving about her mother's new best friend. Something about it had irritated Steffen and made him wonder whether his ex-wife preferred women now.

Steffen sat taut as a bowstring the entire drive. Only when they saw the idyllic farmstead—after having to turn around because Thomas missed the turnoff again—had he finally relaxed. Thomas saw that his brother had come a long way, but he wasn't back to his old self—and might never be. The series of harsh blows had changed him, made him softer, more sensitive. Too sensitive?

Thomas sighed and turned off toward the river. He hadn't seen Janica for days, and he had to admit that he was avoiding her. The redhead confused him and took up far more of his thoughts than he ever would have imagined.

Her freckled face was the first thing he thought about when he woke in the morning, fantasizing about getting to see her that day. All day long, he'd wonder where she was, what she might be doing. At night, sitting in his quiet house, he thought of her contagious laughter and his placid, successful day suddenly seemed meaningless. Thomas had canceled the trip to Morocco he'd planned with two of his colleagues. He told himself it was so he could be there for Steffen, but was it also to stay close to Janica? If so, why was he avoiding her?

"I'm not, though," Thomas grumbled and pulled up in front of Janica's apartment.

The moment he killed the engine, the heat of the day came creeping into the car, but he sat there a few long moments without getting out. What was he doing here? He had no excuse for visiting. Thomas felt familiar butterflies in his stomach, and his heart beat faster. This wasn't the first time he'd driven over like this, but so far, he had driven right back home. What was holding him back? The fact that Janica had found Steffen, not him? The fear of betraying Steffen by coming between him and this fascinating woman? Steffen was probably ready to let his ex-wife go and fall in love again. Was it wrong of Thomas to interfere, especially when his brother was so fragile?

"Thomas? What are you doing here?"

Janica's voice tore him from his thoughts as she tapped on the window. He looked up from the rotten banana peel in the road he'd been staring at as if it held the answers to all his questions.

Janica was wearing black—not her work clothes, but a knee-long skirt and a sleeveless blouse, together with an awful yellow scarf. She'd probably call it Dijon-mustard yellow with a hint of sunflower-seed brown or something like that.

Her face was pale, highlighting her freckles and her carefully pinned-up hair.

Climbing out, Thomas's heart skipped a beat. He felt like a student caught smoking in the toilet.

"Hi, Janica," he replied woozily, trying to regain control of his senses.

"Are you all right?" Worried, she reached into her shapeless, blue shoulder bag with neon-yellow stripes, and handed him a bottle of water. He thanked her and drank. It bought him a few extra seconds to gather his thoughts.

"I just thought I'd come by and say hello."

"I don't live down here on the street, though," she teased.

"Yeah, um, when I got here, I realized you'd probably be at work, or maybe away on vacation."

"I am on vacation."

"Are you going away anywhere?"

"I never go away in summer. It's much too sunny."

Thomas laughed, then realized Janica wasn't joking. He figured she must be protecting that pale skin.

Janica turned and walked across a strip of grass to the gravel path that led back to her metal stairs. Thomas lingered uncertainly by his car until she turned and waved for him to come.

"Sometimes people sit down while they talk, over a cup of coffee or whatever."

"I'd love to!" Thomas replied.

He slammed the door shut and jogged after Janica. Following her up the stairs, he wondered why the athletic woman was climbing the stairs so slowly today. Maybe it was the heat.

On the metal landing outside her apartment, she pulled her jingling bunch of keys from her bag and opened the door. Thomas followed, but jumped back with fright when a huge shadow leapt toward him. He had forgotten all about Balou, who thankfully pounced on Janica first. She knelt down and greeted the wolfhound enthusiastically.

"Go easy on him!" Janica told the dog in a stern voice as she got up.

Balou sat down in front of Thomas with his tail wagging, tilted his head to one side, and panted heavily, despite the pleasantly cool temperature inside the dim apartment. Thomas gingerly stroked the dog's massive head a few times and thought he read disappointment in his eyes. He let his eyes wander through the open-plan kitchen and living room. A dark timber floor and white ceiling beams gave the apartment an elegant touch, while the furniture was a colorful, motley mix, suiting the home's inhabitant. The room was dominated by a huge oak table, which seemed strangely out of place for a woman who lived on her own. Maybe it was an heirloom, or connected to a happy memory for Janica.

Thomas's eyes fell on framed photos of happy, laughing faces. He went closer and recognized several children from the hospice, including Florian, Sven, Jessika, Rat, Derja, and Annabelle. There were also pictures of Helga and the friendly intensive-care nurse, Werner. Two younger women were standing between them, probably nurses he hadn't met, and an older, round woman in an elegant silk blouse, a stethoscope dangling from her neck. Could she be the palliative doctor?

Thomas turned when he heard steps. Janica had emerged from her bedroom and was on her way to the bathroom. She smiled, but it didn't make him dizzy like usual—it pained him instead. The smile seemed wistful and made her look frighteningly fragile. Something was wrong. Usually, Janica's eyes were like sparklers, her face brighter than the sun. Taking a second look at her black clothing, now without the yellow scarf, he suddenly wondered if she'd been on her way home from a funeral when she found him in the street like a stray dog.

Before he had the chance to say anything, she closed the bathroom door behind her. A painting was stuck to the door: turtles in various sizes and strange colors, sitting among rocks, brown sand, and green seaweed. He walked over to read the writing underneath.

"*The Swarm of Butterflies*. By Rat and Janica," he read and frowned in confusion. He jumped when the door swung open. Janica looked up at him with surprise. Her closeness, the smell of her deodorant, her shorts and fitted T-shirt made him gasp. Feelings flooded his heart like the ocean in the picture, and he grabbed her by her shoulders. He simply had to touch her, feel her skin.

"What happened?" he asked in a strained voice.

"You noticed?"

"I may be a boring loner, but even I can see—"

A shiver ran down his body when she placed her index finger over his lips.

"You're getting better already," she said with a smile.

Thomas, having expected a polite contradiction, was surprised by her yet again. And he liked it. Not only because she was so different from most people, but because she was starting to draw him into a new kind of life. He loved how genuinely honest she was. You always knew where you stood with Janica.

He was sad when she took her finger away, and even sadder when she twisted out of his grip and walked to the kitchen, disappearing behind the protective shield of the breakfast bar.

"Do you want to put the cushions on the deck chairs and put up the umbrella? I'll make some coffee. Do you feel like ice cream?"

"Yes," Thomas replied, and wished he could say much more.

He struggled to tear his eyes from her body when she stretched to open a high cabinet. Breathing out slowly through pursed lips to calm himself down, he stepped out into the glaring sunshine and did as he was told. He could hear the hissing and humming of a coffeemaker, which seemed a little silly for a one-person household, just like the massive table, as he moved the wide umbrella so that only one chair was shaded. Happy with the result, he slumped into the sunny chair and crossed his hands behind his head. He closed his eyes and watched the pale-blue dots of color the sunlight painted on the inside of his eyelids.

As much as Janica's physical closeness, especially her smile and her touch, made him nervous, he also felt increasingly comfortable in her presence. For a moment, he allowed himself to fantasize about a future with her. But the thought of Steffen gave him a sharp pang of guilt, and so he swatted his reveries away like a pesky insect.

The minutes went by. He listened to the cooing of pigeons, the chirping of birds, snatches of conversations of cyclists riding along the riverbank. He heard Janica clinking glasses in the kitchen and took a deep breath of the tangy air. Suddenly, there was a new smell. Before he could put his finger on what it was, something wet brushed across his face. Thomas's eyes sprang open and he saw shaggy fur and mischievous eyes. The astonishingly long tongue that had licked salty sweat off his face was hanging out the side of Balou's mouth, and he panted in Thomas's ear.

"Lousy mutt!" he cried, and a few seconds later, Janica appeared.

"Balou, inside!" she commanded.

The animal retreated with its head hung low.

"What did he do?" Janica asked Thomas.

"He licked—" Thomas broke off when he saw her trying to hide a smile.

"If I may give you a piece of advice, Thomas: Greet the lousy mutt properly. As you probably noticed, he didn't jump up on you or beg for your attention. I've been working to teach the big baby to gauge who enjoys his greetings: My father, for example! Balou loves contact, affection. Give him a few of your precious minutes, and then he'll leave you in peace. Mostly."

"I'll be sure to remember," Thomas muttered, although Janica had already gone back inside.

What was she doing in there? He longed to have her beside him. He wanted to look at her, talk to her, find out what was wrong. He wondered how much longer he could keep his feelings, his worries and impulses, all locked up before they spilled out everywhere.

"Thomas?"

He jumped again, then remembered with relief that not even Janica could read the thoughts that circled her incessantly like a bee around a tempting piece of pie.

Finally, Janica came to join him. She set down a tray containing two frothy lattes in long-stemmed glasses, a selection of cold bottled drinks, and two large glass bowls holding generous helpings of ice cream in various flavors.

"You're not running a café up here, are you?"

"Sometimes, when I have visitors," she replied. She sank her spoon into a scoop of chocolate ice cream. "My-first-Icelandic-pony brown."

"Why do you do that?"

"Do what?" Janica closed her eyes with relish as she put the spoon in her mouth.

"The thing with colors. Why don't you just say brown or blue? Or even dark brown or sky blue or something like that?"

"Because I connect colors with memories. They help me remember a wonderful moment I got to experience, and people who were part of that moment. I relive the gratitude to have experienced that moment, to have known those people. That gratitude for all those small and big gifts is the key to a happy life."

Stunned and awed by this answer, Thomas concentrated silently on the rapidly melting ice cream and wasn't surprised when Janica unburdened herself about the day's events. She was an open, uncomplicated person who didn't think much of false modesty or polite restraint.

"I went to Rat's funeral today."

"Rat?" A dark abyss was reaching out for him.

"The girl who—"

"I know who Rat is, Janica," Thomas said, the ice cream suddenly seeming to burn his tongue. "How could she . . . so quickly?" He couldn't get the word out. It was such an ugly, final word.

"The destructive power of a greedy, ravenous disease and the pitfalls of a body not designed for eternity," Janica said and shoved a huge spoonful of vanilla ice cream into her mouth, as if testing how much *her* body could handle.

"I'm so sorry. I got the impression you and Rat had been through a lot together."

"Yes," Janica slurred with her mouth full. "Rat knew a long time ago that her battle with leukemia was hopeless. Everything she went through the last few years, all the chemotherapy and radiation, was for her father and her brother. She wanted to give them more time with her. Time to say good-bye."

"She told you that?"

"A few weeks ago, yeah."

"How could a thirteen-year-old be so mature?"

"Many of these children develop very differently from healthy ones. Of course, they have the same needs, desires, and hopes as their healthy peers, and the same problems, like heartaches or fights with their friends. But their emotional and mental development, their knowledge of good and evil, right and wrong, love and hate, can be far ahead of other children their age. I'm not saying they age faster, but they become . . . wiser, perhaps? Not all of them, of course, but most."

"Admirable."

"You think? They don't really have a choice. They have to live their whole life in a fraction of the time most people get. They learn very early on things that healthy people don't learn until old age, for example that we can't know happiness until we've experienced suffering, that we don't appreciate our healthy body until we've been sick, that human life is worthless unless we give it meaning."

"They see meaning in their lives?"

"Many of them. They make me laugh and dream, teach me hope, dedication and persistence, strength and vulnerability. They make me think about meaning in my life, and force me to become aware of my own mortality. Our culture tries so hard to ignore death. We hide the elderly in institutions, sick people don't get to die at home, children are kept away from funerals. Those kids can't hide from death. They teach me how important it is to enjoy every moment, to take full responsibility for my own life."

"And then they die. Far too soon and far too cruelly."

"Yes, but that's not the end for them." Janica sighed, the pain of Rat's loss showing in her face. She set down the bowl of melted ice cream. "See this ice cream?"

"I wouldn't call it ice cream anymore," Thomas replied.

"Right. Ice cream is made from cream. As long as I kept it cold, it was what it was supposed to be: ice cream. Now it's not ice cream anymore, like you said. But it's still there. It didn't just go away. It returned to its original form."

Thomas ran his hand through his hair. "Kind of a weird analogy."

"Well, it is just ice cream, after all!" Janica had a mischievous glint in her eyes. She reached for her coffee. "Did you see Steffen today? How is he doing?"

Thomas was grateful to shift the topic of conversation to safer ground. But when he looked into Janica's sparkling eyes, he wasn't so sure the ground here was safe after all.

The water gurgled along the riverbed and reflected the evening sun. Janica was glad when the heat finally let up—the cool air rising off the river helped her feel a little better. She didn't do well with heat, and this summer, her body seemed even more sensitive to it than usual. But she'd enjoyed the afternoon. After their ice cream, she had suggested a walk, and Thomas had readily agreed. He had even thrown Balou's tennis ball over and over for him on a patch of grass. The wolfhound hadn't left his side since.

He'd told Janica about the school where he taught, and she could see how dedicated he was to his students. It didn't surprise her, as he took everything so seriously, but she was glad for his students' sake.

But when Thomas told her about his adventures in faraway countries, she was forced to revise her assessment of him. He was more like his brother than she'd thought. Not fearful after all, he possessed a different kind of courage, a thirst for adventure.

But the stories of solo travel also confirmed Janica's suspicions about his reclusiveness. His life was like a river that wasn't following its natural course, but—like so many rivers in Germany—it had gotten penned in between two walls. But that could be changed, Janica thought, and turned to her side.

She and Thomas were lying in the grass on the riverbank, listening to the rushing water and the chirping crickets. The young woman propped herself up on her elbow and rested her head in the palm of one hand while picking a long blade of grass with the other. She brushed Thomas's tanned neck with the grass. Without opening his eyes, he swatted at it, and Janica pulled back just in time. As soon as he relaxed, she tickled his Adam's apple again.

Thomas smacked at the grass a second time, then crossed his hands behind his neck. She went in again, and this time, Thomas gave a little grunt while trying to swat the imagined insect, making Balou lift his head and wag hopefully.

Janica chuckled with delight. She approached once more, but Thomas was on guard this time. He snatched the blade of grass, opened his eyes, and sized her up. Janica let out a laugh like a bell. Before she could react, Thomas grabbed her by the shoulders and whirled her around, pushing her into the grass. He braced one elbow against the ground, some of his weight on top of her.

She saw the sparkle in his brown eyes, felt his breath on her cheek. She held her breath. Her whole body was tingling, as if thousands of ants were crawling on her. Small explosions seemed to go off inside her, making her flush with heat again and again. He held her gaze as the seconds passed.

Suddenly, he frowned. It was as if a voice in his head reminded him of something, pulled him back. And then Balou's head pushed in between them. The tension fell away.

Thomas rolled back into the grass next to her. This time, she couldn't read the expression on his face. Was it disappointment? Relief? Shock?

For her part, Janica felt disappointment with every fiber of her being, right into the remotest corner of her heart. She liked Thomas very much. It wasn't an opposites-attracting thing, or his old-fashioned politeness and reserve, and least of all his organized, boring life. It was the way he worried about Steffen and looked after him. She loved the fervor with which he listened to her father. She was moved by the friendship he had shown Sven, his lack of discomfort with the boy's twisted body. It was his honest laughter—on the rare occasions he actually laughed—and the duty he felt to his students, even though his efforts were often hindered by the peculiar perfectionism that left little room for spontaneity.

Janica watched Thomas nervously run his fingers through his hair again. The gesture underlined his confusion, and the way he avoided her eyes revealed his embarrassment.

She sprang to her feet and was punished with a dizzy spell. She quickly put out both hands to hide it. He looked at her hands, hesitated, and when Janica was about to lower them again, he took hold and pretended to let her help him up. Thomas immediately tried to let go, but Janica didn't let him. She made herself hold still, wait for him to meet her eyes. It wasn't easy, not with butterflies swarming wildly in her stomach. But she'd learned that life was too precious not to show what she felt. So she waited, winked at him, gave his hands a firm squeeze, and only then did she let go.

"I—" He broke off, gave her a crooked grin, and picked up Balou's ball. The dog pricked his ears and chased the young man up the bank, barking loudly.

Janica strolled after them with a smile on her face, watching Thomas turn to glance back at her repeatedly. He wasn't completely sure how to interpret her gesture, but elation showed in his beaming face and his exuberant bearing. Janica smiled as she walked along the gravel path toward home. She was actually falling in love! Who would have thought the sad man on the bridge could cause so many ripples, just like a stone thrown into water.

Chapter 16

July 11

Shrieking with delight, the six-year-old girl rolled across the timber floor. Balou was thrilled to continue the game they had made up—he jumped over the little body again and again. He gave a little bark every time he landed and skidded along the polished wood, until he lost momentum, turned around, and prepared for the next jump.

In the kitchen, Janica paused for a moment to watch the frolicking, then focused her attention back on preparations for tonight's party.

All three of them looked up when someone knocked. Balou ran toward the door, tail wagging. His giddy yelps told Janica the visitor was no stranger.

She washed her hands, hurried over, and opened the door. Janica gave a cry of delight at the sight of long, black hair, a huge pair of sunglasses, an amazing figure, and a beaming smile with perfect teeth. Her sister pushed her sunglasses into her hair, spread her arms, and Janica fell into her embrace.

"Happy birthday, sunshine!" Jenni sang in the deep, full, slightly husky voice that was her trademark. It was increasingly well known, especially in the Netherlands, where she had moved to become a singer.

"You made it!" Janica cheered.

"Of course I made it. I wouldn't miss your birthday for the world!"

"Did you fly in just to see me?"

"Yes, from very slow contract negotiations in New York. Which is why I've got to ask: Do you mind if I crash in your bed for a little while before your crazy friends arrive?"

"You came from New York? Just for me?"

Jenni set her enormous bouquet of red roses on the ground and gave Janica another hug. "No journey is too long to see you, you know that."

Janica giggled. "I hear that's what your fans say about you."

"Well, they just want to hear my voice or admire this carefully maintained body. But you're the whole package. And these are for you." Jenni leaned down and rescued the roses from a curious Balou. "I decided on red this year."

"Sunset-over-the-North-Sea red."

"I knew you'd find the perfect name for it!" Jenni teased. "And now, would you kindly introduce me to this pretty little girl?"

Janica, carefully placing the bunch of flowers in the crook of her elbow, turned around to her young visitor. The girl was standing in the middle of the room like a statue, gaping at Jenni.

"I–I know you. From TV," she stammered.

Jenni pulled her huge sunglasses out of her hair and crouched down in front of the child. "And who are you?" she asked, ignoring the allusion to her growing fame.

"I'm Marie. My real name is Marianne, but no one calls me that—only Grandpa."

"I'm Jenni."

"No, that's not your name!"

"I'm a bit like you, Marie. Hardly anyone uses my real name. Only very special people are allowed to call me Jenni. And I think you're special."

"Really? Marie's eyes widened. She cast a questioning glance at Janica, who nodded with a smile as she filled a vase.

"OK!" Marie said eventually, having decided to accept Jenni's offer, and shook her hand energetically. "You look tired. Like Mommy when she's sad or someone annoyed her."

"You're right, Marie. I really am very tired."

Janica placed the flowers on the wide windowsill in the kitchen, hurried around the breakfast bar, and waved for Jenni to follow her. "Give me a sec to put on fresh sheets for you, then—"

"You don't need to do that. I've got my bags in the rental car downstairs. I just need a couple hours of sleep, and then I'll change the sheets for you."

"Do you need anything?"

"One of your ridiculously large glasses full of tap water would be fantastic," Jenni declared as she headed for the bedroom.

Janica brought her the water while Marie and Balou went back to their game.

"Cute kid. One of your hospice friends?"

"No, thankfully not."

"How nice! You also look after healthy children," she said, kicking off her high heels and flopping onto the bed.

"Marie's mother has a job interview today, so I'm babysitting."

"You're an angel," Jenni mumbled, already half-asleep.

"I'm so glad you came," Janica whispered.

She set the night-blue designer shoes side by side, and gave her sister a kiss on the forehead before tiptoeing out of the room and softly closing the door.

"Jenni is nice," Marie announced when Janica returned to the kitchen.

The little girl climbed onto one of the barstools, rested her elbows on the wooden counter, her head in her hands, and watched her older friend spreading generous amounts of soft cheese on slices of roasted bread, before adding sliced tomatoes, which she drizzled with olive oil and balsamic vinegar, adding a basil leaf for the finishing touch.

"Yes, she's very nice."

"She always seems so . . . distant, on TV."

"Well, she usually is quite far away."

"And I heard someone on the radio say she's not nice."

Janica gave a little sigh, rested her elbows on the counter opposite Marie, and studied the wonderfully bright little girl before replying.

"It's not easy for Jenni to always do the right thing when everyone constantly bothers her and wants things from her, even when they don't really have a right to ask for it. They won't even leave her alone when she's onstage."

Marie made a face, and Janica made it right back. To most people, Jenni was a stunningly beautiful, glamorous celebrity. They admired and envied her. For her talent, her looks, her fame, and probably for her money, too. Hardly anyone saw the dark sides of those things.

Janica turned to the sink and let cold water run over her hands. She was surprised to see a bruise on her lower left arm, and tried to think when she might have banged it. But her thoughts quickly returned to Jenni. Only two years ago, shortly after Jenni's career had taken off, her sister had been a mess. Exhausted from the impossible demands of the media, burnt out from the wild expectations of her manager and the record label, and dumped by her fiancé, who couldn't handle her constant traveling, the young woman had turned first to alcohol, then pills. The rising star had nearly killed herself with increasingly dangerous drugs. She'd been clean for about a year now, was more successful than ever, and had gained the wisdom that bitter, painful experiences can bring.

Since rehab, Jenni no longer teased Janica about her work at the hospice. She'd come so close to throwing her life away, and now she understood why Janica wanted to bring joy and distraction to the children there. In fact, she'd been giving charitable performances at the hospice every few months, inspiring generous donations from the awed spectators. Just one of her gigs had paid for the therapeutic swimming pool, and the arts and computer rooms received new additions following another call she made for donations.

A knock on the door made the snoozing Balou jump like he'd received an electric shock. Janica was pleased to see that Larissa, Marie's mother, had put aside her natural reserve and let herself in.

Marie jumped off the stool with a cry of joy and threw herself into the arms of the short, tired-looking woman in her late twenties.

"How was it, Mom?"

"Good, I think. The personnel manager and I got along well. She's a single mother, too." She addressed the last part to Janica.

"That's good," Janica agreed. "So she won't be prejudiced against your application."

Larissa turned to Marie, who was tugging at her hand with urgency.

"Janica's sister is a famous singer," Marie yelled, jumping up and down. "But I'm allowed to call her Jenni. She's asleep in Janica's bed."

"How exciting."

Larissa stroked the girl's blonde curls. It was obvious she didn't deem Marie's message nearly as important as her daughter would have liked. "Thank you, Janica. I don't know how—"

"It was my pleasure. Marie is a darling. She played with Balou the whole time. I even managed to prepare all my hors d'oeuvres for the party. Can you stay awhile?"

"I'm exhausted, but thank you for the invitation. Marie really needs to get to bed on time tonight. Four nights in a row now she's stayed up late playing with her dolls and toys."

Marie made a silly face, and Janica winked at her.

While the child packed her things into her little backpack, Larissa overcame her shyness and gave the younger woman a cautious hug good-bye.

"Thank you. Thank you for everything," she said. "I hope your party is amazing."

"I'm sure it'll be great—it always is when my family and friends take over this place!"

"Oh, yes, the singing sister."

"Her, too, yes."

Larissa, swept up in Janica's contagious warmth, turned around at the door to smile and wave.

Thomas had never approached the metal staircase with such trepidation. Swarms of mosquitoes danced in the evening light, and a pair of ducks complained loudly in the river as if they were trying to warn him off. It was ridiculous to be scared. He was just going to a birthday party. What could possibly be dangerous about that? He noticed a woman walking in the opposite direction, a child by her side. She disappeared behind some trees, but he felt certain he knew her from somewhere.

Curious, he followed, but she and the blonde child were nowhere to be seen. After an indecisive glance at Janica's place, he meandered along the riverbank and eventually sat down on a stone bench, rethinking his decision. On his knees, he balanced a bulky present and a small bunch of flowers: stargazer lilies, gerbera, and chamomile. With a wildly beating heart, he pulled himself together as well as he could and stood up. For the second time that evening, he headed toward Janica's house, purposefully taking long, confident strides.

Loud laughter made him look up. Two men around his age were sitting on Janica's deck chairs with beers in their hands, talking animatedly. A wave of disappointment washed over Thomas. He had hoped to be the first guest at the party. He'd imagined having her to himself for a few minutes, and already being there when the other guests arrived, putting the onus of introductions on them. Now all he could do was hope for a few familiar faces from the hospice.

"Hey, you, new guy, up the stairs, third landing!" one of the men called, pointing his beer bottle toward the staircase.

Thomas thanked him with a wave and started the ascent, making the stairs hum and sway slightly.

"New guy," he growled with indignation.

What was that supposed to mean? Was Janica telling everyone about the latest guy to follow her around the city like a puppy dog? Thomas shook his head. That wasn't like her. It probably just meant that the other guests had known each other for a long time. But that didn't make Thomas feel much better. He wasn't the most outgoing person in the best of times, and he'd really feel out of place with a bunch of people who'd known Janica forever.

Yet he climbed on, stepped onto the landing outside Janica's door, and stopped in front of the men, who raised their beers in greeting.

"Ugh, flowers," said the blond mop of hair who'd called down to him, grimacing as if Thomas had offered them as a snack.

"You better get rid of those quick," advised the other, who must have been six foot five.

The giant leaned forward, snatched the flowers from a stupefied Thomas, and stuffed them under his chair. Then he leaned in again and grabbed Thomas's right hand, squeezing it like a vise.

"Good to meet you, man. I'm Lars, and this short guy here is Finn."

Thomas gave his first name, too, although he found their familiarity a little strange.

"What's wrong with my flowers?" he asked, glancing through the open door.

Inside, more men he didn't know were moving the huge table from the wall to the middle of the room, two women were setting up folding chairs, and a third one was scurrying around, setting the table. Everyone appeared to know their way around perfectly. Thomas felt a pang of jealousy.

"If you'd known Janni a little longer, you'd know she only likes flowers when they're still in the ground. The sight of cut flowers hurts her."

"Oh, I see. Thanks for the heads-up."

"Anytime!"

"By the way, Janni's sister is here," Lars warned.

"So . . . ?" Thomas asked, raising his eyebrows quizzically.

He didn't know much about Janica's older sister, but if she was anything like Janica or their parents, he'd be very pleased to make her acquaintance.

Lars beckoned for him to come closer and Thomas leaned forward, setting down the cumbersome present on the metal grating.

"Jenni is somewhat . . ."

Lars looked at Finn, who shrugged and said, "Difficult?"

"What woman isn't, am I right?" Lars laughed, turning back to Thomas. "But listen: Jenni has a striking, almost scary, resemblance to a famous singer. She even dresses like her to emphasize the similarity."

"So she likes people to compliment her on the resemblance?" Thomas concluded.

"He's a clever cookie!" Finn said to Lars, and raised his bottle to his lips.

Lars followed suit.

"Thomas?"

He spun around and found himself face-to-face with Janica. She was wearing a thin light-blue dress, had her red curls tied up in a ponytail, and—as he noticed immediately—was once again barefoot. Thomas swallowed hard, and with mechanical movements, he picked up the parcel wrapped in green paper and held it out to her.

"H–happy birthday," he stammered, and managed a smile.

Janica beamed at him, took the present, and raised her eyebrows with surprise at its weight.

"It's nothing special," Thomas explained with a look at the deck chair, glad the bunch of flowers was well hidden. "It's a strawberry plant for the balcony railing. Next summer, you can harvest your own strawberries."

"What a wonderful present! Thank you!"

Thomas breathed a sigh of relief. The strawberry plant was firmly rooted in the ground—just the way Janica liked it.

"Looks like you already met Finn and Lars. Come inside so I can introduce you to everyone else."

Janica walked inside and placed the present on a sideboard that was already covered with wrapped boxes and cards. Thomas followed the birthday girl inside and was greeted by the beguiling smell of flowers. Every windowsill, even the one in the kitchen, was covered in vases holding bunches of flowers ranging from simple and small to opulent and elaborate. They transformed the windows into oceans of color. Thomas ran his hand through his hair with confusion. Had he misunderstood something?

"This bustling, always-busy woman is Julia," Janica introduced the dainty, dark-haired woman Thomas had noticed earlier.

"Those two are Barbara and Susi," Janica continued, pointing at two women who were clearly sisters, if not twins. "We've known each other since elementary school."

"Nice to meet you."

Barbara—or was is Susi?—held out her right hand and he squeezed it, while Susi—or Barbara—waved at him and set up the next chair.

"You know Werner."

Janica nodded to the intensive care nurse, who wasn't wearing his colorful T-shirt designed by the children today, but a plain white shirt.

"Hi, Thomas!" Werner called and opened the huge fridge, another thing Thomas had been surprised to see in a one-person household.

It was filled with sweet treats, hors d'oeuvres, and a ton of drinks. Werner reached for a bitter-lemon soda and looked at Thomas solicitously.

"Coke, thanks."

Janica had left him; apparently a guest required her help in the bedroom. The two remaining guests introduced themselves as Kurti and Angelo. Kurti spoke with a broad Bavarian accent, and Angelo was obviously Italian. Angelo said he'd come to Germany for a semester abroad as part of his engineering degree, but ended up staying for love. His gaze turned to Susi—or Barbara—as he spoke, and she smiled back fondly.

Janica returned and began to stack more drinks into the fridge, but Thomas's attention was drawn to the stunning woman who emerged from the bedroom.

"Angelo! Kurti!" she called out in a melodious voice and gave Kurti a hug before allowing the Italian to kiss her on both cheeks.

Thomas wondered how many men would pay to be in his place right now. His fear of not knowing which artist Janica's sister was supposed to look like had been unfounded, as her resemblance to a pop singer his students were crazy about was astonishing.

"Oh, a new face, how nice!" The beauty walked over to him and held out her hand, jingling a number of bracelets that perfectly matched her earrings and necklace. "I'm Jenni, Janni's sister."

Thomas nervously wiped his palm on his black jeans before taking the woman's hand.

"Thomas," he said. "You look so much like—"

Suddenly, everyone fell silent. All conversations stopped, as if he had set off a bomb with his insinuation. He looked around with alarm.

"Er . . . ?" Thomas wished the earth would actually swallow him up.

But Jenni handled it like a pro. She kissed him dramatically on the cheek and stage-whispered, loud enough for everyone to hear, "I don't just look like her, I am her. And if the two idiots out front told you to mention my resemblance to myself: Don't worry, they do that to all of Janni's new friends."

"I should have known better after they took Janica's flowers off me, but—"

"They what?" Janica shouted and stormed outside, where she beat Finn and Lars with a dishrag until the tall man finally handed over the flowers.

A happy smile on her face, Janica returned, sniffing the flowers.

"White like Aunt Erika's china; a star-shaped, dotted rosé, first strong, then almost white at the edges, like the color of a sunrise behind a fog bank; and the pale pink of monkey bars that used to be bright red but have been faded by the sun," she raved, walking up to Thomas and kissing him on the cheek Jenni had neglected.

But Janica's kiss was different. Not just one of those superficial, polite gestures from people you didn't really know, but a proper kiss, and Thomas felt a tingle from his cheek right down to his toes.

"They're beautiful!" she whispered.

"Well, looks like it was worth the trouble, huh?" Angelo laughed, and wrapped one arm around Susi—or Barbara.

Thomas just grinned and looked happily around the apartment, which looked a flower shop had exploded in a restaurant. He'd never felt anything like this before. It usually took him a long time to warm up to new surroundings and people, and sometimes it didn't happen at all. But something was different today. He felt like he was . . . home.

Chapter 17

Janica leaned back in her chair and watched Kurti and Thomas's animated conversation. She suspected they were talking about their travels, because Kurti had also visited many interesting places. A deep sense of happiness warmed her from the inside. She had been worried about introducing uptight Thomas to her quirky circle of friends. She probably owed the fact that he hadn't immediately turned around and run to Lars and Finn, the pair of clowns, and Jenni's well-practiced grace.

Kurti laughed at something Thomas said, and Janica saw how the man's shoulders relaxed a little. His back finally touched his chair, and his hand wasn't constantly running through his hair any longer. She gazed around the room. Her guests were crowded around the huge farm table, Susi on Angelo's lap, everyone talking at a volume that made Janica wonder if she should have bribed her tolerant neighbors with more of Barbara's perfect Black Forest cake.

Janica loved the music of the voices, the laughter, the hissing of drinks being opened, the clinking of glasses.

But when Susi returned from the kitchen with three bottles of champagne, presumably brought by Angelo and herself, Janica felt an anxious tingle in her stomach. Champagne with her friends could only mean one thing, and it might get uncomfortable for Thomas. Janica tried to catch Susi's eye, but the young woman was too busy ferrying in champagne flutes. The first cork shot out the open front door like a firecracker and disappeared into the darkness.

The table fell silent in expectation of a familiar ritual. Julia grabbed the second bottle and popped the cork, while Barbara swiftly positioned several glasses underneath the gushing liquid, which glowed like amber in the candlelight.

Innocent Thomas happily accepted the glass Susi handed him before she sat back down on her husband's knees and cleared her throat.

"Honest and Positive!" she announced, opening the round of talks they nearly always held when they were all together.

Janica considered calling the game off, but changed her mind. If Thomas wanted to belong here, he had to go through this.

"I'll start!" Barbara announced and stood up. It was unusual for her go first, so she must have had news she was dying to share. "I lost my job three weeks ago."

"Oh, no," Kurti exclaimed. "What did your boss say?"

"Downsizing, the economy."

"How could they do that? You did your internship with them. How many years have you worked there, and how many nights did you stay late, come in early—all unpaid, of course?"

"Whatever." Barbara waved dismissively and raised her glass.

"To your boss. He'll miss you!" Julia said, and everyone bent forward to clink glasses.

Thomas looked a little confused, but raised his glass like everyone else. Instead of taking a sip, however, everyone fell silent again and looked at Barbara expectantly.

"Easy to see the positive side this time," Barbara announced. "I got a call from my agent yesterday. They sold my YA novel to a big publishing house, wrangled an unusually big advance, and scored a respectable advertising budget on top of it. Guys, as of yesterday, I'm a writer!"

The table erupted in loud exclamations, until Finn's voice drowned out everyone else.

"Cheers to the agency and the publishers! They made a good decision, which I know because I had the privilege of reading the manuscript."

The glasses were raised again and this time everyone took a sip.

"Our turn!" Susi decided and slid forward on Angelo's knees. "As you know, we've been trying for a baby for more than two years now."

Nods. Janica leaned forward and squeezed Susi's hand. She knew how her friend had struggled with this, and how she always told herself to have more patience.

"A week ago, we found out for certain: I can't have children."

Shocked silence fell over the table. For a long while, the only noise came from Balou, who had found something to eat under the table, and the crickets outside.

"I'm so sorry," said Werner, the father of three young children himself.

Angelo raised his glass. "To . . ."

He hesitated, his eyes wet with tears. His friends gave him time, suffering with the young couple.

"To all the happy couples who can have children. And to those who have no idea what they're missing because they don't want to lose their so-called liberty."

The glasses clinked, and a few droplets of champagne splashed on the tabletop, where they gleamed like tears.

"At least now we know," Susi said bravely, but her smile looked forced.

"We've been talking about adopting," Angelo said. "Susi will have to give up her job teaching kindergarten, but it's something we really want. Don't worry, we're not going into this with our eyes closed—we know that the kids will come from difficult backgrounds and probably will have had some bad experiences. But we want to give those kids a chance to sort out their lives—"

"—and we hope that you'll support us."

"To a good, if challenging, decision. And to the lucky children who will become part of your family." Lars raised his glass to the center of the table. "We've always got your back. You know that, right?"

"Now Thomas," Jenni said as she put down her glass.

Janica pursed her lips. Would Thomas be willing to take part? Was it too much for him?

"This is . . . all quite new for me. But since you . . . even though you don't know me—" He broke off and shrugged.

"We trust Janica's judgment and assume that she didn't invite a spy into our midst," Finn joked.

Suddenly, Balou barked, ran to the door, and jumped up on Peter, who was followed by Heidi and Steffen. Janica and Jenni jumped to their feet and ran to greet their parents, while Steffen hugged his brother and introduced himself to the others. Chairs were moved and space was made. Not long after, Helga and two pediatric nurses from the hospice turned up as well, followed by Rat's father and brother. Gottlieb and Karsten gave Janica a huge bouquet of flowers, smiled wistfully at *The Swarm of Butterflies*, and left the party soon afterward.

Janica didn't waste much time wondering whether to be glad Thomas had been interrupted. Maybe he would have felt overwhelmed by the pressure, but on the other hand, it might have done him good to open up a little. But the moment had passed, so it was irrelevant now. She just wanted to enjoy this wonderful evening with her friends.

Janica said good-bye to Angelo, then hugged Susi. The young woman held her hostess for a long time and whispered, "Thomas is very charming. Perhaps a tad serious and . . . pinched?"

Janica laughed and whispered back, "You should have seen him when I first met him. Pinched wouldn't even come near it."

"Well, it's part of who he is, so don't try to change him. But he really relaxed after a while and blended into our crazy circle nicely. I like him!"

"Me, too."

"How much?"

Janica gave Susi a kiss on the cheek and said nothing, especially since Angelo was waiting impatiently. He had to get up early the next day, and it was already long past midnight.

Susi pointed her index and middle fingers first at her own eyes, then at Janica's, but Janica already knew her motherly friend would be keeping a close eye on her and Thomas.

Finn and Lars pushed the heavy table back against the wall while Thomas folded up the chairs and stacked them neatly in her storeroom, which led off from her bedroom.

"Can you take it from here?" Lars asked, grabbing Janica by the waist.

"Perfectly. Good night."

"Sleep well."

Lars bent down to her and breathed a kiss on her forehead, then Finn gave her a hug, waved to Thomas, and both disappeared.

"We'll be on our way, too," Heidi declared and let the dirty water drain from the sink.

Jenni immediately dropped her dishtowel on the wet glasses. Her father, also holding a dishtowel, grinned and rushed to finish drying the plate in his hand.

"Steffen, will you ride with me?" Jenni asked. "You can help me stay awake so I don't hit a tree."

"Sure. I'll sing for you—that's sure to keep you awake!"

There was a rush for the door and, within seconds, Janica and Thomas were alone in the apartment.

Janica heard Thomas breathe a sigh of relief and watched with amusement as he leaned his back against the now-closed front door.

"They are exhausting, aren't they?"

"A tornado is a mild breeze in comparison," Thomas replied, and Janica laughed. "But I could get used to tornadoes like those," he added, pushing himself off the door and picking up the dishtowel Jenni had dropped.

"You don't have to—"

"But I want to!" Thomas looked at her reproachfully and picked up one of the large glasses. "Or they'll get horrible water stains."

"That doesn't matter."

"I know you don't mind. Believe me, that much I have figured out about you by now."

"Are you saying I'm not hard to figure out?"

Thomas turned to her.

"Basically, you're an open book. But I have a feeling there's a secret message hidden in the pages."

"You sound like my father."

"Your father is a great man."

"That's beside the point."

Janica smiled and tried to turn her attention to sweeping. She felt a flutter in her stomach and was painfully aware of Thomas's presence. She was grateful for his help, but his nearness also put her in a state of unsettling excitement. Cautiously, she glanced at him, and saw that his eyes were fixed on her, even while he was drying the dishes. His gaze didn't even waver now that he'd been caught, but held hers confidently. Thomas might appear shy and withdrawn around others, but he definitely knew what he wanted.

Janica forced herself to break eye contact and reached for the dustpan, crouching down to collect crumbs, a piece of tomato Balou had spurned, and four bottle tops. She dumped everything into the garbage can.

Balou paced restlessly in front of the door, signaling that he needed to go for a walk. She thought she'd better take her bike, just like the night three months ago when she found Steffen on the bridge.

"Why don't you go put on something warmer while I put the rest of the dishes away. Then we'll take the bear for a walk together," Thomas suggested, as if it was the most natural thing in the world for him to walk the dog with her.

"You don't have to come," she said with surprise.

"But I want to. If only because it's very late and I'm not sure how good a bodyguard this playful puppy is."

Janica laughed, which made Thomas frown and pause in the middle of drying a plate.

"Are you the same guy who admiringly called Steffen the 'protective type' a few weeks ago?"

"He is my brother, after all. One or two things about him might have rubbed off on me."

Janica laughed out loud again.

There were sides to this man she'd never have suspected. But didn't they say that still waters run deep? She knew what it was like to stand in the shadow of a confident, talented, extroverted sibling. Janica had been a quiet child, almost shy unless she was with her family or good friends. Around them, she had talked a mile a minute, thought up the craziest ideas, and was always first in line to try new things, until . . . well, until that dark cloud had gathered above her head. It had turned her life upside down and made her the person she was today.

At a leisurely pace, she put away the broom and walked toward her room to get changed. When she passed *The Swarm of Butterflies*, she ran her fingers over the turtles affectionately, saddened at the thought that Rat would never get to experience being wooed by a young man. But Rat had been fortunate in a different way: She'd had the most loving and imaginative father one could wish for, and an older brother who'd cared for her with humor and charm.

Janica put on a black cardigan that, like her dress, ended just above the knees, buttoned it up, and returned to the living room. Balou was already wagging his tail in anticipation, his eyes fixed on Thomas. Thomas had thrown the leash over the shoulder of his blue shirt, the top buttons undone, and was busy wiping down the kitchen counter.

"Ready to go?" he asked before looking up.

His brown eyes wandered up her body to her face and the wild mass of curls she'd unleashed. His face changed, becoming soft and flushed.

"Are you sure you're going to be warm enough?"

"It's summer." She laughed. "But thank you for your concern."

She sent Balou ahead down the stairs, and Thomas joined her on the metal landing. The crescent moon shone in the dark sky, and a few gauzy-gray clouds meandered past the sparkling stars. This part of town was fast asleep.

Janica switched off the light and was about to pull the door shut, but Thomas stepped in close and blocked her way. She raised her head questioningly, but his face was backlit by the moon, while he saw hers perfectly in its pale light.

"Thank you for this wonderful evening," he said quietly, and in an unusually deep voice, which conveyed more emotion than he probably realized.

"You mean this crazy evening?" she teased.

His closeness made her feel drunk. This man aroused feelings she'd never experienced so intensely. Where were they coming from? Had they snuck up on her, waiting for the right moment for an ambush?

"If I say wonderful, I mean wonderful," he scolded.

"I was afraid we'd be too much for you."

"Is that why you sounded so standoffish when you invited me? I thought maybe you were just doing it to be polite."

"No!" she replied, her fierce reaction making him laugh.

He took another step toward her. She could smell his aftershave and the leather of his jacket. The butterflies in her stomach multiplied a hundredfold.

"The Honest and Positive thing—do you always do that?"

"Almost every time we get together," Janica replied. "We joke around a lot and talk a lot of nonsense, so one day, Lars suggested that we try to be honest and vulnerable. We came out with surprisingly sad stories. That's when we decided that each of us had to try to find something positive in our experiences."

"Sounds intriguing."

"It's good to know what's really going on in the lives of our closest friends, what battles they're fighting. But Lars didn't just suggest the game because he's such a sweet guy. Back then, he was in the middle of his theology degree—we were his guinea pigs! Now he's the pastor of a small congregation in the suburbs."

"That giant prankster is a pastor?"

Thomas's laughter made Janica's heart beat even faster. She had never heard him laugh as much as this evening. It was the best birthday gift of all.

"I was relieved when my parents and Steffen interrupted your turn."

"Why?" Thomas asked, and moved even closer.

She felt his warm breath on her forehead and resisted the urge to gasp with excitement.

"Well, for someone who doesn't know the game . . ."

"Am I still just 'someone'?" he murmured and took her by the shoulders.

"Not to me, but—"

He squeezed her tighter.

"Do you want to know what I was going to say?"

Janica mumbled an unintelligible reply. Every fiber of her being was focused on his closeness. She wanted to lean against him and feel the warmth of his body, find out what it felt like to be in his arms. But the confusing, childlike shyness inside her grown-up body was holding her back.

"I would have told them how you stopped my brother from jumping off a bridge and saved his life."

He paused when she opened her mouth, and placed two fingers on her lips to prevent her from speaking. His fingers lingered there for an exciting, heart-stopping moment, then brushed across her cheek, and eventually buried themselves in her hair, cradling the back of her head. His touch set off millions of tiny pinpricks in her body. She couldn't hide the tremor rising in her body, and he laughed softly.

"But I suppose your friends already know, don't they?" he asked without waiting for a reply, which Janica wouldn't have been capable of anyway.

She had never lost control over her body and mind like this before.

"And the positive side?" she finally managed.

"You know very well," he replied.

"That's right," Janica said, pleased she managed a mocking tone. "You met a lovely bear and visited a beautiful farm which, according to you, doesn't exist on this earth."

She giggled, but her heartbeat was still galloping at breakneck speed.

"Keep talking," Thomas replied, amused.

"You've become more relaxed and broken out of the constraints of your daily routine. And you met Sven and other wonderful kids who now mean a lot to you."

"And?"

"Let me think."

"*I* don't have to think."

"No?"

Janica leaned lightly against Thomas, and he let go of her shoulder and placed his hand against her back instead, though without pulling her any closer. His restraint and sensitivity didn't surprise Janica, just deepened her feelings for him.

"Do you think your crazy friends would mind if I tried to see you much more than they do? If I became part of your life?"

"Why would they?"

Her words came out as a breathless whisper.

Thomas shrugged. "I can't help wondering how Kurti, Lars, Finn, and all the other men who met you before me could have missed their chance with the most beautiful and amazing girl in the world."

"Probably because they didn't feel that way about me. And I didn't feel that way about them."

"Their loss, my gain!" Thomas whispered and leaned down.

His kiss was gentle. Restrained enough to not make her feel pressured, but intense enough to make it clear how serious he was.

They climbed down the stairs to the ground, where Balou greeted them excitedly. Together, they walked down the moonlit path along the chilly riverbank. Thomas touched Janica's wrist.

"May I?" he asked, but Janica had already put her hand in his.

"Want to tell me how you met Susi and Barbara, who I can't tell apart, by the way, and Julia and the boys?"

"You want to learn all about them so you don't put your foot in it again next time?" Janica laughed, nudging him softly with her shoulder.

"That, too, yes," Thomas sighed. "But I was mostly hoping to learn more about your past."

Janica smiled at him. His look, his embrace, and the passionate kiss that followed set off colorful fireworks inside her, making her feel like she'd never be too cold or hot again. The cold gray of winter would turn into a cozy blue, and the glaring white of summer sun would mellow into warm orange. Thomas's love seemed to tone down colors that were too garish and brighten ones that were too dull. To Janica, it painted the picture of a perfect life.

Janica

In love!

But those two little words weren't nearly enough to describe what was happening inside me. My heart wanted to dance, my mind cheered, and the rest of me wanted to somersault. Who would have imagined it back then? When I was ten, the doctors said my chances of beating non-Hodgkin's lymphoma were slim. But my parents, Jenni, and I never gave up. We fought this malignant illness together—and won. I survived, my routine checkups got further and further apart, and I decided to enjoy every moment of life. And now Thomas was in my life! Thomas!

I felt free, happy, grateful, and alive like never before. If you like, imagine me dancing in a meadow full of flowers, my pale-pink skirt billowing around my legs. I could already picture myself standing at the altar in a white dress. Perhaps I was getting ahead of myself, but for a woman who had been told as a child that she had no future, the here and now was all that counted. And now I loved you! In white and pink, sky blue or hope green, in bright red or soft orange, it didn't matter. The only thing that mattered were those three words: I love you!

Chapter 18

July 18

With nimble fingers, Annabelle strung glitter-covered purple and white beads on the string, talking incessantly. The girl was doing very well, and she constantly reminded everyone at the hospice that she was just visiting for the day. Janica smiled. Perhaps Annabelle was another lucky child who would beat her illness in spite of having been declared a lost cause. Annabelle strung one day after another on the necklace of her life.

Derja, on the other hand, was looking frailer than ever. Selina practically wouldn't let her out of her sight—as if it was the only way to prevent her daughter from disappearing like a drop of dew in the sun. Janica had talked the young mother into lying down in the family room to rest for a while.

"Which bead would you like next?" Janica asked the girl, who gave a start at her words.

She held out the necklace she was putting together for the little girl since she was too weak to do it herself.

"Red," Derja decided. She lifted her trembling hand and reached for a green bead.

It slipped through her fingers and bounced off the table. But Derja barely reacted.

Annabelle opened her mouth to say something, but closed it again when she caught Janica's look.

Janica got down under the table to search for the bead, and Annabelle followed.

"Red?" the child asked quietly, and Janica saw painful understanding in her prematurely wise eyes.

She nodded at Annabelle and pretended to keep looking, though she had already spotted the bead. She just needed a few seconds to swallow back the tears.

"It's all right, Janni. Derja stopped fighting weeks ago. She doesn't want all this anymore."

Janica didn't ask how Annabelle knew. The children here spoke openly to one another, and they had an uncanny sense for these things.

"We have to tell Werner and Helga and the doctor. Her family needs to say good-bye soon. Or she might not understand them," the girl urged.

"I'll tell Werner, but I bet he already knows."

"Yeah. He's very nice for a man."

"What do you know about men?"

"A lot," Annabelle giggled. "I know Thomas likes you."

"What makes you think that?"

"He's standing by the door, staring!"

Annabelle grinned, and snatched up the bead on the ground like it was a race.

Janica crawled out from under the table. Thomas smiled when he saw he'd been discovered. He uncrossed his arms and stepped into the round room, which was surprisingly empty that morning.

"Hello, Annabelle. What are you doing here?"

"I'm visiting!"

"It's nice to see you!"

Annabelle beamed at him, but he was already looking at Derja, who sat slumped in her chair. His smile disappeared as if someone had flipped a switch.

Janica reached for his hand instinctively. Perhaps it wasn't such a good idea for him to be here so often.

"Maybe I should carry Derja to the couch," Thomas said in the place of a greeting.

"That would be good."

Janica let go of his hand, but he grasped hers again and raised it to his lips. Annabelle giggled, and Thomas breathed a kiss on her hand as well.

"Eeeeee! Romantic!" Annabelle declared in a high-pitched voice and with a roll of her eyes, which she seemed to think looked grown up. "But you should only kiss Janni. She deserves you!"

"That sounds like it's a punishment for Janica," Thomas grumbled, and the girl laughed.

Janica watched with a smile as Thomas gently picked Derja up and carried her to the couch. He carefully set her down, sat beside her, and whispered something in the girl's ear. His words put a smile on the pale, sunken face. Thomas grabbed a light, orange blanket and covered her with it.

"You should have been a nurse."

Werner closed the door behind himself, nodded at Janica, and walked over to Thomas.

"Or a father. But that's still a possibility."

Werner winked at Janica, who put her hand on her hips and glowered at him.

"Is there anyone who doesn't—?"

"No. Do you really think you could fall in love without your friends noticing?"

"But—"

"Plus, Susi and Angelo saw you at a café in town two days ago."

"Why didn't they join us?" Janica wanted to know, while Thomas frowned, looking wonderfully out of his depth.

"Susi said something like: 'You should have seen them gazing into each other's eyes. I don't think Thomas and Janni would have seen us if we'd danced on the table!'"

The silence following Werner's words was broken by Annabelle's giggling, which Janica joined shortly after. Thomas shook his head.

"I'm sorry, but your secret is out."

Werner grinned and gave Thomas a friendly slap on the shoulder. Then he leaned down to Derja, felt her forehead with one hand and her pulse with the other, and left the room whistling.

Thomas sat down heavily between Janica and Annabelle, and the girl immediately claimed his attention.

"You can make yourself a necklace, too. Or a bracelet."

"I'm not really into pink or glitter," he replied.

"But I also have blue and green and brown and black."

Annabelle hauled up the big case of beads she carried everywhere.

"Then I might try my hand at a necklace for Janica. She's got this beautiful blue sundress."

"Glacier-ice blue," Janica explained to the girl with an amused grin.

"Good idea. But!" Annabelle was holding up her index finger, and Thomas raised his eyebrows to signal his undivided attention. "You have to put a white glitter bead in the middle."

"Because it'll be pretty?"

"Yeah," Annabelle said, looking at the couch. "But mostly to remind Janni and you of me, in case I'm not here anymore."

Thomas had retreated behind the glass door to the round room, absent-mindedly fingering the blue beaded necklace. But his eyes and his attention remained on the bright room beyond the door. He could see the hunched back and twitching shoulders of Selina, who was hanging onto Janica as if she were drowning. Drowning in the treacherous waves of Dr. Kraus's words. Selina had known for a long time that she'd have to let go of her child, but, like any loving mother, she'd held on with every fiber of her being. Annabelle had been sent to play in another room, but her beads still lay scattered across the table. They shimmered like colorful tears.

Werner sat with Derja, who seemed not to understand why her mother was so upset. The intensive-care nurse picked her up and carried her to her room. When the door closed behind them, Selina lost any remaining self-control. She threw herself to the ground, screaming. With desperately controlled movements, Janica sat down beside her and stroked the young mother's back. What could anyone possibly say in the face of so much pain?

"Pardon me."

Thomas startled and turned. An elderly woman with dark hair and narrow glasses reached past him to press the electric door opener. He stepped back and watched the psychologist enter the room and wait off to one side. Janica made to get up, but the woman waved her off decisively, signaling that she should stay with Selina. She would wait.

"Why does God allow this to happen?" Thomas asked, not realizing he'd said the words out loud.

"Has he ever said he wanted to protect us from the storms of life?" Helga replied, stepping closer. "God isn't supposed to spare us grief, illness, or pain."

"I know," he said, not taking his eyes off Selina, who had curled up into a ball, her head resting on Janica's knees.

"We live in an imperfect world," Helga continued in a whisper. "Somewhere, it says that God never gives us more than we can bear." She grunted approvingly.

"How can anyone bear this?" he hissed, struggling to resist his urge to punch the glass.

"One can learn to bear the loss of a child. It is an incredibly painful, hard road, and it rips out a piece of your heart. The pain and loss and grief never go away, but they get gentler. At some point, there'll be better days again, easier days. Hopeful days."

Thomas nodded lamely.

"The important thing is never to lose hope."

"Hope?" Thomas asked quietly. "With a diagnosis like that?"

"I suppose it depends what we invest our hope in. Should we invest it in the skill of the doctors, the progress of science, and the strength hidden in such a tiny body? Yes, we should. At the same time, when everything humanly possible has failed, it is a good idea to place your hope in the one you mentioned so reproachfully before."

"Yeah, sure. I've heard the bible stories about miraculous healing."

Why was he picking a fight?

"I'm not talking about healing," Helga said dismissively and began to walk away.

Thomas's eyes followed her back to her office. He would have liked to continue the conversation.

The psychologist had stepped in now and Janica was walking over. The emptiness in her gaze shook him. It was as if Selina had drained all her energy.

"What do you think, want to take a drive to the farm that doesn't really exist? Jenni won't be there much longer, and I wouldn't mind checking in on Steffen."

Janica placed her hand on his shoulder, stood up on her tiptoes, and kissed him on the cheek.

"That's just what I need right now," she replied, taking his hand.

Thomas breathed a sigh of relief when the sparkle returned to her beautiful green eyes.

Chapter 19

Thomas's gaze followed Janica, who had been meandering across the flower-filled meadow and was now perched on the log fence, watching the horses. He heard familiar footsteps approaching. Steffen.

His brother sat down on the bench beside him, stretched his tanned legs, and wiggled his toes.

"So, you two are an item?"

"Is it that obvious?"

Thomas felt his heartbeat accelerating. Every time he thought of Janica, every time someone mentioned her name, and every time he realized she was nearby, he was overcome by happiness. Yes, they were an item. This wonderful, soulful girl actually loved him.

He felt a tiny pang of guilt. Once he'd realized how deep his feelings for Janica were, he'd stopped worrying that Steffen had feelings, too.

"I'm very happy for you both."

"Really?"

"Why shouldn't I be?"

"Well, it was *you* she—"

"Talked off the ledge?" Steffen laughed. "And you thought this was a bad movie? The heroine falls in love with the suicidal guy? I never knew you were such a romantic."

Thomas watched Janica jump down into the paddock and walk toward the grazing Cesar. Balou jumped in after her but was ordered to settle down. He wasn't allowed to chase the herd around today.

"You know that Janica battled an aggressive cancer for almost two years?"

"She told me."

Thomas's stomach turned every time he thought about how close Janica had come to sharing the fate of Derja, Rat, and so many other children.

"There's your movie: Doomed cancer patient saves suicidal man and they fall in love," he suggested, feeling sick.

"What a load of trash," Steffen replied. "This isn't a movie. Janica is real. And she's good for you. I haven't seen you this relaxed in a long time."

"Relaxed? She has crazy friends, and a bear-dog that, for some unfathomable reason, won't leave my side. Also, she lured me into that hospice and introduced me to those amazing kids, and now I can't stop going back, even though I know that I'll be destroyed when they die."

"She fills your life."

"Completely."

"Anyway, I like what I see. After Mom and Dad died, you just shut down and never let anyone get close. Why? Were you afraid to lose them, too?"

Thomas said nothing for a long time.

"Well. You seem to be doing well, too," Thomas finally observed.

His brother sighed.

"I should have gone back to the city weeks ago. But I just can't bring myself to leave this paradise. Heidi can see right through me, of course, and we had a long talk yesterday. She practically kicked me out.

I was planning on driving back with Jenni tomorrow, but maybe it's better if I pack my bags and go back with you today?"

"Because of Jenni?"

"Jenni?"

Steffen leaned forward and gave Thomas a puzzled look, dashing Thomas's suspicions that his brother might have feelings for Janica's glamorous sister.

"No, I just don't want Heidi to feel like she actually has to kick me out," Steffen joked.

Thomas grinned and crossed his arms.

"So you think you're ready to go back to work?"

"I'm going to leave the SFU and look for a job with the Federal Criminal Police Office."

"I beg your pardon?"

"I can't handle the SFU anymore. No, let me finish." Steffen took a deep breath. "I never want to go through anything like this again. It's time for me to find out where my strengths lie and how I can best put them to use. And, also . . ." Steffen paused, running his fingers through his hair—a gesture they'd both inherited from their father. "Lara called yesterday. A reporter harassed her outside her workplace. He wanted to know whether her ex-husband was a member of the Special Forces Unit and if he'd be willing to talk about the events leading up to the child's death."

"No!" Thomas gasped.

"I reported it to my boss."

Steffen spoke through clenched teeth, but otherwise appeared calm.

"How could your identity have gotten out?"

"The guy probably was just acting on a hunch. Thankfully, Lara handled the situation perfectly and didn't react at all."

"She's so great."

"Yes."

Thomas, who'd been watching Janica again, turned his head to study Steffen. His tone of voice told Thomas how much his brother still cared for his ex-wife.

"I asked Lara to take Marie and go to her parents', but she didn't want to give up her new job. Plus, she thinks running away would be an admission of guilt." Steffen punched the bench with his fist, sending little green pieces of moss flying in all directions. "My boss said he'd take care of it, so I'm guessing Lara is being watched for now. Marie is at her grandparents'."

"Is that the reason you want to get back to the city?"

"One of the reasons. But it really is time for me to face life again. Being here was great—especially the conversations with Peter—but I can't hide out forever."

"I'm not at home as much anymore as I used to be, Steffen. If you need me . . ."

"I know, Thomas. That's another thing I've learned. I need to talk to the people close to me before blowing a fuse. Now, run along—your girl is waving to you like crazy."

"She probably wants to show me a flower with flamingo-colored petals and flaming-sunrise dots, or a butterfly with a mix of elderflower white and early-spring-cloud white."

Steffen laughed and gave him a playful box in the ribs.

"You just hang on to her, buddy."

"Oh, I will!"

Thomas had never felt so sure about anything.

Janica

Thoughts were swirling around my head in a wild tumult. Swallows and swifts would have had a field day with them. But I was tortured by fear, despair—and a fiery pain that wanted to leave nothing in its wake but destruction. And death.

I had found Thomas, and with him love and all that went with it. From butterflies in my stomach and a thousand other clichés to a yearning in my body—a hunger for more and increasingly intimate touch. Everything was just the way it was meant to be. Except for me.

Defiance, anger, refusal, and denial—I had been to all those places before, so this time I just skipped them and went straight to desperation.

Would I have the strength to fight it off once more? Would I get the chance?

The first thought on my mind was: I must protect Thomas. I must protect him from me!

Chapter 20

August 29

Thomas hurried past the reception area and peered through the glass door. Relief and joy washed away the paralyzing dread he'd been carrying around for weeks now.

She was there! Janica was sitting together with two mothers he hadn't seen before. He saw two sick-looking teenagers, along with several assorted siblings.

She had dyed her hair. It was dark brown now, a lot like his. But why? He loved her red curls and the way they shimmered in the sun. They harmonized perfectly with her athletic body, her green eyes, and the late-summer freckles on her face.

Thomas studied her sluggish movements and forced smile, and noticed she was unusually pale. She was always careful to avoid direct sunlight, but today she looked particularly . . . tired? Had she been missing him as much as he'd missed her?

A few weeks ago, without warning or explanation, she'd started avoiding him. He'd found her at home with a packed suitcase and the vague explanation that she had to go away for a few days. She'd asked him to leave, and, stunned with surprise, he hadn't objected. When he'd asked if her trip was work related, Janica hadn't replied.

The following weeks had been bleak. Thomas was relieved when the time came to start preparations for the new school year, and he attended teacher conferences and meetings with more relish that he'd ever have thought possible. Steffen moved into an apartment at the other end of town, and Thomas helped with renovations and moving. Then the school year started with all its hiccups and challenges, and before he knew it, another week had passed without any sign of Janica. In his desperation, Thomas had called Janica's parents. Peter told him Janica was staying with them, but she was asleep and would call him back later. She never did.

He called Barbara and Julia, Finn and Lars, but they didn't know any more than he did, and advised him to be patient.

But how was he supposed to be patient when his heart was about to break from the separation, the questions and doubts? Finally, worrying he'd been played for a fool, he'd driven out to the farm. To his surprise, he found the turnoff on the first try, but the farmstead was deserted.

Thomas waited as long as he could, but in vain. On the highway back to town, he'd wondered whether Janica, Heidi, and Peter had ever actually existed.

But now, here she was, back at the hospice and back in his life—or so he hoped.

"She's back," Helga said, and Thomas looked at her anxiously. "Has anyone ever told you how she turned up here the first time?"

"No," Thomas said, pulling back his hand from the door button.

"She was still an intern when the chimney company sent her over, wearing black clothes but a bright-orange scarf. I think she called it 'Grandma's-freesias gold.' First, she worked on the heaters in the basement, then she needed to see the flues in the back rooms. When she walked through the round room, a woman with a three-year-old jumped up, carried the boy over to her, and said to him: 'Quick, touch the chimney sweep. She'll bring you luck, and you need all the luck you can get!'" Helga paused. "Janica let the boy touch her, but didn't say a word, and practically ran out the room. The following day, she turned up at my office, asking if she could help out. She wanted to play with the children, and, if possible, bring her dog from time to time. Back then, she had a shaggy Newfoundland, which the kids loved almost more than Balou. Balou just doesn't look quite as much like a teddy bear as Captain Cook did."

"Do you think she was offended by that woman treating her like a good-luck charm?"

Helga shrugged and smiled. "Janica wanted to give the children a different kind of hope—real hope. I don't think she realizes that she's also spreading 'luck.'"

"What do you mean?"

"Take Annabelle, for example," Helga said, and leaned against the wall. "She loves beads more than anything."

"That's for sure."

"Janica told Annabelle that, if she ever has to leave this world, she will go to a city whose streets are paved with gold and whose twelve gates are made of beads."

Thomas nodded. He wondered whether Helga and the others at the hospice knew about Janica's battle with cancer as a child. Did Werner?

Just then, Janica stood up, spotted him, and uncertainly raised her hand in greeting.

He frowned. Her hesitation and sad expression pierced his heart like a knife, and her reluctant steps toward the door felt like someone was twisting that knife.

Something was broken. Between them.

What had he done? Had he made a mistake, overlooked something important, said the wrong thing? A thousand questions attacked him like a swarm of wasps. Suddenly, he wished he had more time to think.

But the door opened with a soft hydraulic hiss, and there she was in front of him.

"Hello, Thomas."

"Janica?"

Her name conveyed all his doubts, his pain, and the longing he felt for her. She nodded as though she heard all his unspoken words, and gestured toward the exit.

"Let's go outside, OK?"

He managed a nod. He walked ahead and held the door for her, and a smile scurried across her serious face. But that was all. She was hiding behind a mask that would have made any poker player proud. He knew what was coming: She would dump him, destroying the magical love he'd naively believed would color the rest of their lives. He wished he could defend his heart with a wall of steel and concrete, but Janica had torn that wall down, shown him it was preventing him from living life to the fullest. Now, his heart would be reduced to rubble, too.

Chapter 21

September 13

Janica helped herself to another bottle of water and sunk into Barbara's couch. Her friends' cheerful banter filled the room.

Several times, someone asked why Thomas wasn't there, and she avoiding giving a straight answer. She was open, honest, and tough by nature, but these days, she simply lacked the courage. She didn't want to tell her friends anything before she even knew how she felt herself. But she felt trapped on an emotional roller coaster.

When Barbara placed several bottles of champagne on the table, Janica considered running away. But no: It was time to come clean. She reached nervously for her flute, knowing she wouldn't be able to drink anything.

"Us first!" Susi called out. "Honest and Positive! Adopting a child is a bureaucratic nightmare. We never imagined how strict the conditions would be. We assumed child protective services would be glad to find somewhere safe for the kids. It's so frustrating!"

"But," Angelo continued, "it's given us time to talk to other adoptive parents, and their advice has been invaluable. Now we know we're not ready to take in a child older than two. If we hadn't spoken to those parents, we would have approached all this much more naively."

"To the ladies and gentlemen of child protective services. They've got a tough job!" Finn said.

The glasses clinked merrily, but to Janica, it sounded like a blunt saw cutting through metal. She felt sick.

"And to the parents who share their wisdom!"

The flutes chimed once more, but Janica didn't even raise her glass this time. The others were still drinking when she burst out: "The cancer is back."

The whole room seemed to go cold.

"No!" Julia gasped tearfully.

"Janni," Barbara whispered.

Her glass came down hard on the table, then she covered her mouth with both hands, as if holding in a scream.

"And I can think of absolutely nothing positive about that," Janica said into the shocked silence.

Lars was the first to regain control. He put down his glass, reached across the table, and took her hand, which had been tracing the grain of the wooden table erratically.

"How bad is it?"

"Bad," Janica croaked, dizzy with relief at having spoken the horrible truth out loud.

"I went in for a routine checkup. Two days later, the doctor called and asked me to come in. It's another form of the non-Hodgkin's-lymphoma. It is classed as highly aggressive, and I'm already at Stage IV. That means not just lymph nodes, but also organs like the spleen, liver, bone marrow." Saying it out loud didn't change the facts, but she felt lighter, somehow.

"The prognosis?" The man of God wanted answers.

"I just completed one round of chemotherapy, but it made practically no difference. Six months—if I'm lucky."

Janica heard several of her friends inhale sharply. She kept her head down, not wanting to see their faces, not wanting to see where the sobbing came from, or who was frantically fidgeting with a packet of tissues.

A chair was pushed back with a scraping sound. Janica stiffened. She didn't want to be touched right now. It would burst the dam she was trying so hard to hold up. But the person left the room, slammed a door, and hammered against it with fists. Each blow hit Janica's heart. She was hurting the people she loved. Her family, her friends . . .

"Thomas?" Kurti asked.

"I cut him loose." Her words came out choked.

"Wait, are you saying he doesn't know?" Lars asked.

"How could I put this on him?" Janica snarled, her eyes flashing at Lars. How could this man dare judge her? "Everything was brand new—we'd only just gotten together. How could I ask him to get in deeper with a girlfriend who's just going to die on him? I didn't want to put him through that!"

"Or maybe you were afraid of history repeating itself? Afraid it might be like with your classmates when you were a kid? Because *they* couldn't deal with it, never came to visit you?" Lars persisted.

"What protects him protects me, that's the deal."

"So you pushed him away? Back into his sad, narrow life? But worse, because his heart is broken and he doesn't even know why?"

"Lars, it's for the best!"

"I disagree. Thomas has a right to his love for you! And you have a right to be loved and desired by a man, even if it's only for a few months!"

"Desired, Lars?" Janica ripped off the wig she'd had made from her own hair.

Susi yelped at the sight.

"Desired?" Janica repeated. "In just a few weeks, the rest of my body is going to be wrecked, too. It'll be weak, deformed, a shell to house the pain."

"When did you get so shallow?"

Janica stared at him, knowing he was right, but unwilling to concede. She had to win at least one of her battles, right?

Then it dawned on her that there would be no more victories for her, only defeats. She crossed her arms on the table, dropped her head on them, and cried bitterly. Finally. They were her first tears since that terrible morning at the clinic, when she had been confronted with the all-too-familiar images of her organs and realized: Those strange spots were her death sentence.

Finn was back, having vented his anger on Barbara's bathroom door. Susi wrapped her arms around Janica and rested on her shoulder. Barbara's body twitched as she cried. Cried for a life lost.

Chapter 22

September 14

Janica went to the hospital, the wide corridors and anonymous rooms reminding her of those months fifteen years back when she'd been a constant visitor. After her appointment, she pushed open the heavy door to the oncology wing and scurried out. At the top of the stairwell, she heard hurried footsteps coming up and paused to avoid a collision. Suddenly, Thomas stood in front of her.

His hair was a little longer, somehow dashing and wild, and his three-day stubble was undeniably sexy. He froze. His eyes scanned her white jeans and gray shirt before coming to rest on her face. Small furrows formed on his brow, as if he was wondering where her colors had gone.

"Hey," he said in a husky voice, looking at her as if she'd just accused him of every crime under the sun.

"Hey," she replied, fighting the urge to throw herself into his arms. "What are you doing here?"

"One of my colleagues from school had to have surgery. What about you? Visiting one of your protégées?"

"They're in pediatrics. This floor is adult oncology."

"Oh, yes—"

"I just had an appointment—" Her pulse was throbbing in her temples. She felt weak and confused. But she knew what she had to do. She took a deep breath, straightened up, and lifted her hand. Slowly, she pulled down her wig.

The lines on Thomas's brow grew deeper. "Janica," he said in a strained voice. The pain in his eyes gave way to a new, different one. "That's why you pushed me away!"

Thomas clearly didn't need any explanations. He didn't even need an apology. He accepted her choice, even though he was hurt that she'd thought him weak or superficial. Janica's love for him overflowed, burst the box where she'd locked away her feelings.

Thomas closed the gap between them and took her in his arms tenderly, as if afraid of breaking her. That tenderness was precisely what Janica needed right now. It conveyed understanding, dedication, and strength at the same time.

"I'm here for you, my silly girl," he whispered.

Janica nodded into his shoulder and knew how right he was with his hidden reproach. She had shut him out when she needed him the most. She had deprived him of the opportunity to prove his love for her. He tightened his embrace and Janica was filled with a sense of security that almost made her sing with joy. How could she ever be thankful enough for this gift?

"It's not fair. Just when I've found you," she cried, her tears soaking his shirt.

"Janica, I don't know—

"Six months, Thomas. That's all we've got. Six months, maybe less."

Thomas didn't reply for a long time. Janica could feel him processing the news, how his insides rebelled, cramped, twisted, turned, protested. Then an electric shock seemed to go through him. He pushed her away gently and took her pale face between his strong hands.

"It's going to be the best six months of our lives."

"Thomas!"

Shocked, she looked into his dark eyes, unable to read what she saw in them. Love and pain? Hope and despair? Didn't he understand what she had just told him? How hard these six months would be? But she knew this kind of irrational reaction all too well. Denial and refusal—she had been there as a child, and so had her family when they first got the diagnosis. Her classmates had never gotten past it. But what about Thomas? Was he reacting the way she'd feared, after all? Would she have to lock away her feelings all over again, sit on the box to force it shut?

"I know what this means, Janica. It will be the most intense six months of our lives, and the most painful. But it'll be our time together."

She didn't feel relief but more a kind of sweet pain. "I'd hoped and wished for so much more."

"Me, too."

Thomas pulled her close again, and they held each other for several long minutes in the cold hospital staircase, warmed by their love, their mutual understanding, and the colorful blossoming of their brief past and future together.

Chapter 23

A gust of wind blew across the picnic blanket. Janica and Julia jumped to their feet, laughing as they chased fluttering napkins across the meadow.

"How did you describe them again?" Julia called.

"Canaries in the light of the setting sun."

"Perfect!"

Julia reached out for a napkin, but the wind was quicker and snatched it away again.

She laughed and kept running while Janica slowly walked back to the blue-and-gray-checked blanket, trying hard not to stumble. Everything was spinning and she felt frighteningly light-headed. Julia returned, weighed down the recaptured canaries with a cup, and sprawled out on the blanket. Janica lay down as well, and the two women watched the kites their friends were steering across the blue sky in wild somersaults.

"Like flamenco dancers," Janica muttered. "IKEA-plate blue, forsythia yellow, and the pink one is the same shade as the baby blanket my grandma knitted for me. The violet reminds me of the lavender fields of France. I can practically smell them now."

"Me, too," Julia sighed. "What about the two kites on the right?"

"You mean Lars's wild-grass-yellow one and Thomas's Kermit-the-Frog-green one?"

"Perfect!" Julia giggled. She sat up and reached for a red thermos. "Coffee?"

Janica shook her head but gratefully accepted a bottle of water. Her meds didn't mix well with caffeine or alcohol.

"I'm so glad you and Thomas worked things out."

Janica gave her a smile and pushed aside the stinging pain in her heart, the voice that whispered time was her biggest enemy. She was determined to appreciate every single moment she had, and this wonderful fall day was just made to be enjoyed. A cool breeze was blowing, rustling the pines, spruces, and fir trees on the rolling hills. The air smelled of dry hay, and every gust of wind flooded the meadow full of daisies with the earthy smell of freshly harvested fields. Next to the forest, between them and the road, stretched a huge sunflower field. The yellow-and-brown heads nodded to the rhythm of the wind, and the soft blue of the autumn sky was filled not only with colorful kites, but also birds of all sizes and species, from inconspicuous sparrows to majestic hawks.

"Thomas is spending every free minute with me. I'm afraid he's neglecting his students."

Julia tilted her head, and Janica knew what she was thinking. He'd only be neglecting his students for a little while.

"Is he smothering you? Do you need us to keep him busy from time to time?" Julia teased.

"I'm enjoying every second! But I'll be sure to let you know if it's too much."

"Deal!"

Julia held out her coffee mug and Janica tapped it with the water bottle.

"What are we celebrating?" Barbara sat down on the blanket beside them.

"Thomas!" Julia said.

"He's a darling. Especially since he's loosened up a little. At first, he was like a steak defrosting in the fridge after years in the freezer."

"I love your images!" Julia giggled. "And I can't wait to read your book!"

"It's going to be a little while," Barbara said with a surreptitious glance in Janica's direction.

Janica nodded, knowing she wouldn't live to see Barbara's book come out. But she didn't ask for the manuscript. There was no point trying to squeeze years of life into a few short months. She'd miss out on so much more than just this book or Angelo and Susi's child, meeting her friends' future spouses and children, taking care of her parents in their old age, or her sister's unpredictable future.

Julia poured Barbara some coffee and laughed as she watched Lars and Thomas fight with their kites. In the end, both kites crash-landed, their strings hopelessly tangled.

"Let's go ahead and break out your cake, Barbara. Looks like Lars and Thomas will be busy with their toys for a while," Julia joked.

"What delicious creation did you bring us today?" Janica asked, leaning forward and lifting the lid off the chilled plate.

She was so grateful to her friends for helping her to have this beautiful, normal day. And yet she continuously had to beat back the dark shadows that kept returning like storm clouds, trying to smother any joy. Her experiences from childhood had taught her how to keep them at bay, but this time, her prognosis was even worse.

"Orange cream!" Janica announced with relish. "My favorite! Julia, could you please make sure the others' kites get tangled up, too? I don't want to share this."

The three women laughed, which caught the attention of Susi, who'd been taking turns flying a kite with Angelo.

"What's going on over here?" she asked and helped herself to a bottle of water.

"Fine! You can have a piece, too," Janica said, and Susi grinned when she spotted the cream-filled object of Janica's desire.

"My dear sister, you should write a novel about a pastry chef next!" she suggested, and swiped a dollop of cream with her index finger. "With all your delicious recipes at the end."

"I was more thinking along the lines of a young woman who meets her true love, but then finds out she has cancer," Barbara joked, cutting up half the cake.

"A challenging topic," Janica said, reaching for a plastic plate and holding it out to Barbara. "I'll have this piece here, thanks," she added, pointing at the uncut half of the cake.

Barbara pinched one eye shut, grinned, and hauled half of the cake onto Janica's plate with the help of the cake slicer and a knife.

"And I vote for a happy ending!" Janica added before setting down her bounty on the blanket, rolling onto her belly, and digging into her cake with relish.

"Me, too!" Julia said.

Janica winked, her mouth too full to speak.

Out of nowhere, the men and Balou descended like a swarm of bees.

Finn scrutinized Janica's slab of cake. "I've always admired your self-restraint!"

"I'm just helping with your diet plans," she replied, patting his slightly protruding belly.

"Selfless as ever!" Finn said. He grabbed a spoon and stole a big chunk.

Thomas lay down in the grass beside Janica and also helped himself from her plate.

"Did you get the kites untangled?" she asked.

He made a face and shook his head.

"I'm afraid we managed to knit a scarf midair," he said when he'd finally swallowed, then he leaned forward and gave her a light kiss on the mouth.

"Oooooo!" their friends teased as Thomas rolled his eyes.

Janica giggled and told him, "Angelo and Susi had to go through it, too. We finally left them in peace after six months or so."

Once again, she was rocked by the fact that they might not have even that long, but she pushed the thought back down with another mouthful of cake.

Thomas gave her an intense look, and she wondered whether he was thinking the same thing, but then a mischievous smile crossed his scruffy face. He kissed her again and again while the others oohed and aahed like they were at a fireworks display. Eventually, they had to give up, and Thomas completed his successful scheme with one last long kiss, which no one commented on.

"That's settled, then," he said and held out his hand for some cake. "Janica, your friends are just like my students."

"Hey!" Kurti exclaimed indignantly. He, Finn, and Lars jumped to their feet, but Thomas was already halfway across the meadow. Only Angelo stayed with the women.

"Kindergarteners!" he snorted, waving his fork.

"Maybe we should save a tiny slice for Thomas?" Janica asked.

"Mr. Teacher got it wrong, my dear," Angelo explained with a full mouth. "His punishment isn't getting chased, but me eating all of this divine cake."

"Easy, buddy," Susi said. "You've been putting on weight lately."

Angelo sat up and gave his wife a peck on the cheek. "Have you forgotten, my love? There's a child for us somewhere out there. I'm allowed to put on weight: We're pregnant!"

Chapter 24

September 18

The day following the wonderfully happy picnic started at 5:00 a.m. for Janica. While wafts of mist crept up the riverbank like carelessly dropped strips of organza fabric in the early-dawn light, she drank a cup of herbal tea but passed on breakfast, as she wouldn't be keeping it down, anyway. She packed her hospital bag with well-practiced efficiency. Her oncologist wanted to try out a new chemo plan, and after thinking it over, Janica had consented. Her decision might have been different if Thomas hadn't loved his way back into her life, but for him she wanted to try to eke out a few extra weeks or days, and at least delay a rapid decline.

It was just past six when Janica opened her front door and nearly jumped back.

"Thomas? What are you doing here?"

"I wanted to take the day off to go to the hospital with you and your mother, but the school wouldn't let me, because you're 'just' my girlfriend."

Thomas made a face, climbed out of the deck chair, and took the leash from her.

"Go on, Balou!" he said, gesturing down the staircase. "So I thought I'd go for a walk with you this morning."

Janica beamed and let him take her in his arms, snuggling against his warm body. She felt safe and secure and at home, and the sensation brought tears to her eyes. She was so grateful for Thomas's attentiveness and affection, the enormous strength he'd found. Perhaps it had been selfish to get back together with him. Her original plan would probably have been kinder. But didn't she deserve a little love amid the pain and fear? She accepted Thomas's love for what it was: a gift.

Hand in hand, they walked along the softly gurgling river. The houses on the opposite bank were wrapped in cotton wool, only a few vague outlines visible. Janica and Thomas were alone in their foggy cocoon, alone with their hushed conversation. Thomas wanted to know every last detail of Janica's impending procedure, and she didn't hold anything back. It was good for her to speak openly about her fears, to brace herself. On their way back, Thomas offered to look after Balou so her mother wouldn't have to take him back to the farm. She agreed enthusiastically, knowing how happy it would make the creature.

By the time they returned to Janica's house, it was nearly time for Heidi to pick up her daughter. They hitched Balou's leash to the bottom of the stairs and climbed up to Janica's apartment. The moment they went inside, Thomas grasped Janica's arm and spun her around. She threw herself into his arms and clung to him like a person drowning. Thomas moaned and held her tightly, his hands stroking her back.

"I'll come and take over for your mom as soon as I'm done at school."

"You don't have to—"

"But I want to."

"I'm not going to be a pretty sight."

"You're always beautiful. You have a beautiful heart."

"Thomas, I—"

"No excuses. You can't get rid of me."

"I love you!"

Thomas's kiss made her want more, and she wished she could go anywhere but the hospital.

The doorbell rang, but it took them a long minute to let go.

Heidi entered, giving Thomas a slightly confused look.

"How's Steffen?" she asked.

"Good. He's happy in his new apartment, quitting his job went smoothly, and he's put in several applications for new jobs. He's in the middle of several training courses at the moment, and thanks to the latest political scandal, the media seems to have lost interest in the SFU's deadly shooter."

"Nothing's as fickle as the media!" Heidi replied, reaching for Janica's bag.

"Thank goodness," Thomas agreed. "But he's still struggling with that police psychologist."

"I'm not sure how useful it is to go over a terrible event again and again. It's important to talk, but it's OK to stop at some point to let things heal themselves and hope for forgiveness," Heidi said as she headed for the door.

Janica breathed deeply and smiled into her apartment. It was such a relief when people talked about things other than chemo and cancer.

Janica stared at the tube that delivered the solution into her subclavian vein through the port near her collarbone. She knew it was silly, but she still imagined she could feel her body turning into a battlefield. The cytotoxic agent caught a ride with her blood, pushed its way through the vascular walls, and attacked the abnormal cells, which paused in their cell division, attempting to deflect the attack, to force the intruder back. But the toxic chemicals also wandered past the cancer, fighting in places it wasn't needed, destroying everything in its path—which was most outwardly noticeable with body hair. She still had her eyelashes and eyebrows, but nothing else.

Nurse Bettina, who'd just arrived, called it "full-body baldy." Heidi closed the book she'd been reading to Janica.

Bettina, rather round and just under five foot two, had to stand on her tiptoes to change the IV bag. Despite the fact that she was only forty, her short-cropped hair was completely gray, and her ice-blue eyes revealed the sorrow they witnessed day in and out. Only the nurse's black humor saved her from quitting or becoming depressed.

"The rest of the chemical solution isn't due in till later, Janica. The chief physician used it all up. I think he must drink the stuff for breakfast."

"That's Bettina's way of telling you that someone forgot to put the order in on time," a male voice called from the next partition, and Janica knew it belonged to the chief.

The nurse winced, but then showed one of her rare smiles.

"Don't worry, honey. The culprit will be sent to the bottom of the river."

"To do what?" Janica joked.

"Um. To collect the used packets, which get dumped in the river with all the other hospital garbage, and combine the leftover drops into one bag so you don't have to wait?" Bettina suggested.

"You're making this sound like a terrible place, Bettina," the voice called.

"Do you get the impression anyone likes coming here? I don't!" the nurse replied, and received a soft chuckle from her boss.

"OK, Janica. Which receptacle would you like? Small and green?" Bettina held up a vomit dish. "Or big and red?" she asked, pointing at the garbage can.

"I'm leaning toward shiny-rust red."

"Good choice!"

Terrible retching noises and sobs came from a few cubicles away.

"I better check on Mrs. Schmidt."

"Is the poor woman on her own again?"

"Watching people lose their lunch isn't for everyone," Bettina replied, hurrying off. Her joke seemed callous, but the sad lines around her mouth showed she was anything but.

"I'm so glad you're here, Mom," Janica said quietly.

Heidi promptly handed her a glass of water and her lip balm.

A few hours later, Janica was hanging over the garbage can, retching heavily. Hot and cold at the same time, she ripped off the scarf around her head and kicked the blanket off her legs, then waved to her mother a minute later to cover her again. Heidi was calm and collected, having seen it all before when Janica was little.

"Is the can enough or should I get a dumpster from out back?" Bettina asked, sticking her head in. They were obviously short on nurses again, as the formidable woman was working double shifts.

"Didn't eat anything on purpose," Janica said and retched.

"Was that a good idea?"

"Would have been a waste. And you don't like waste."

"That's true! Very considerate of you." Bettina placed an arm around her shoulder for a moment. "You're doing great, Janica."

"Puking's not that hard," Janica grumbled, but she knew what Bettina meant, and so she squeezed her hand before sticking her face back into the trash.

"By the way, there's a Mr. Hejduk waiting by the nurses' office. He looked like he was going to pitch a fit when I told him he couldn't see you right now."

"Thomas is here already?" Janica looked up too fast and heaved. She trembled so hard that her mother had to help her hold the rim.

"So the polite but impatient boy who looks like a mother-in-law's dream come true is named Thomas?"

"And I'm the proud mother-in-law!" Heidi said with a laugh, stroking Janica's hair.

"What shall we do? Send him to the bottom of the river until you can sit up straight again, or allow him in to witness your unusual exercise?"

"Let him in," Janica croaked.

"Another wise decision."

Bettina smoothed the sheet on the hospital bed, tugged Janica's twisted sweatpants back into position, fetched a second chair, handed Janica a clean bowl, and nodded happily. "Are you ready?" she asked softly.

"Is he?"

"That's right. We need a plan. If he runs away, should I let him go or hold him back? And am I allowed to use force or must I limit myself to handcuffs?"

"Let him go."

"And what's our code word if you want me to get rid of him?"

Janica couldn't help but giggle, which—together with a renewed urge to gag—sounded like the grunting of a piglet.

"Agreed, an excellent signal."

"Ten minutes?"

"All right, I'll give you and him ten minutes."

Bettina left their cubicle and went to check on Mrs. Schmidt, her shoes clattering like a horse's hooves.

Janica gave her mother a worried look.

"It'll be fine. He's a champ," Heidi said, wiping her daughter's face with a damp cloth for the hundredth time.

Janica couldn't stop the tears welling up in her eyes. She groaned and leaned against her mother's shoulder. "Why now?"

"Why did you fall in love now, or why did the cancer have to return now?"

"Both."

Heidi sighed heavily and kissed her daughter's forehead. "Maybe because you need him? And he needs you?"

"I'm going to hurt him so badly."

"It's not you who's going to hurt him. You are a great gift to him. Losing you is going to hurt him. But you do know that we'll be here to catch him?"

"You'll be hurting, too."

"That won't prevent us from understanding his pain and getting through it together. We won't have you, but at least you'll be somewhere far better."

"Still: Why now?"

"When is it ever the right time to die, Janica? It's much too early as a child. As a young woman, newly in love, it's unfair and wrong. The same for newlyweds. Then we want children. As soon as we have them, we want to be there for them and watch them grow up. Next, we want to help them through the turbulence of becoming adults, and then we don't want to miss out on the grandchildren. And then? Travel, perhaps? Discover the world, take up painting, and volunteer somewhere so we feel we're still needed? Tell me, when is the right time? And what is the best way to go? A sudden accident? An unexpected heart attack? Or knowing that death is near, giving you the chance to say good-bye? It's always hard. How lucky that death isn't the final chapter in our lives."

"But I still don't want to die," Janica wheezed, clinging to her mother's thin sweater with both hands.

Heidi balanced the bowl in one hand and tightened her hold on her trembling daughter with the other. She could no longer stop the tears running down her cheeks.

Chapter 25

Thomas paced nervously. What was that nurse still doing in there? And how was Janica? Didn't she want to see him?

He ran his fingers through his hair and wished he had an instruction manual that told him what to do. What he should say, what he shouldn't. Would Janica want him to touch her, or should he keep his distance? Should he have brought a present, or was it better to pretend like it was a day like any other? Thomas felt somehow cut loose from the world. And there was no way out of this liminal space. In the last few days, he had felt as if he was staggering through thick fog, not knowing where he was going, unable to find a beginning or an end, crushed by an overwhelming sense of helplessness and fear. The feeling intensified whenever he had to leave Janica, and waned again the closer he got to her. Soft colors flowed into the white mist around him—pastel, beautiful and soothing—then came the bright colors of joy and happiness. But every colorful dream eventually ended in front of a pitch-black wall.

He ran his trembling fingers through his hair once more and paced even faster, as if that would make the nurse come back sooner. A voice in his head told him to run from the pain waiting for him behind that door. But hadn't he already spent too many years running from intimacy, trying to preempt loss? How ironic! He'd finally opened his heart, and now the woman he loved was dying of cancer. How much easier life would be if he'd just never allowed Janica in. But what would he have missed out on? Her frenzy of colors and all those little, joyful details in the world he suddenly noticed again. Her wonderful family, who had practically adopted him and his brother, her quirky friends, who'd welcomed him with open arms . . . life itself, perhaps?

Lost in thought, Thomas almost ran right into the short nurse from earlier. She gave him an almost-menacing look.

"Follow me," she ordered.

He grabbed his bag and followed her past several closed doors. He could hear sobs coming from behind one of them, snoring from another.

"The ten-minute visit from the-mother-in-law's dream," Bettina announced to the room, which made him frown with confusion.

Thomas walked through the door. His eyes first took in the IV pole, drawers with various labels, and the sharp odor of disinfectant. Then Heidi on an uncomfortable-looking chair, bluish-gray walls, and a hospital bed, its backrest up, holding a frighteningly fragile-looking Janica. Her bare head reflected the fluorescent lights overhead. Her skin was translucent; even her freckles looked like they'd been bleached by the sun. A film of sweat covered her skin, and she was shivering. One hand was clutching a light-brown bowl, the other dug into Heidi's arm. She looked ill and helpless.

He had never seen her like this before. His heart skipped a beat, stumbled, as if it was wondering whether it should even go on. But then Janica looked up. He gazed into her green, now strangely large-looking, eyes, and thought he might drown in them, like in a deep lake. As though the sun was brushing over the water, Janica's eyes lit up. He read love there, and happiness that he had come. Just that one look, the gleam in her eyes, swept away all his fears and reservations. He was exactly where he needed to be. His place was here, by her side.

"Her beauty leaves you speechless, eh?" the nurse prodded.

"Yes," he breathed, noting the nurse's surprised smile.

Janica grinned, then her eyes widened and she leaned over the bowl. Waves of pain rolled through her body, and she trembled. She heaved and heaved, but in vain. Before the nurse knew what was happening, Thomas had handed her his bag and pulled the chair as close to Janica's head as the bed allowed. He wrapped his arm around her convulsing body, his other hand on top of hers, as if she needed help to hold the bowl. He bent over and kissed her softly on her temple, her body still racked by useless cramps.

"I'm in love!" the nurse muttered, dropped his bag in the corner of the room, and disappeared.

"What a dragon," Thomas whispered to Heidi.

"A defense mechanism," Heidi explained. "She always knows when it's time to joke and when tenderness is needed. She's a fantastic nurse who is exactly where she ought to be."

Thomas nodded thoughtfully and heard the nurse's voice from outside.

"Thank you for the defense and the compliment. But you forgot to mention that I'm hopelessly underpaid."

"So true! The fatal flaw of all caregiving jobs!"

"By the way, Thomas," Janica squeaked from inside her bowl, "the walls here are made of cardboard."

"Can I take that bowl?" he asked.

"Certainly not. It's my best friend today, and probably tomorrow, too."

"But can I rinse it out?"

"It's not worth it."

"Doesn't matter."

Heidi stood up and showed Thomas around the hospital wing. Then she picked up her jacket and handbag, and, without asking Thomas whether it was OK to leave him alone with Janica, she said good-bye and disappeared.

He looked around in panic.

"What's wrong? Spit it out," Janica said, direct as ever, but with an unusual hint of aggression in her voice.

"I'm out of my depth. I have no idea what I'm supposed to do."

"It's enough that you're here. You don't have to hold the bowl or rinse it if you don't want to. That's Bettina's job, though the nurses are glad for any help they can get. Sometimes, just for fun, we practice synchronized spewing to keep them on their toes."

"I knew it!" Bettina crowed from another cubicle.

"The important thing is to call for help if my eyes roll back and I stop making any sound."

"If you what?"

"She's only kidding, mother-in-law's dream."

"I'm talking to my boyfriend," Janica yelled.

"And we're all ears, aren't we, Mr. Elsässer?"

The patient's affirmative grunt came through the wall. It sounded more plaintive than enthusiastic.

"These ridiculous cubicles. You'll never get used to it. But you don't have to. Anyway, I'm glad you're here. Back when I was a kid, not a single soul from my class had the guts to visit me at the hospital. Not even the teachers. They couldn't cope."

"You must have felt so hurt and disappointed."

"I learned from it. It taught me to tell the difference between a 'friend' and a friend."

"You'll let me know if there's anything I can do for you, or if I'm doing anything wrong, right?"

"Hey, he's attractive, charming, and smart! Congratulations, Janica. Are you also available in an older model, mother-in-law's dream?"

Just then, Janica's energy ran out. Frantically, she snatched the bowl and launched into a long spell of retching and trembling, sweating and shivering. Partway through, she lost all sense of politeness and patience with Thomas. She hissed when he put the blanket over her too soon or took it off too late, or tried to wipe her face at the wrong moment, or took her arm when she didn't want him to. Thomas took everything stoically. He knew Janica had bigger things to worry about than good manners, and she never became abusive.

After some time, she sank back into her pillow and closed her eyes. Her chest rose and fell rapidly—she was still trembling, and her face seemed pointed and pale as never before. In that moment, Thomas's heart truly registered that Janica was fighting a battle she'd already lost. He didn't say anything, gave her time to settle down, emptied the nearly empty bowl, and rinsed the cloth again. He waited until she opened her eyes and gave him an apologetic look before he wiped the sweat from her face, neck, arms, and legs, finally covering her with the blanket.

After he sat back down, the nurse came in. She glanced at the bowl, scrutinized her patient, checked the drip, and then held out her hand to him with a satisfied expression on her face.

"I'm Bettina."

"Thomas."

"Welcome to the Hero Club, Thomas."

"Thanks."

"Janica, you're a lucky girl!"

"Yes," she replied, and the smile on her dry lips filled Thomas's heart with pride.

"Psst, lip balm," Bettina said, pointing at a tube on the shelf, which he immediately grabbed. He waited until the nurse had left the room before bending over the exhausted patient.

"Lip balm," he whispered, kissing her softly.

She smelled awful, but he didn't care. The kiss was for Janica, and she thanked him with another feeble smile.

Chapter 26

It was past midnight, but oncology was still busy. Janica, who had been struggling with severe dizziness, had been moved to a three-bed room and finally managed to fall asleep. Thomas leaned back in his chair with relief, completely exhausted. They hadn't spoken much, since Janica hadn't been able to. Turbulent periods had alternated with quiet ones; she'd shown strength and weakness, willpower and stamina. At one point, she hadn't been able to hold back the tears. Thomas hadn't left her side apart from two quick bathroom breaks when she had briefly nodded off. He felt like he'd been chewed, swallowed, and spat out again. But he knew that what he'd gone through was nothing compared to what Janica had. He also knew that she'd mostly agreed to this round of chemo for him. During a particularly bad episode, he'd come close to begging her to quit the treatment. Was there really any use in her suffering so terribly during the last months or weeks of her life? Wouldn't it make more sense for them to enjoy their remaining time together, even if it meant there'd be less of it?

He didn't know the answer to this or any of the self-pitying questions that flooded his mind.

The night nurse came in. She checked the two other patients first, then she walked over and whispered, "You can go now, Mr. Hejduk."

Thomas couldn't stand the thought of leaving Janica alone here, but reason told him he ought to go home and get some rest.

"Miss Meier's mother will be here first thing in the morning," he replied defensively.

The night nurse nodded and headed out of the room, leaving the decision up to him.

He knew he was probably on the verge of overstaying his welcome and didn't want to try the patience of the staff and the two other sleeping women in the room. Afraid of waking Janica, he didn't let himself touch her, even though he longed to.

He studied her pale face for several minutes in the glow of the night-light. Her freckles seemed more pronounced again. He wished he could kiss every single one of them.

He took a deep breath and held it as he slipped out into the cold, harsh light of the corridor.

The night nurse came out of her office and walked him to the exit. "It's good for Miss Meier that you're here now. Where were you a few weeks ago, during her first round? Away on business? Ill?"

Thomas considered ignoring the disrespectful question, but then he said, "I was in her heart."

The young woman sighed and held the door for him.

When the cool air of the night hit him, Thomas couldn't even remember how he'd gotten outside. He walked to the parking lot with heavy steps, thinking how deserted it looked at night. He felt as though he was the only person on the planet worrying about a loved one, but knew it wasn't true. There were so many . . .

His thoughts turned to Sven, Jessika, and Annabelle and all the other sick children. Did they know Janica was like them?

Thomas climbed into his car, leaned back, and closed his eyes. Then an idea shot through his mind, which he thought had already entered a nebulous state of semiconsciousness. Suddenly wide awake, he fished his phone out and dialed Lars's number.

"This is Pastor Lars," said a voice that sounded like it was still asleep. The generous man obviously felt obliged to be on standby for his flock at all hours.

"Hi, Lars. It's me, Thomas."

"Thomas?"

"I know—it's late."

"But?"

"I was at the hospital with Janica tonight—"

"How is she?"

"She's asleep. Listen, I'm dead tired and so are you. Can you do me a favor?"

"Sure."

"Could you please get Janica's friends together? Tomorrow, if possible, at a time when as many of them as possible can make it?"

"They're your friends, too. You can call."

"Lars!"

"Fine, fine, what do you want?"

"I've got a few ideas, and I'm going to need all the help I can get."

"We'll help."

"But you should warn them. At least one of my ideas is . . . probably—"

"Spit it out, dude."

"Well, not entirely legal."

"And you're telling a pastor?"

"I think you're the craziest of the bunch."

"Guess I need to work on my image."

"Well?"

"Consider it done. I'll send you a text as soon as I know the time and place."

"Thank you."

"Get some rest. You sound like you've been cheering at a soccer match for hours."

"That's pretty much right."

"Good night."

"Thanks. Good night."

Thomas put his phone down, started the engine, and drove home with wide-open eyes, loud music, and the windows down. Balou greeted him at the gate, and Thomas was glad for the bear's company. At least he wasn't coming home to an empty house.

A pale crescent moon hung in the night sky, but only a milky glow told the onlooker where it was hiding behind tufted clouds. Heidi wrapped her arms around herself in defense against the strong autumn wind. She was shivering, but didn't want to abandon her position in the yard. It was as though she hoped the wind might carry away her pain.

"Why?" she whispered, wanting to scream the word.

Strong arms embraced her from behind, and she leaned against Peter with a sigh.

"It's bad, huh?"

"The first time was bad enough. But this time, her chances are so bleak—" Heidi broke off and took a deep breath. "It's a death sentence. And there's still so much she wanted to do!"

Heidi felt her husband nod and was grateful for his silence. She didn't need any wise replies right now, no sermon about the transitory nature of life, just someone who listened, someone she could lean on.

"She's so brave. And Thomas . . ." She let out another sigh, but this one was different. Hopeful. Admiring.

"He's coping well," Peter said.

"Her friend Finn isn't, though. He's sending me multiple e-mails a day about alternative medicine or new research from the US. He's trying to respect Janica's desire for normalcy, but it's tearing him apart. He wants to help her—"

"He's a typical doer. It's hard for him to accept a fact as unchangeable."

"Well, it's hard for me to read his e-mails and not start clutching at straws, too," Heidi said.

"Then ask him to stop e-mailing you."

"I already hinted at it once. His reply was almost aggressive. He wrote that I couldn't force him to give up on Janica. I think he needs this outlet."

"Maybe. But not at your expense. You're suffering enough."

"He needs a task, something he can do to help Janica. Or a distraction." Heidi shrugged helplessly.

"I'll talk to Lars about it," Peter decided.

"Finn will have to let her go. Just like . . . all of us!"

Heidi's legs gave out. Peter held her up and turned her around at the same time, hugging her tightly. Blank despair descended over Heidi like the rafters of a collapsing building, threatening to bury her heart under the rubble.

"She's my daughter!" she howled. "How can we lose her now?"

"We won fifteen extra years together."

"It's not enough! It's not enough at all!" Heidi sobbed, clinging to her husband, the cold wind blowing in her face.

Chapter 27

Janica's numbers were good enough for her to be allowed to go home, but not on her own. She really did have Bettina's "full-body baldy" look now, having lost her eyelashes and eyebrows. But that didn't bother her nearly as much as the weakness. Janica couldn't walk more than twenty steps at a time, climbing stairs was torture, and even the simplest tasks were exhausting. She loved being on the farm and being looked after by her parents, but she missed Thomas. He came straight from work every day, graded exams and did his lesson planning at her side, but the hours when he was off at work seemed endlessly long to her.

The following weekend, Angelo, Susi, and Barbara came to visit. In the company of Thomas and her friends, Janica dared the walk down the path, across the bridge, and over to the horse paddock. They had a picnic, and Janica beamed when she managed the whole return walk by herself as well. Her happiness also had something to do with the fact that Thomas would be staying in one of the guest rooms that night. They wouldn't have to say good-bye all weekend!

That evening, Peter built a fire, and, in spite of the cool night, they cooked and ate outside, sitting around the fire until late. Thomas ensconced himself in a deck chair, and, with her express permission, pulled Janica onto his lap. She snuggled against his chest, let him warm her, and listened to the soothing rhythm of his heartbeat. She could hear the crackle of flames and burning wood, and the animated voices of her friends.

Janica must have nodded off, because she was a little confused when Barbara called her name and Thomas nudged her repeatedly.

"Hey, my little snuggle bug, the others are going home," he whispered.

Janica straightened up sleepily.

"See you again soon," Susi said, and hugged her delicately. "Have a nice Sunday with this boyfriend of yours."

Angelo stroked her bare head, then leaned down and planted a kiss on it.

Barbara crouched beside her, holding a pen in one hand and a birthday card on a book in the other. A piece of paper was sticking out from the bottom of the card.

"It's Kurti's birthday this week. Could you sign his card?"

Janica frowned at the flowery image on the card, thinking it was an odd choice for the jolly Bavarian. But she didn't know what her friends had planned and, anyway, she was half-asleep and couldn't see properly in the flickering light of the fire. Without asking any questions, she put her name on the piece of paper inside the card, and handed back the pen. She noticed neither the look Barbara and Thomas exchanged nor his triumphant grin.

"When are you coming back?" she asked with a heavy tongue.

"Very soon, I promise!" Barbara replied, squeezed her arm with both hands, and followed Susi and Angelo to the car.

Shortly afterward, Janica heard the Fiat's engine start up, then the noise receded, until all she could hear was the rustling of the leaves, the chirping of crickets, and the occasional crackle of the dying fire.

"It's time we got to bed," Peter groaned as he got out of his chair and headed inside.

Janica's mother followed but returned with a fluffy blanket, which she spread over Janica and Thomas. She wished them a good night and went inside.

Janica snuggled back against Thomas, ready to enjoy their time alone. He held her tightly, and they listened to the peaceful sounds of the night.

"I had a wonderful day," Janica said, breaking the silence.

"Me, too. And I'm very proud of you."

"Because I walked so far?"

"Yes, and you made it through the whole day with only one tiny nap."

Janica leaned her head back and gave him a little kiss. Thomas took it as an invitation and returned it with a long, passionate one. She felt a tingle of excitement running through her body, followed by a disappointing dullness.

She snuggled back up to Thomas and muttered sleepily, "I could stay here all night."

"What's stopping us?"

"I'm heavy and the chair isn't that comfortable."

"Do you think you're the only one who can endure hardship? I've been incredibly impressed by what you've gone through recently. Surely I can hold you in this chair for a few hours?"

"Bettina calling you a hero must have gone to your head!"

"You're my hero, Janica! And has anyone ever told you what a beautifully shaped head you have?"

"Flatterer!" Janica laughed.

They spent the rest of the night kissing, dozing, and talking quietly, and eventually watched with fascination as the day dawned, announcing itself with a spectacular display of colors, carrying the hope of something new.

Janica

It may sound weird, and I didn't want to see it at first, but the best thing that happened to me when I was sick was my love for Thomas and his unconditional love for me.

He saw me at my worst. Helplessly at the mercy of the chemo cocktail, weak, decrepit, desperate, and possessed by mood swings that no one should have to be exposed to that early on in a relationship. I guess it might help couples to find out whether they're meant for the long haul, having to face tough times at the beginning of a relationship. Of course, I don't wish hardship on any couple—least of all, a situation like ours: to have just begun and to already see the end.

My treatment options had been exhausted. After speaking with the doctors, my parents, and Thomas, I decided to stop chemotherapy. It was too hard on my body—it robbed me of too many of the good days I had left, especially for the minimal result I could expect to gain.

Time is precious. Every minute we give to another person is priceless, even if we're not staring death in the face.

What can I tell you? I had made the most of life since my first bout of cancer, seeing something special in every color of the rainbow, a miracle in every little thing, heaven in every smile. But never before had I felt so alive as at Thomas's side. He was the crowning glory of my life—of this life.

Chapter 28

September 29

Rays of sunlight dipped the fields in gold, dissolved the high fog on the bluish mountains, and triggered a concert of birdsong. It was the beginning of a beautiful fall day.

Janica had risen early. Accompanied by Balou, she'd taken the horses to the paddock, fed the chickens and geese, and started cooking breakfast for the two guests, Thomas and Steffen.

Then, suddenly, as if someone had given a signal, the entire household came to life. Her father mucked out the stables in record time, while Heidi bossed Thomas and Steffen around in the kitchen.

Breakfast was anything but relaxed that morning. For some reason, everyone seemed to be in a hurry. Janica had no idea what was going on, and eventually crossed her arms over her chest in protest, enabling her mother to snatch her plate away, though she hadn't even finished yet. And it was her mother who always pestered her to take another bite!

"What's going on?" she asked, eyeing Thomas suspiciously.

He shifted nervously in his chair and ran his hand through his freshly trimmed hair. He cleared his throat awkwardly and was saved by his brother, who replied, cool as ever, "We have a surprise. This day is a present for you, and it's just fantastic how quickly you've recovered."

"A surprise?" Janica felt excitement welling up in her. She loved surprises, and did indeed feel well enough to let herself get spoiled for a whole day.

"I'll just load the dishwasher, then we'll go and find something for you to wear."

"What's wrong with what I'm wearing?" Janica asked.

"We're dressing up today," her father replied.

He had already showered following his work at the stables and was sitting at the breakfast table in an elegant, silver-gray suit with shirt and tie. Janica had assumed he had a work appointment, but apparently not.

"I can't wait!" Janica squealed, jumped to her feet, and rushed to her room with Balou hot on her heels. Once there, she realized she'd left all her nice clothes in the city.

But her personal event organizers were well prepared. A moment later, her mother came into her room carrying four of her nicest dresses.

"Oh, we really *are* dressing up!" she exclaimed, reaching for a light-green shift dress. "Pistachio ice cream in Genoa," she remarked to her mother, who handed her a new white bra with matching underpants, and a pair of fancy pantyhose.

"Whoa. Where are we going?"

"Your friends have planned an unforgettable day for you, so stop asking questions and start enjoying yourself. All right?"

Janica tilted her head, studied Heidi for a moment, and decided not to ask who exactly this day was supposed to be unforgettable for or voice her fear of not having enough energy for it. She slipped on the dress and matching ballet flats, and slung the white cardigan her mother had picked out for her—as if she'd known Janica was going to pick the shift dress—over her shoulder. The dress hung a little loose in places, as she had lost a lot of weight.

"At least I don't have to worry about bad hair days anymore." Janica laughed, and her mother hugged her tightly.

Janica reached for her wig and studied it thoughtfully. "Thomas says I've got a beautifully shaped head," she whispered.

"Then leave the wig."

"What if I regret it later?"

"You could take it in the car."

"No, it's staying here," Janica said decisively.

"Ready to go, then?" Heidi asked.

"I'm ready—for whatever!" Janica laughed.

"I'll run and get changed."

Janica climbed down the stairs to the living room, where she found her father and the two brothers. She stopped on the landing, unable to take her eyes off Thomas. He looked like he'd climbed straight out of a fashion magazine in his gray suit, its color reminding her of the vintage Mercedes of her neighbor in town, and his light-blue shirt and tie, which reminded her of her grandma's parakeet. When she noticed his hungry eyes on her, she blushed. Now she couldn't even lower her head and hide behind her curls.

"My head must be red as a fire engine."

"Nonsense! You look stunning," Steffen assured her. He and Peter walked outside.

Thomas crossed to the bottom of the stairs and held out his hand. Janica climbed down the remaining steps, took his hand, and let him pull her into his arms.

"Have I ever told you how beautiful you are and how much I love you?" he asked in a husky voice.

"Many times. But I enjoy hearing it over and over, and every single time feels like the first."

"Will you allow me to abduct you into this day?"

"Yes."

"I apologize in advance for all the crazy plans your friends, family, and I hatched."

"I'm not sure right now if I should be excited or worried."

"Me neither."

"Come on, let's go!" Janica said, then kissed him on the cheek and darted out of the house.

Filled with anticipation, eager for the day with her loved ones to begin, and a little anxious about the secrecy, she climbed into Thomas's car and let him drive her to town.

He parked near the city center, and the shop windows greeted her with the harmonious colors of fall, accentuated by the surprisingly warm sun.

She climbed out of the car, smoothed her dress, and let the brothers and her parents lead her to the square in front of the city hall, where she spotted her friends. Janica whooped with joy and waved in greeting, then froze and clasped her hands to her mouth in shock.

The men had lifted the hats they had—strangely—been wearing, Susi was untying a beautiful headscarf, and Barbara took off her baseball cap, while Julia stepped out from behind Lars. Every one of them had shaved their head.

"What have you done?" Janica gasped. "Susi, your beautiful hair!" She rushed toward her friend and gaped at her in disbelief.

"It'll grow back," she assured Janica, and wrapped her arms around her.

"Y–you did this for me?" Janica stammered, staring at the shiny heads across Susi's shoulder.

"Barbara?" Janica touched Susi's sister's smooth, soft scalp, tears welling up in her eyes.

"We all went to the barber together yesterday. It was so funny!" Barbara explained, and hugged her.

"Even funnier when her phone rang this morning and it was the agency's publicity guy asking for a current photo for the book jacket!" Finn whooped.

Janica hid her face again and shook her head. Peering through her fingers, she saw passersby stopping to look at the strange group—one even took a picture.

Her parents, Steffen, and Thomas appeared to be just as surprised as she was, and Heidi declared, "If I'd known, I would have joined you!"

"There's a salon just across the square, Heidi," Angelo said, pointing.

"How much time do I have?"

"None," Thomas replied with a glance at his watch.

Janica turned to him. He was running his fingers through his hair again, clearly nervous.

"Why don't you guys go ahead?" Thomas said. "I just want to have a quick chat with our guest of honor."

"Are you sure you don't want me to stay, for protection?" Lars offered, but Kurti grabbed him by the arm and dragged him away.

Janica would have liked to see where they were going, but Thomas took her face between his hands and gave her a serious look.

"Well," he started shakily, cleared his throat, and squared his shoulders.

Janica grinned, stood up on her toes, and kissed him. Thomas pulled back with surprise and cleared his throat again. Janica, taking advantage of his nervousness, kissed him again, harder.

"Janica, I—we can do that later—please, let me just say what I need to say, OK?"

"Are you embarrassed by me kissing you in public?" she asked mischievously.

Thomas leaned his face closer to hers. "Never. Anyway, I can't see anyone but you," he said softly, his voice breaking. He straightened up again, pursed his lips for a few seconds, took a deep breath, and said in a surprisingly calm voice, "We have an appointment at city hall to get married."

"What?"

Janica took a step back, but Thomas anticipated it and followed without letting go.

"Everything's all set. There's only one thing left to do: Janica, will you marry me?"

"Today? Now?"

"Right now!"

"But we can't! I would have had to sign something, and—wait! That birthday card from last week?"

"Barbara did a good job, didn't she?" Thomas laughed.

"That borders on coercion, on deceit, on fraud, on—"

"Love?"

"Oh, my goodness!" Janica exclaimed.

She began to realize the extent of the surprise her friends, her family, and Thomas had planned behind her back. Admiration for all her loved ones welled up in her. And something else? What was that other feeling, rising up like it was about to boil over? Boundless happiness?

Before she could reply, Thomas continued, alarmed by her long silence, "I'm sick of getting told 'family members only' when I ask for information at the hospital. I'm sick of not being able to take time off from school because the person I want to look after doesn't count as family. I'm sick of having to leave you behind at the farm every night when I want to be with you every minute of the day! And most of all, I love you. I want to be the one who's responsible for you, the one by your side, the one who holds you and carries you, and loves you and loves you, and loves you more."

"But, Thomas . . . ?" Janica struggled to surface from the whirlpool of exciting and frightening emotions.

"I know, Janica! I get it! I'm perfectly aware of everything this means, and I still want to do it. For both of us."

Janica placed her index finger on his lips, silencing his ecstatic and, for a taciturn man like Thomas, long speech.

"Yes."

Thomas blinked. A lopsided smile spread across his face, then he grabbed her around the waist, lifted her in the air, and spun her around several times. He took her face between his hands again and gave her an infinitely soft kiss on the lips.

"Then let's go."

"Yes, even if it's utter madness."

This time it was he who placed several fingers on her lips, silencing her. Janica took his hand and led him toward city hall.

Thomas stopped just outside the door. "One moment."

He reached into the pocket of his suit jacket and fished out three little jewelry boxes, opened them, and held them out to her. Each one contained a set of his-and-hers gold rings.

"I stole one of your rings to get the right size. The jeweler was kind enough to size three rings for you, so you can choose. The ones we don't want, we'll return."

"He did that?"

Thomas shrugged and said nothing. Janica realized he must have told the jeweler about the cancer. And not only the jeweler—the story had probably moved a whole number of people to break protocol for this special day.

She looked at each ring, and spontaneously chose the one made of intertwining strands of white gold and red gold.

Thomas snapped the two remaining boxes shut and returned them to his pocket, keeping the third one in his hand.

"Shall we?"

Janica nodded in amazement. She was getting married! She wasn't wearing the extravagant white gown from her childhood dreams, but nevertheless, Thomas was giving her the gift of experiencing how precious it felt to be a bride.

An hour later, Janica walked out of the city hall as Mrs. Janica Hejduk, and threw herself into the arms of her mother. Heidi held her tightly, as if she feared the fall breeze sweeping through the streets might carry her feather-light daughter away. When they let go, Janica saw the silent tears her mother had cried.

But her friends gave her no time for sentimentality. Julia squeezed her hand and pointed at a photographer setting up his tripod at the bottom of the stairs.

"Now a group baldy photo!" Kurti announced, following shots of the newlyweds, the newlyweds with the parents, and with their witnesses, Steffen and Barbara.

The friends stormed the stairs and gathered around the bride.

"What a blinding sight we are," Peter said with a wide grin, and everyone roared with laughter just as the photographer pushed the button.

"See you later!" Susi called to her husband, and Angelo waved as he trotted off.

"Where . . . ?" Janica asked.

She watched with confusion as her brand-new husband left with her parents and the other men. Julia and Barbara took her by the hands and dragged her off in the opposite direction.

"Where are we going now?" she laughed, taking her two friends by the elbow, while Susi linked arms with her sister.

"We're only just getting started," Barbara said ominously, and Julia, who lived near city hall, jingled her keys.

Janica stopped short in the doorway of Julia's tiny apartment, thunderstruck. Standing in front of her was a tall clothes rack holding five white wedding dresses and one cream-colored one.

"No!" she gasped.

"You have two hours to pick *your* dress, then we have half an hour to get you ready, and then another forty-five minutes to drive you to your church wedding."

"You guys are nuts!"

"You knew that, didn't you?"

"I never realized to what degree, though!"

"Come on! Make the most of your time!" Susi laughed and sat down on the couch, crossed her arms in front of her chest, and looked up expectantly, like a fashion designer waiting for the first glimpse of her creation on a live model.

"Whose idea was this?"

"Your mother's, together with that crazy-in-love guy. What was his name?"

Julia lifted the first dress off the rack and walked into her bedroom. Janica followed in a daze. She never would have thought she'd get another chance to try on wedding gowns. When Susi had picked hers, she'd naturally come along and tried on a couple, too.

She knew right away she didn't like the first dress. While it matched her childhood dream of puffy sleeves and a voluptuous hooped skirt, it didn't suit the taste of grown-up Janica. Kind of grown up, at least. But the second dress she tried stayed on. The others were all cut to hide the port showing through Janica's skin, which showed her friends' thoughtfulness, but Janica didn't give them a second glance.

She spun around in front of the mirror. The lacing in the back looked elegant and made the corset mold to her dwindling body mass. The transition to the skirt was fashioned with two pointed triangles, and the satin below was only slightly flared and made of curved layers, so it flowed down to her ankles like waves, neither overloaded nor plain. The back hem of the skirt tapered into a pointed train. The corset top revealed her collarbone with the surgery scar and the port, but the dress came with a satin shrug that covered the scar in the front but was short enough in back to reveal the lacing.

"Absolutely stunning," Julia whispered. She opened the door and waved for Janica to show herself to the sisters.

Barbara gasped when she appeared in the doorway, and Susi clapped her hands in excitement, shouting, "I knew that dress would be perfect for you! We were already on our way out of the shop when it practically jumped out at me!"

"Quick, try shoes, and then I can take the other dresses back. I promised I'd have them back by noon, since most brides-to-be go dress shopping on Saturdays," Julia said.

Janica tried on three of the five pairs of shoes before she found the ones she liked. She didn't even notice Julia wrapping the dresses in plastic and taking them to the car, because Barbara and Susi were helping her with the tights and makeup. Susi powdered her nose one last time so it wouldn't be shiny in the photographs.

"Now we'll have a bite to eat, and when Julia comes back, we'll toast with a glass of alcohol-free champagne. Then off we go," Barbara explained, and fetched a platter full of hors d'oeuvres from Julia's tiny kitchen.

Underneath a white pavilion, by the murmuring creek on the meadow beside the horse paddock, Lars blessed the beaming couple's union. In addition to the friends who'd already accompanied them to city hall, more guests filled the benches decorated with lilac-colored fabric. Among them were Janica's colleagues, Nurse Bettina, and Janica's oncologist. Helga, Werner, and two other nurses from the hospice had also come, as well as Annabelle with her mother, Petra; Jessika and Sven, each with their parents; Liana, the girl who'd arrived the day Rat died; Dr. Kraus; Derja's mother, Selina; Rat's father, Gottlieb and her brother, Karsten; and several of Thomas's colleagues, as well as a great-aunt of the Hejduk brothers.

Aside from Petra and Annabelle, who wasn't feeling well, everyone stayed after the ceremony for coffee and cake. By early evening, when two of the Meiers' neighbors served a light meal, the party had shrunk back to the people who'd organized this day with so much blood, sweat, and tears. And suddenly, Jenni was there, too, glowing in the light of several torches that had been set up between the buildings and the sloping meadow.

Janica ran into her sister's arms, and the first thing she said was, "I'm so glad you've still got your hair!"

Jenni laughed, kissed her forehead, and whispered, "If I'd known . . ."

"No!" Janica replied, but to her relief, Jenni just winked at her.

"I'm going to go say hello to that extremely attractive pastor over there, and the others."

Janica let her sister go, smiling to herself as she watched ever-confident Lars turn crimson when Jenni greeted him before anyone else. "Another happy ending I'm going to miss," she whispered with a touch of melancholy, which Thomas dispelled by wrapping his arms around her from behind.

"I'm going to abduct my enchanting bride now!"

"Sounds exciting." She turned her head and let her kidnapper kiss her.

Janica had no illusions when they secretly stole away into the darkness and climbed into Thomas's car. The others were bound to know what he had planned, but she didn't care. She enjoyed every minute of their clandestine escape.

Chapter 29

It was after midnight when Thomas led her into the dimly lit hotel room. Countless white roses exuding a strong, sweet smell were standing in vases on the floor, the bedside tables, and along the panorama windows.

"I think that's enough for today," Janica said, laughing at the ocean of flowers.

Thomas grinned and loosened his tie.

"I had nothing to do with the roses. Did you know that Finn, apart from being an organized, funny guy, and, when necessary, a total badass, is also a secret romantic? The ceremony by the creek, the pavilion, the carriage ride up to the house, and, presumably, the roses, are all his doing. He even recommended this hotel by the lake."

Janica nodded, her thoughts jumping about like grasshoppers. She was married! She was alone with her husband! They didn't have to part any longer, not ever, not until—

She didn't have to tell him she was still a virgin; she was sure he knew. But—and that was unusual for her—she had no idea what she could or should say right now. Slowly, she turned to him, the hem of her dress floating around her ankles.

"Your dress looks almost blue in this light," Thomas said softly, devouring her with his eyes.

"Snow-in-moonlight blue?"

"Mermaid blue," he replied, hinting at the waves around her legs. He came closer and held her hands. "My beautiful wife," he whispered, and leaned over her and kissed her.

As he kissed her, he slipped the shrug off her shoulders, and it rustled to the floor. His lips traveled down her neck, to her port, and over to her shoulder without pausing, as if it was the most natural thing in the world for a woman to carry a hard round device under her skin.

His mouth returned to hers. The kiss was more passionate this time. Janica buried her hands in his thick hair and pressed herself against him. Hot excitement rolled through her body in waves, burying all her fears and insecurities, and she felt like she couldn't get close enough to his body. Thomas lifted his head. His eyes gleamed, and the cheeky grin on his face made Janica giggle. He put his hands on her shoulders again and spun her around, so she was standing with her back to him. She felt his hands slowly moving down her shoulders, leaving a trail of fire. She closed her eyes and enjoyed every second, while Thomas undid the lacing in slow motion. Each time he loosened the ribbons in their hidden loops, he pulled the corset apart a tiny bit further and kissed every inch of exposed skin, as if he was rewarding it and himself for his success.

The dress slid down, tantalizingly slow at first, then very fast, landing on the floor around her feet. Janica was about to step out, but Thomas scooped her up and carried her to the bed in his arms.

Chapter 30

Kurti, Lars, Finn, and Steffen—the last wedding guests—were sitting at one of the tables decorated with ivy-and-white gerbera, surrounded by candles flickering in old jam jars and a huge number of empty or half-empty bottles, which scattered the moonlight in an array of colors.

"Well, I think we can pat ourselves on the back," Finn sighed contentedly, and raised his beer.

The three other men raised their drinks. The dull clinking appeared to disturb an owl, which hooted mournfully.

"We should keep going while we're on a roll," Kurti said, casting a meaningful glance at Lars.

Finn and Steffen followed his example and stared intently at the clergyman.

"Will you at least let me grow my hair back first?" Lars replied coolly.

Kurti dropped his shoulders with disappointment. "You could at least plead innocence or pretend to be upset," he scolded. "It's no fun this way."

"So you like her, this Jenni?" Finn asked.

"Sure do," Lars said. "Even more after talking to her all evening."

Steffen expected a mix of deafening jubilation and mockery from Finn and Kurti, but he was mistaken. Kurti merely grinned, and Finn nodded sagely, as if he hadn't expected anything else. Evidently, the boys were feeling just as content and pleasantly tired as he was. His thoughts turned to Thomas, and one corner of his mouth curled up when he realized the newlyweds must be consummating their union. Desire flared up inside him. He'd been on several dates since his wife kicked him out, but he'd never let them go beyond chitchat. He didn't just miss his daughter, but her mother, too. Still.

She had been the real thing, his one true love—a passionate love, matching his reckless personality. But Lara had struggled with the lifestyle his job had imposed on them, and the problem became greater once they had Marie. Who could blame her? He would be gone for days at a time, leaving her in constant fear that something might happen to him. Plus, he never spoke about his work, and the secrecy ate away at her trust in him. Perhaps even more so since she wasn't beautiful in the popular sense, like the Barbie-doll types that used to turn his head. She'd probably been haunted by a fear of losing him to a—in her eyes—more attractive woman and not even knowing, because he might be guarding that aspect of his life like yet another state secret.

Steffen rubbed the stubble on his chin. He should have tried to fix things much sooner. But back then, he hadn't been ready to give up the job he'd fought so hard for, and his status on the force. This compulsion to hold on to what he'd thought was important had destroyed his marriage. Tonight, sitting in the cool breeze at the Meiers' farm, following his brother's marriage to a terminally ill woman, the question forced its way in and wouldn't leave: What was really important in his life? Where was he headed? What did he want to have achieved, if he looked back on his life in many years' time?

Steffen looked into the tired, distracted faces of Janica and Thomas's friends. There were great people outside the SFU's sworn band of brothers. And the reason he was finally in a position to enjoy their company was because he no longer had a job he couldn't talk about, and no need to make up excuses for his sudden, frequent deployments. This fact had always put a strain on any relationship Steffen had tried to have—not just his marriage.

He had quit his beloved job and lost contact with his old comrades, and now he was lonely. From time to time, the terrible feeling of being lost, which, together with the wrong dosage of drugs, had pushed him onto the bridge railing that night, resurfaced like an ugly, grinning demon.

His phone vibrated in his shirt pocket, tearing him from his gloomy thoughts. He reached for it instinctively, feeling adrenaline rush through his veins and his muscles tense up. His body always reacted that way when his phone rang—another psychological remnant from the Special Forces Unit.

Three pairs of eyes stared at him, puzzled by his fierce reaction. He would have to think about how to tell them what job he had recently left. Like so many times before, he had to weigh carefully who he could tell, and how much.

It was his ex-wife's number. At this hour? His stomach seized up. He leapt across two rows of tables and chairs, which earned him a whistle from one of the guys, and answered the phone with the question: "Is Marie all right?"

"No! Yes?" Lara sounded scared.

"Relax and tell me what's going on," he said, trying to sound collected despite his racing heart.

"I think someone's sneaking around outside," she said in a choked voice.

Steffen could feel her anxiety through the telephone. He felt for his car keys in his jacket pocket and pulled them out.

Lars stood up and came toward him. "Trouble?"

"Gotta go," he replied curtly, and turned around. He could hear Lars following him but focused on the phone. "Lara, did you see anyone?"

"No, I just heard something."

"A cat? A fox?"

"I don't think so. It sounded like footsteps."

"Could it be one of my former colleagues, still keeping an eye on the house?"

"Nothing happened for a long time. They left," Lara said with a trembling voice, so quietly that he could barely make out the words.

"Have you locked every door and window?"

"Of course," she whispered irritably.

He'd made her practice their emergency drill regularly, which she always hated.

"Where is Marie?"

"Asleep in my bed."

"Go join her. Lock and barricade the bedroom door like I showed you. I'll be there in thirty minutes. I'll call when I want you to let me in, all right?"

"Yes."

"Do you want me to stay on the phone with you?"

"No. You have to drive."

Steffen hung up turned to Lars, who was looking at him quizzically. "My ex-wife. She might be in danger."

"Danger?"

"It's a long story. I have to go."

"Can I come?"

Steffen yanked the door of his BMW open. "You might regret it."

Lars jumped into the passenger seat and hurried to close the door, as the car was already moving. A fountain of pebbles spurted out from under the wheels as the vehicle shot into the dark. For a brief moment, he considered calling his former boss, but decided to wait. So far, they were merely dealing with a vague suspicion by Lara, who'd always been overly cautious.

The tires squealed as he spun onto the winding country road.

Lars clung to the door handle. "Now I understand," he muttered, fished out his phone, and texted Finn to let him know that he'd left.

"I doubt it," Steffen grumbled, and sped up even more. "Take my phone and call back the last number. My ex-wife, Lara, will answer. Explain to her who you are, and talk to her, or let her talk. It's what she needs now."

Lars did as he'd been told, and a short while later, he was speaking with Lara in an easy, pleasant tone. "Lara wants to know if she's allowed to tell me what's going on?"

"Just this once."

Steffen accelerated on the ramp to the highway. He pushed the powerful engine to its limits, ignoring Lars's terrified expression. He focused all his senses on racing through the night, forced aside all the worries and fears that would only slow him down.

A few minutes later, Steffen braked hard and took the exit on the outskirts of town. He sped through the silent, deserted-looking suburb far above the speed limit. Finally, he slowed down and switched off the headlights. He forced himself to pull over very slowly.

"You stay here for now," he told Lars in a hoarse voice, took the phone, and said to Lara: "I'm in front of the house. As soon as I've secured the area, I'll call so you can let me in."

He hung up, put the phone in his pocket, and reached past Lars's long legs to the glove compartment. His passenger watched with knitted eyebrows as Steffen pulled out his SIG Sauer P229, inserted the magazine, and opened the door. "You have to stay right here, OK? I need to know where you are."

"Of course!" Lars agreed, but gave the shimmering blackish-blue weapon a suspicious look.

Steffen climbed out and stealthily shut the door. He scanned the street for any movement, and checked the neighboring gardens as well as he could without night-vision goggles. Then he entered his former property, gun stuck in his waistband. The bushes and trees formed sharp outlines against the moonlit surroundings. The swing he'd bought for Marie hung limp and lifeless in its frame. Next to it, Steffen could see the outline of the huge sandbox Marie's grandparents had made for her. The grass was long, and it rustled under each slow step he took. The patio's sand-colored stone tiles gleamed among the blades of grass, the pruned rosebushes, and the bamboo. This part of the garden appeared quiet, deserted. Steffen turned around to scan the ground and saw his own dark footprints in the ankle-deep grass. No one else had walked across the lawn. Had Lara been mistaken?

Not satisfied yet, Steffen continued on, around the corner and the blue rain barrel, onto the narrow strip of lawn alongside the semidetached house. He stopped dead. There were footprints in the grass, and they led straight to the basement. Steffen frowned. Beads of sweat formed on his forehead. He fought down his fear for Marie and Lara. Fear was a useful warning signal, but not a good adviser. He took a deep breath and tried to assess the situation. The footprints could be Lara's. She might have been out in the garden late in the evening. Or not. Was someone lurking in the basement? Inside the house? Was the thing he'd been so afraid of all those years actually happening? A revenge attempt? Had his identity been compromised now that he had left the SFU?

Slowly and carefully, he pulled the gun from his waistband and released the safety. Holding the weapon with both hands, he raised his arms into position and snuck along the wall, crouching, until he reached the metal railing over the descending steps. With a sudden movement, he leaned over the railing. There was a shuffling noise down below. Steffen felt danger like pinpricks all over his body.

"Don't move!" he barked.

A glaring light cut through the night. Blinded, Steffen closed his eyes. When he forced them open and desperately tried to make out something—shadows at least—all he could see were dots of light dancing in front of his face. His trained ears heard someone moving in a hurry. Should he fire?

Instinctively, he threw himself to the ground and rolled under the boxwood hedge he knew started here. Hurried footsteps ran up the stairs and away from him. Steffen jumped to his feet and raced after the shadow figure. He reached the street with his pulse hammering in his temples. A few yards ahead, a door slammed and an engine roared to life. A dark hatchback pulled out with no lights, so Steffen couldn't even make out the number plate. Revving loudly, it sped off. Steffen ran to his car and jumped in the driver's seat. Lars gingerly took the gun from him. Steffen immediately started the car and raced off with smoking and squealing tires, crossed several intersections, and turned sharply down various side streets. But there was no one on the road. The driver of the hatchback might have simply pulled into a driveway or parked inconspicuously between two other cars.

Angry, disappointed, but also relieved, he slowed down and drove back to Lara's house. Once there, he turned off the engine and rested his forehead against the steering wheel. His hands trembled. He had held a gun in his hand again—almost used it. Since the shooting, he hated the feeling of the cold, hard steel in his hands, and he'd avoided firearms. His fear for Lara and Marie's safety had forced him to cross this line.

"I put the gun away in the glove compartment," Lars said, reminding Steffen of his presence.

Steffen sat up with a jerk.

"Thanks. I'm sorry if I scared you."

"Looking forward to the explanation. But maybe we should check on Lara and your daughter first?"

"I'll call her. They're safe now."

"I'm sure she'd rather hear that in person," Lars said, and opened his door.

Steffen wasn't so sure, but followed Lars nonetheless. He dialed Lara's number and asked her to open the door for them. They waited in silence in front of the door, until it opened a crack at first, then fully.

"Hi, Lara. I'm Lars. We spoke on the phone."

"Er, yes, hello," Lara replied, uncertain, and threw a confused glance at Steffen.

She was a bit like Thomas before he met Janica: reserved, not very spontaneous. Gentlemanly, protective Steffen had always liked that about her.

"Lars is a pastor and a friend," Steffen told her, and saw her face soften with relief. Apparently, Lara had more faith in a man of God than in his old friends from the SFU.

"Is Marie asleep?" he asked awkwardly.

Lara nodded. He saw that she was shaking and wrapping her arms around herself. For a brief moment, he considered taking her in his arms, but denied himself. He couldn't handle being rebuffed right now. Also, touching her would chip away at the protective wall he'd put up between him and his feelings for Lara.

"Shall we sit down?" Lars suggested, and led the way into the open-plan kitchen and living room. He switched on a light. "Is it all right if I make us some tea?"

Lara looked to Steffen. He nodded reassuringly, and was glad to see her clenched fists loosening a little.

"The cups are in the dishwasher—it's clean, I just haven't emptied it yet. Tea is in the pantry next to the fridge," she said, sounding a little bewildered by Lars's familiarity.

"Great!" Lars replied, and started to fill the kettle.

"Come on, let's sit down," Steffen said to his ex-wife, who was standing indecisively in her own living room, and took her gently by the elbow.

She pulled her arm away, sending a searing pain through his heart. And yet he almost felt grateful for the rejection. It was better this way. His feelings for her were still far too close to the surface.

"So did you see anyone?" she asked, looking at him anxiously. She knew she had a tendency to be overly cautious, and was worried that she had bothered him over nothing.

"Yes," he said, his voice grim.

"Brief and without explanation, as always, right?" she replied bitterly, folded her arms across her chest, and slumped onto the couch.

Steffen gritted his teeth, ran his hand through his hair, and took off his jacket.

"Lara, I can't give you an explanation, because I don't know anything. The guy blinded me and took off."

"Blinded you?"

"Camera flash, I think."

"Oh, God. Could it be that journalist from the other week? He was hunting for the shooter who—" Lara gave him a shy look, and lowered her head without finishing her sentence. "So there's a photo of you now?"

Steffen nodded grimly. He could just imagine the picture: an angry man with flexed muscles, viewed from below, which probably made him look beefy and massive, eyes and lips pinched, gun pointed straight at the photographer. The perfect image of the trigger-happy member of the Special Forces Unit who'd shot an innocent child.

"And they've got your name," she whispered, her eyes instinctively going to the bedroom, where little Marie was blissfully asleep.

"I'm going to call my old boss. Maybe he can do some damage control," Steffen said, and sprang to his feet.

"I'd better change back to my maiden name as soon as I can—and Marie's, too!"

"I thought you did that ages ago?"

"I filled out the forms. But I've been so busy—I've had to make so many decisions, so much to do. I've been putting it off."

Steffen ran both hands through his hair. Had she waited because his name still meant something to her? He dropped the thought immediately and cringed, angry at himself.

"Pack your bags. I'm taking you and Marie to your parents'."

"What about my job?" she objected.

"Is your job more important to you than Marie's safety?"

"You're impossible!"

Lars set three cups and a steaming teapot on the table. With a disdainful look at Steffen, he said, "Communication isn't your forte, strong man!"

"They had trained psychologists for that at the SFU."

"Maybe you should have brought one with you," Lars replied drily, not commenting on Steffen's revelation about his job.

"You're welcome to demonstrate your communication skills now, Lars—I have a phone call to make!" Steffen snarled and walked out of the room.

He heard Lars say: "He's afraid for you and your daughter. That's why he's putting on the tough-guy act."

"He always puts on the tough-guy act!"

"He's the protective type."

"There was a time I used to like it," Lara admitted quietly, and Steffen leaned back toward the living room to listen.

"That changed at some point?"

Lara sighed deeply. "I think we always overinterpreted each other's actions and reactions, never talked about them—half the time, we weren't allowed to talk about them."

"I'm guessing Steffen used to be away a lot, on dangerous deployments, and sworn to secrecy?"

Steffen closed the door, leaving Lars to talk to Lara about him, their past, and their difficult present. Right now, he had to try to stop an overly curious journalist from passing on his photograph and name to the media, especially to protect Lara and Marie. He still had his former boss on speed dial. Despite the late hour, it only took the man a few seconds to answer, and—following Steffen's succinct report of the night's events—blow his top. Steffen nodded grimly. It seemed that highly confidential information had leaked. That could not happen.

Chapter 31

Steffen's former boss had arrived, together with several of his old colleagues. They searched the garden, took fingerprints around the basement entrance, and talked to Lara, who was upset all over again at the commotion.

No one paid any attention to Steffen when he left the brightly lit house and garden. He looked at the dark windows of the neighboring houses, glad to find that the fleet of SFU vehicles hadn't seemed to have woken anyone.

His heart threatened to burst with fear and anger, but his head felt strangely empty. When he reached for the door handle of his car, his hand shook uncontrollably. All he wanted was to get away, escape this chaos he'd brought to Lara and Marie's home. His name and picture would be all over the media by tomorrow. Friends and neighbors, old and new, would recognize him. He'd been marked as the child shooter, and the hunt was on. He and—worse—his family would be fair game for the media and the Internet. The criminals and assassins the SFU had arrested, foiled, kept away from key witnesses, or crossed paths with in whatever form were now being handed the perfect victim, or victims, on a silver platter. If any of them had a taste for revenge, it wouldn't matter whether Steffen had even been part of the operation that affected them, or whether it had been a unit from another part of the country entirely.

Steffen climbed into the car and leaned back. He closed his eyes. All the old ghosts were back: the burning wreck. His mother's screams. His fruitless attempts to save her. The flames against his skin. The search for his only friend. The days of not knowing. The agonizing helplessness. The certainty of his death. The confusing situation in the dark house. The father and husband's desperation. The shots inside the house. The shadow in the window. His voice, declaring a clear shot. The flash. The recoil. The bursting glass. And, suddenly, the silhouette of a child.

Steffen's heart skipped a beat. His brain felt like it was bursting.

Was there any way to keep Lara and Marie out of this? How could he prevent the press from besieging them, the children at kindergarten from bullying Marie, Lara's work friends from ostracizing her? People always needed someone to blame. If they couldn't find anyone, they'd blame an unfair God. This time, though, the outraged masses wouldn't have to go that far. The culprit had been identified. They would demand a harsh punishment.

Steffen leaned over and opened the glove compartment. There it was. Black as death. It would be quick and easy. It would save Lara and Marie from what was to come, and acquit his colleagues at the SFU. It would certainly help with his conscience.

Steffen was dragged down into a well of self-doubt, self-reproach, and panic. Sheer walls surrounded him. There was no foothold, nothing to stop his fall into the infinite blackness. The hand that held the pistol was trembling, the muscles in his legs felt like stone. He was panting like he'd just run a half marathon.

He reached for his cell phone to call Janica's parents. He needed help. But then he paused. Did he really? And was he entitled to bother the Meiers with his worries, his fears? Hadn't he done enough of that already? Hadn't he doubted enough, feared enough, felt guilty enough? Accepted enough help from others? They had their own battles to fight, after all. Poor Janica! The guardian angel who'd saved him on the bridge and brought him to paradise.

While he was sitting here with a gun in his hand, thinking about a quick end, she was fighting for every single day, grateful for every moment, every breath.

The thought of her strength and her joy was like a kick in the pants. Like a friend trying to tell him he was running in the wrong direction. He couldn't fall back into his old patterns. He couldn't give up! Guilt wasn't something you could wipe away like chalk on a blackboard. Reason was arguing with . . . what? With a demon, trying to destroy him? Which would emerge victorious? It would be so easy to just let go, free-fall into the depths, away from this hopelessness. That way, he would escape misery once and for all. But Thomas and Janica wouldn't, and neither would Lara and Marie, or his colleagues from the SFU. Not even the little boy's family would be helped by his final, desperate act. Steffen closed his eyes and realized he only had two options: allow himself to keep falling and use the gun, or raise his head and look up past the slippery black walls to focus on the starry sky. Fight or flight. Sneak off selfishly and bring more pain to others, or scale these high walls and be of help to those he had dragged into this disaster with him. Which way should he choose?

Chapter 32

Janica was greeted by rippling waves that sparkled like diamonds when she stepped out on the wooden balcony, wrapped in her blanket. The water sloshed against the pillars, brown reeds swayed gently in the waves, their hard, rough leaves rattling softly in the breeze. It brushed over the lake, adding a dark, almost-gray cast to the already multicolored surface.

Looking at the rumpled bed, which at this moment revealed nothing more than a pale leg, a muscular arm, and a dark head of hair, Janica knew exactly where she belonged. At least for a while. Her next home lay in another world, still invisible and unknown to her.

She smiled and arranged two chairs to face each other, sat down, and wrapped her blanket around herself. She slid down until she could rest her head against the back of the first chair, but still watch the lake over the chair her feet rested on. The first rays of sunshine drew silver flashes of light on the ever-moving surface. Surrounded by blue-and-green hills, the lake lay peacefully before her, looking like the mirror of a divine soul.

A pair of white swans swam past at a leisurely pace, their feathers puffed up to keep dry and warm, making them look like oversized cotton balls. Far out, a flat-bottomed fishing boat rocked on the waves, but aside from that, the lake was still untouched. Windsurfers and other sports enthusiasts were still sleeping in their beds, leaving it to Janica to greet the day and enjoy the clean air, the rising sun, and the play of colors across the sky, the wooded hillsides, and the water.

She didn't take her eyes off the enchanted fairy-tale world even when she heard footsteps approaching. Thomas stopped behind her chair, and she knew he was also taking in the view. Finally, two strong hands reached down and tucked her blanket more firmly around her.

"Aren't you cold?" His voice sounded husky, not quite awake.

"Not at all."

Janica leaned her head back and smiled up at Thomas. His hair was messy and he wore nothing but a tight T-shirt and boxers. She freed one arm from the blanket, grabbed his T-shirt at the chest, and pulled until Thomas bent over her. She wrapped her arms around his neck, buried one hand in his hair, and kissed him.

"I was going to suggest a nice, relaxing breakfast," he muttered once he'd caught his breath.

"And what's stopping you?" she teased, running her index finger across his cheek, down to the stubbly chin, and further across his neck before he clasped her hand firmly in his.

"Who are you?" he asked, laughing, and pulled her to her feet.

"Your wife."

"In that case . . ." He energetically steered her through the balcony door into the hotel room.

Following a very late breakfast, Janica and Thomas packed the little luggage they had into the trunk of the car, and walked hand in hand through the woods along the lakeshore before returning to the small village by the hotel. A handful of tourists were sitting on the patios of the cafés enjoying the fall sunshine, a few sailboats were gliding over the sparkling lake like feathers.

Suddenly, Thomas froze. Janica winced when she saw the horror in his face.

"What's the matter?" she asked.

Thomas let go of her hand, rushed to a kiosk that exuded the unpleasant smell of stale coffee, and tore a copy of a tabloid newspaper from the rack. He was back at her side in a few long strides, followed by the distrustful gaze of the skinny old woman behind the counter.

Janica gasped and held her breath. Covering almost half of the front page was a picture of Steffen. He was still wearing his suit from the wedding, his striped bowtie hanging loose around his collar. Steffen was leaning over a metal handrail, and his face looked pinched, almost cold, while he appeared to be pointing a gun directly into the camera. The picture was a little blurry and poorly lit, adding to the sense of menace. Large black letters above the picture read: "The SFU's Angel of Death?!"

Janica scanned the article below, which was all speculation, but left the reader with the sense that the clever journalist had uncovered a well-kept secret.

Thomas balled up the paper and pulled out his cell phone, but had to wait for it to turn on. Meanwhile, Janica paid for the newspaper, placed her arm around her husband's waist, and guided him gently, but firmly, toward the hotel parking lot. It was time for them to go home. Steffen would need all the support he could get.

Janica

Isn't it amazing how quickly life can go from perfection to utter chaos? One minute you feel safe and carefree, and the next, fate knocks you down without mercy. Why is life that way? I don't know. Perhaps to teach us to appreciate the good times, to see them and taste them. Because how could we, if we didn't know the flipside? Light, happy colors get lost if there's no gray or black in the painting of our life.

Or should we avoid putting down roots in this imperfect earth, lest we forget to turn our eyes beyond the horizon? Just how limited is our perspective? Are we even capable of grasping the truth with our physical senses? It seems too large to fit into my human brain, my vulnerable heart, or the thing called my soul. But every now and then, I'm permitted a glimpse of a faint echo, a colorful speck, a hopeful inkling of what lies beyond our understanding. They are enough.

Thomas and I were granted some wonderful hours together before the next disaster descended, tearing us from of our happy dream and throwing us back into harsh reality. I wouldn't allow this darkness to blot out all the bright colors of my world. No matter what lay ahead, I loved and I was loved back. I was a married woman whose friends and family had given her the most wonderful gift in the world. Nothing could take away my joy or my gratitude.

Chapter 33

Thomas had dropped Janica off at home and driven straight to his house, where he'd arranged to meet Steffen. When he entered, he exchanged nods with an exhausted Lars, who hadn't left Steffen's side. His brother was pacing like a caged tiger. He was still wearing his best suit, which looked pretty wrecked by then, but he'd taken off his bowtie and unbuttoned his top button. At least he didn't seem anywhere near suicidal.

"Where are Lara and Marie?" Thomas asked.

"I took them to Lara's parents. I practically had to force Lara to go and explain that she couldn't risk her and Marie's safety for her job. How could she even think that her job was more important than—"

Steffen broke off, probably realizing that he and his ex-wife had had this exact discussion many times before—just with the roles reversed.

"What's your . . . boss saying?" Thomas asked, careful not to use a name with Lars in the room.

"He's furious. The leak is causing him a huge headache. But he doesn't think Lara and Marie are in any immediate danger. This isn't about extorting names from me or punishing an SFU member, just sensationalism and finding a scapegoat for people to tear apart," Steffen hissed.

Thomas understood his brother's anger all too well. He knew how much his brother loved his daughter and that he'd never gotten over Lara. The fact that someone had trespassed on their property in the middle of the night was shattering. Then there was his fear that his daughter would get bullied at kindergarten, and his wife at work.

"What can we do?"

"I'm supposed to lie low," Steffen growled, which told Thomas he wanted to do the exact opposite.

"Why didn't you stay with Lara and Marie?"

"I can't," he said, gritting his teeth.

"Because Lara's parents haven't forgiven you?"

"Unfortunately, they blame Lara for our divorce. After all, it was she who ended things because she couldn't take it anymore."

"Well, Janica is packing her bags as we speak. She's moving here, so you can use her apartment for now."

"I thought you might move in with her and let me hide out here?"

"I've got the same name as you, remember? How long will it take someone to figure that out and come looking for you here?"

"But then they'll come after you and Janica."

"We can handle it."

"Thomas, I don't know—"

"Janica reckons her bald chemo head will exact a drop of decency even from the most persistent journalists. Also, Balou would be extremely grateful to you."

"Balou?"

"He can't stand Janica's metal staircase. And he'll keep people away from here—as long as they don't figure out what a teddy bear he actually is."

Lars, sitting quietly on the couch with his eyes closed, smiled.

"We'd already decided on my house anyway, just for practical reasons," Thomas added.

Steffen sighed deeply and nodded as he realized that Janica might not be able to climb all those stairs for much longer. "All right, I'll go and grab a few things from my apartment before the mob figures out where I live."

Lars stood up, stretched his six feet and five inches toward the ceiling, and said, "I'm coming with you. I'm a kind of human Balou." He ran his hand over his shaved head. "Give Janica a hug from me when you pick her up, OK?"

"Will do, Lars."

In the doorway, Lars turned to Thomas. "We'll talk about your other ideas as soon as things quiet down."

"That would be great."

"For now, let's agree that you and Janica only open the door if the visitors call you within a minute beforehand? Hopefully, that will spare you from unwelcome guests."

"That's a good idea. I hope this whole mess blows over soon. There's a reason why the members of this special unit are supposed to remain anonymous."

"At least it's a good opportunity for Steffen and Lara to think about where their priorities lie, and how similar they might be after all."

He winked and pulled the door shut, leaving Thomas staring at the grain of the wood, and thinking how Lars was one of those amazing people who always found a silver lining.

Chapter 34

October 5

From the day Janica moved in with Thomas, he almost forgot how to spell the word *routine*. Of course, he still taught, did lesson planning, graded tests, and went to faculty meetings, but every day, when he got home from work, his wife surprised him with some new crazy idea—sometimes she even dragged him out for an escapade before school. The ever-adventurous woman had quit her job and was set on making the most of their time together.

Janica repainted the rooms of their house, and he soon found himself surrounded by "granny-smith green" and "cherry-blossom pink," as well as "old-fashioned-but-still-pretty blue" and "sun-bleached mint green." She arranged for her huge fridge, coffeemaker, and the pot with her strawberry plant to be brought over, brushing aside his concerns with the beguiling argument that now they'd just have to stand close together in the packed kitchen. The next day, her table took over the entire length of his living room, and the folding chairs were stacked along the garage wall.

After his fourth day at work as a married man, Thomas came home from a frustrating meeting only to find that all their friends were there, not giving him any time to worry about school. The following morning, Janica, having recovered well from chemo, chased him out of bed at five-thirty to join her on a walk with Balou.

This woman was turning his life upside down at the same speed she had entered it. She was the sunshine that warmed him on cold fall days, his North Star in the darkness, both the wind in his sails and the deep lake at whose shores he came to rest. She taught him how to let go of little things, and yet marvel at the magnificence of every detail. And perhaps the most important thing: She taught him to pray. Openly and honestly, straight from the heart, without holding anything back, and with the deepest gratitude.

He watched as Janica held on tightly to Balou's leash, her eyes following several crows that emerged out of the dense morning fog, shot past them with a few strong wing beats, and were swallowed back up by the white-gray wall. Janica seemed completely spellbound by the spectacle. He knew her well enough by now to know that she wasn't merely entertained by the birds, but actively thankful for the sight. This gratitude for every tiny, seemingly insignificant experience was the key to her joyful life.

Thomas glanced at his watch. He had to be at school in forty-five minutes, but he let Janica watch the crows in peace. His hair was drenched, and his light tracksuit felt damp. Shivering, he cast a worried glance at his wife, but she was much more warmly dressed. Since this fall had started out so sunny and mild, he had grossly underestimated the predawn cold.

Janica spun around as if she knew that, right at that moment, the first rays of sunshine would begin to penetrate the thick fog. She watched how the colorful leaves on the trees along the river lit up under the golden light, and the drops of dew began to sparkle. Squinting, her eyes wandered over the stunning display of colors, and she smiled like a child seeing a Christmas tree for the first time.

Thomas watched her face with fascination, but the sound of the church bells reminded him that it was high time for them to go home.

Hand in hand, enveloped by peaceful silence, they turned into their street, and Thomas recoiled at the scene in front of their house.

Two vans with the logo of a well-known magazine were parked outside the gate. A woman with a laptop under her arm was talking on a cell phone, and a man who was just coming out of their gate stepped onto the sidewalk and lit a cigarette. He didn't look like he had any intentions of abandoning his post, even though clearly no one had answered his repeated ringing of the doorbell.

"What the—"

Thomas pulled Janica behind the hedge in a neighboring yard. When Steffen's picture had been published the previous week, the reaction online had gotten even more violent. Without any context whatsoever, people kicked the child shooter as if he wasn't already down. Brainless clichés, abuse far below the belt, and judgments that spat on the right of presumed innocence were hurled all over social media. The family who had lost their son was being harassed without any consideration for their grief. Both the family and the SFU were using every legal means available to them, but the hungry mob wasn't silenced. At least Steffen hadn't been discovered so far, and no one was showing any interest in Lara and Marie, who were still hiding out at Lara's parents'.

"You better get—"

Janica interrupted by putting one hand on his lips and shaking her head.

"No, Thomas. I'm going to go in through the front door with Balou and distract them. Then I'll open the patio door so you can sneak in and get changed. Then you can leave through the back and take the bus to work."

"Janica, no! I don't want those horrible people harassing you," he said, horrified.

"Don't worry. I've picked up a few tricks from Jenni." Janica laughed, stood on her toes, and gave him a peck on the cheek.

Before he could object, she was marching down the sidewalk with Balou. She'd taken off her hat and was clearly determined to demand respect from these vultures.

Thomas watched as the overly made-up young woman put her phone away, took a few steps toward Janica, and addressed her. Thomas took in the cocky smile on her face and felt sick to his stomach. But Janica jovially held out her hand to the journalist, who took it, suddenly confused. Janica also shook hands with the man, who quickly threw away his cigarette, and a second man who had been sitting in one of the vans. Even from a distance, Thomas could see the three strangers exchanging puzzled looks. Clearly, Janica's warmth had taken them by surprise. Now it looked like she was inviting them in!

Thomas took a deep breath and checked the time. There was no other choice but to trust that she knew what she was doing. He ran down the side street and climbed into their small garden from a neighbor's yard. As she'd promised, the patio door was unlocked. Inside, the coffeemaker grumbled loudly, indignant about having to make so much, and Thomas heard Janica set a pile of plates down on the table and ask who wanted eggs. Shaking his head, he slipped into his bedroom, changed, and paused outside the closed living room door on his way out. He could hear voices and laughter; evidently, this amazing woman had the reporters eating out of her hand.

On his way to the bus, Thomas tried in vain to get ahold of Steffen, and eventually called Lars, who promised to drive over immediately to help Janica. He also called Julia and Barbara, but neither of them picked up. He considered calling in sick, but he'd never done so before, and was unwilling to start now. He feared, however, he'd be so preoccupied today that his students would practically be better off teaching themselves.

Lars, Barbara, and Janica laughed as Thomas asked his wife one concerned question after another, repeatedly touching her hand, arm, or shoulder, as if he had to reassure himself that she was really here, and that her lightheartedness was as real as it appeared.

"You wouldn't believe how hungry the men were! And Ms. Keck, the journalist, is a coffee junkie. I think she downed four cappuccinos and two espressos before we left."

Janica leaned back in her armchair and winked at Lars, who looked down with embarrassment at the third cup he'd guzzled since Thomas's arrival half an hour ago.

"What did you tell them about Steffen?" Thomas asked again, his brow still furrowed. He still hadn't been able to talk to his brother.

"Nothing! I talked so much they couldn't get a word in edgewise. I started by telling them that they didn't need to be shy with me because of my cancer, thereby laying the foundation for telling them my whole story, which really threw them off. So many healthy men and women struggle to act normal around handicapped or terminally ill people. But I must have impressed them, because they were more than happy to chauffeur me to the hospice. Unfortunately, I forgot to mention that it was a hospice for children!"

Janica clapped both hands to her mouth in mock embarrassment, giggling like a child.

"I wonder if they were hoping I'd start telling them about Steffen like I was going on about myself and the kids? Anyhow, Helga and Werner were great. When they were asked about 'Mr. Hejduk,' they told them how lovingly he cared for the sick kids and their siblings."

Janica giggled again, and Thomas lifted his eyebrows.

"Y–you—" he stammered, grinning and shaking his head.

"Well, they didn't mention a first name, so . . ."

"They interviewed me, too," Lars said. "The article about Mr. Hejduk's amazing work at the hospice will also include a call for donations. And I'm pretty confident no one is going to bother you here anymore."

"The confusion should give you all a break—at least for now," Barbara said, and watched as Janica ran to switch off the coffeemaker when she saw Lars about to help himself to another cup.

He rolled his eyes, sat back down, and said, "I think the fact that those reporters were so easily derailed shows how little they actually know about Steffen. Just like the trespassing photographer at Lara's place, they took a stab in the dark."

"I guess the SFU's managing to keep things relatively contained," Thomas muttered with relief.

He felt immensely grateful to his clever wife, and to Lars, Helga, and Werner, who'd immediately grasped the situation and even turned it to their advantage.

"And maybe they didn't want to push too hard, since there was a threat of legal action after last week's disaster. What's it called again? Slander? Even defamation is punishable with a prison sentence."

"As if that has ever stopped them in the past," Thomas grumbled.

"Luckily, Janica's visitors were from a reasonably decent publication, not some tabloid," Barbara said. "But it would have been better for them to call first."

Janica straightened up.

"We'll probably never know what's happening behind the scenes right now, what avalanches have been triggered by the publication of Steffen's picture. I believe the SFU's employees and their families deserve any protection they can get. And I don't understand why the press and people on the Internet can't respect that, too."

"Sometimes you're a tad naive, Janni," Barbara said with an indulgent smile.

"Why should bloggers be allowed to trash whomever they want anonymously, while the people who are trying to protect us, sometimes risking their lives for us, have to have their identities revealed, putting themselves and their families in danger? I don't think that's naive."

"I didn't mean it like that. You're right. I just think you expect too much of people."

"Well, my *naïveté* in dealing with those reporters got Steffen out of the spotlight and, hopefully, got donations for the hospice."

"Of course! You have the gift of changing people for the better. Just because you're the way you are," Barbara said.

"Bossy?" Lars asked with a longing look at his empty cup, and everyone erupted in laughter.

Chapter 35

Janica adjusted the pillow at her back, pulled the duvet up to her neck, and reached for her book on the bedside table. She could hear Thomas in the living room on the phone with Steffen. His brother had finally called after having spent the whole day in meetings with his former boss, talking to a second lawyer, and discussing strategies.

Janica heard Thomas pacing, and she could just picture him: frowning, the phone pressed hard against his ear, running his hand through his hair again and again. With a sigh, she opened her book and tried to focus on the story.

To her surprise, Balou came plodding into the bedroom, even though he'd already settled down on his blanket in the hall. He walked to her side of the bed, nudged her arm with his damp nose, and looked at her with his head tilted to one side. She felt something warm on her hand. A drop of blood. Then a second one appeared on the page of her book. Janica frantically rummaged for tissues in the drawer of her new nightstand, which they had bought together with the bed on Monday. She felt blood gushing onto her pajamas and the duvet.

Balou barked with alarm.

"Thomas!" Janica called, threw the book aside, and pressed her pajama sleeve to her nose.

Thomas walked into the bedroom, phone at his ear, free hand in his hair.

"Janica!" he gasped, dropping the phone and pushing the wolfhound out of the way to sit beside her.

"What can I do?"

"Cold, wet cloth for my neck. Paper towels, so I don't make an even bigger mess," she sputtered.

"I'll be right back!"

He returned a moment later with a roll of paper towels and a dripping washcloth. She could feel him tremble even though he tried to appear calm as he placed his arm around her, pulling her close so she could rest against his shoulder. She felt dizzy and her hands and feet were tingling: old acquaintances, unwelcome visitors she'd forgotten about.

"Should I call the hospital?" Thomas asked, watching fearfully as she ripped off more and more paper towels to staunch the bright-red blood.

"Wait. It might stop any minute."

"How long should I wait?" he persisted.

"If I faint . . ."

"Oh, my God," he mumbled, tightening his embrace.

As if this gesture, his warmth and his love, were enough, the bleeding slowed. A few minutes later, it stopped completely. Janica sunk back into the pillows heavily. She felt dull and empty.

"I'll clean up this mess and put fresh sheets on your bed. Try to move as little as possible. As soon as you feel up to it, I'll help you change and get cleaned up. All right?"

"Thank you, you're doing great!" she whispered, closing her eyes with exhaustion.

She didn't object when Thomas sent Balou out of the room, replaced her duvet cover, carefully helped her out of her pajama top, and washed her face, neck, and chest with warm water. She put on a fresh shirt, and Thomas awkwardly did up the buttons.

He put the roll of paper towels within reach on her bedside table with her book next to it, and adjusted her pillows until she was comfortable, then picked up the phone.

"Everything's OK now. She had a bad nosebleed," she heard him say, after expressing his surprise that Steffen was still on the line.

"Janica?" he asked. She blinked several times to let him know she was still awake. "Steffen says hi. He doesn't want you to ever pull a stunt like today again. He says it's his problem, not yours."

"Tell him I only used the reporters for the sake of the hospice."

Thomas repeated her words and then handed her the phone, while he disappeared into the bathroom. She answered with a grunt.

"Janica, you're a hero," Steffen began, unable to keep the reproach from his voice. "My hero! But still: I want you to take it easy. I can fight my own battles."

"It's not the end of the world to need help from time to time," she muttered.

"Don't you know how much you've helped me already? During the first few days at your parents' farm, when I felt like dirt, I kept telling myself that I couldn't give up. Because of you. You had done so much for me, and I couldn't let your effort be for nothing."

"Do you always keep score like that?"

Steffen ignored the question. "The night I caught the photographer outside my old house, it all came back: the misery. The misery I helped create. I felt like the whole affair was going to grow into a hurricane, dragging down innocent people. That night, I considered ending it all again—"

"Steffen!"

"Please, Janica, let me finish. You're supposed to rest, so shut it!"

Janica grinned a little despite herself.

"I was holding my gun, Janica. It would have been so easy, quick, and painless."

Janica could hear anger in his voice, and despair.

"But you were there, in my mind's eye. You, as a beautiful, beaming bride, and Thomas's happy face. I would love to give you many happy years together, if only I could. But I can't. And there I was, coward that I am, once again considering throwing away my life! I sat in the dark car for a long time, and knew that I never wanted to think those thoughts again. The SFU may not have any use for me anymore, but there are still people who need me. Lara, even if she doesn't want to admit it. Marie, definitely. She needs a father! And Thomas is going to need me, when—"

"There are so many people who need your abilities," Janica whispered. "In your job, even if it won't be with the Special Forces Unit, you're always going to come across tragic stories, people who depend on your help."

"Maybe you're right, Janica, but that's not important. What matters to me are the four people I had before my eyes that night. Lara, Marie, and Thomas—and you, for as long as you need me."

Steffen cleared his throat, and it occurred to Janica that this big, strong man was crying silent tears.

"That's good!" she said. "I need all the support I can get. Every smile, every little gesture helps me come to terms with what's coming, and to deal with the thought that I have to leave Thomas behind. It's good to know that he won't be alone."

The line was silent for a while. Janica could hear the splashing of water in the shower, Balou's smacking as he gnawed on a toy, and a car driving past the house.

"Thomas told me what you did today, and it's just amazing. The fact that you not only managed to distract the reporters from me, but also made them write about something worthwhile instead!"

"They were nice, not the kind to bully you or twist your words. The photographer lost his mother to cancer when he was only a child, so it was easy to get him onboard."

"But I still want you to take it easy."

"Steffen," Janica began, and switched the phone to her other hand. "What I'm going to tell you now might sound silly, or even pretentious."

"Go ahead."

"I believe that every person on this earth has a purpose. If I just lie in bed sick from now on, I don't think—"

Steffen laughed softly. "But you do so much."

"Only because I get out of the house while I still can. I want to use my energy meaningfully, as long as I still have any. I want to honor my work at the hospice. I want to share my friends' worries and joys. I want to give Jenni the support her glamorous world only pretends to. I want to show Thomas—and you—that life can be hard and sad, and yet contain joy and happiness. I already had to give up my job, so I—"

"Janica, I understand."

"Good."

"Say good-bye to the happiest newlywed husband in the world. Promise me you'll be there for him when—"

"I'll be there, even if it tears me apart!"

Janica sighed with relief. Steffen sounded as if he had won the fight for his life once and for all that night with the gun. She knew he was finally safe.

"Thank you, Steffen."

"Sleep well."

But Janica had already fallen asleep before she could hang up.

Chapter 36

February 25

Janica leaned back in her chair, let her eyes wander through the round room, and tried to relax her cramped muscles. Pain in her shoulder limited her mobility. Annabelle babbled cheerfully while threading bead after bead on an almost-transparent string. She was like a bubbling fountain, fresh and lively, despite another round of chemo that had robbed her once more of her soft black hair and made her lose a lot of weight.

"You're too skinny!" the six-year-old scolded her. "And your eyebrows and eyelashes weren't right. Now they're pretty again."

Janica nodded. She, too, was surprised that, while her body was slowly falling apart, it still spent energy on such minor matters as hair growth.

"I haven't been very hungry," Janica admitted, and the child nodded sagely.

Apart from Werner, no one at the hospice knew about Janica's childhood illness, or that it had returned. She wanted to be there for the children and their families, not attract pity herself. But she wondered whether the children who knew her best could sense it.

Annabelle's mother sat down beside her daughter. Janica scrutinized the young woman and pursed her lips. Petra's eyes looked haunted, her cheeks hollow; and she tried to sit as close to Annabelle as she could. Not a good sign.

Their eyes met, and when Janica tilted her head in a silent question, tears came to Petra's eyes. A flame flared up inside Janica and singed her heart. The test results following Annabelle's chemotherapy and the isolated aplasia must have come back.

Annabelle chattered on, threading her beloved beads onto the string like a well-oiled machine, happy in her small world.

"Can you tell me about the city made of beads?" Petra asked quietly. Her eyes were screaming with pain, and she was clutching at any shred of hope.

"I can tell you, Mom! Janica and I have talked about it a lot. I know all about it, don't I? I'll tell you about the gates made of pearls and Janica can rest. She looks tired, don't you think?"

Janica smiled with a heavy heart. How come Annabelle saw right through her but didn't notice the change in Petra? Or was this wise little girl beginning to carry her mother? Just like her mother had carried her, cared for her, protected her. And where was Pierre, Petra's husband? Would he finally come support his daughter and his wife?

Janica closed her eyes. She didn't want to judge Pierre. Losing a loved one was impossibly hard. Losing a child—unimaginable. She let herself drift and listened to the patter of soft conversations in the big room.

When she heard footsteps approaching, Janica opened her eyes and tried to straighten up in her chair.

Helga sat down beside her and said, "Thomas called. He's on his way from Sven's to pick you up, so you don't need to take the bus."

"He didn't stay at Sven's for long. Thanks, Helga."

"If you see Werner, could you please tell him I finished his schedule for the next two months? I know he's on vacation, but he really should take a look—I couldn't accommodate all of his requests."

"I'll tell him."

"Thanks."

Helga duly admired Annabelle's half-finished necklace, and squeezed Petra's shoulder as she walked past. The gesture told Janica that pediatric oncology had already forwarded Annabelle's test results.

Taking her time, Janica strung a few more of the tiny beads and watched Annabelle telling her mother about the city of beads with sweeping gestures and enthusiastic shrieks. Every time Janica and Annabelle talked about the city of beads, it became a little more colorful, a little grander. Petra drank in her daughter's exuberance.

"And one day, I'll move there. Isn't it going to be wonderful?"

"Am I invited?"

"Of course! Everyone's invited!" Annabelle proclaimed, before turning her attention to Thomas, who was walking into the room.

She leapt up and skipped toward the young man, who caught her, picked her up with an exaggerated groan, and asked, "Have you been eating gold beads?"

"They're heavy, aren't they?"

"Yes, as heavy as you."

"I wonder how you could carry your wife since you can't even carry me."

"I'll tell you a secret, Annabelle: Janica carries me."

Annabelle burst out laughing and buried her face in Thomas's neck. "You're funny!"

"Yes, since I have Janica."

"Yeah. She used to make me laugh all the time, too. Now we have to make her laugh."

Janica's eyes met his, and he smiled at her wistfully. The sight of Thomas and Annabelle together was bittersweet. Thomas would never hold a child of theirs in his arms, but perhaps one day he'd hold his child, the child he'd had with another woman. Janica hoped that woman would recognize her tremendous luck, and treasure it. She fought back a soft pang of jealousy.

Thomas set down the squirming girl, said hello to Petra, and kissed Janica on the top of her wig.

"Can we?" he asked quietly. "Finn called. He got off work earlier than expected and wants us to get to his birthday party as soon as we can. Apparently he wants us to meet someone special."

"A woman? Finn has a—? Oh, yes, let's go!" Janica exclaimed and held out both hands to Thomas.

He pulled her to her feet so no one could see how much Janica's joints ached after sitting still. Janica made her round of the room and said good-bye for the day. Annabelle was waiting for her by the door. While Thomas stepped into Helga's office—apparently they had to discuss something or other—Annabelle wrapped both arms around Janica's hips.

"Why hasn't anyone else noticed your eyelashes?" the child asked.

Janica loosened the girl's arms and crouched down, even though a stabbing pain shot through her knees. She gripped the small shoulders tightly.

"Sometimes, people don't look very closely. I think grown-ups, especially, have forgotten how to. Also, here at the hospice, it's about the children, not about the volunteers."

"How sick are you?"

Janica took a deep breath.

"Can you keep a secret?"

"Yes. I didn't tell anybody about your hair weeks ago, 'cause I thought you wouldn't want me to."

"You're a very, very smart kid, princess."

"Well?"

"I was ten when I was diagnosed with non-Hodgkin's lymphoma for the first time. I fought for more than a year—and won. Until last fall."

Annabelle looked at her with those blue eyes that seemed to see deep into her heart. Then she wrapped her arms around Janica's neck and hugged her so tightly that Janica had to get down on her knees to keep her balance.

The child was wracked with small sobs, but they quickly eased off again. Annabelle's breath brushed Janica's ear before she whispered, "Mom talked to the doctor on the phone for a long time today. You know, the one with the sticky-out ears? I have to go back to the clinic tomorrow. I know what they're going to say."

Janica denied herself any reaction, but it seemed Annabelle hadn't expected any. She laid her cheek on Janica's shoulder and continued in a whisper, "I thought I'd live more years. I want to be a teacher like Thomas. But now I think I'm going to the city of beads before you, even. When I get there, I'll pick a good room for you. And I'll wait for you by the gate so I can show you the way. The best thing would be to find you a room right next to mine. And I'll save the one on the other side for Mom and Dad, even though it'll be a long time before they come."

"That sounds like a great plan!" Janica pulled back a little and looked at the child without wiping away the tears that were rolling down her cheeks.

Annabelle tapped her index finger on each of the tears like it was a game.

"And then the one who made the city comes, the one who loves us so much he built rooms especially for us, and he wipes away our tears. Right?"

"That's what I heard!" Janica confirmed.

"And we won't hurt any more, right? Because stupid cancer can't come there."

"That's right!"

"So we win in the end, not cancer!"

Janica nodded. It felt so good to hear the words she had told Annabelle reflected back at her. Hearing the girl speak them out loud seemed to make them true.

"When are you going to tell?" Annabelle asked with a gesture around the hospice.

"Werner knows. And judging by the way Thomas and Helga are whispering, Helga does, too. She's responsible for the volunteers, so I guess she needs to know."

"My mom likes you a lot. Can I tell her about the reserved room?"

"All right, you can tell your mom," Janica replied reluctantly.

Annabelle straightened up and said reassuringly, "She'll be glad. Because you'll be living next door to me until she gets there."

"Princess of beads, may I reclaim my wife, please?"

Thomas's question made Annabelle giggle. She gave Janica another hug and skipped off.

"What secrets are you two telling?"

"I could ask you and Helga the same," Janica retorted, and took Thomas's arm.

"We were talking about you."

"I thought so."

"It was high time Helga knew, and the rest of the staff should, too."

"You're worried and want them to keep an eye on me?"

"That's part of it," Thomas admitted. He helped her into her warm coat and boots, and wrapped a scarf around her neck. Holding on to both its ends, he pulled her close.

"Ready to go party with our crazy friends?"

Chapter 37

At least twenty people were gathered in Finn's huge living room, most of them his colleagues from work. Loud music shook the house and rows of icicle lights lit up the room, making it wonderfully inviting and cozy, especially since the cloudy sky was already dark at five o'clock.

Finn grinned as he made his way toward Janica and Thomas, taking them both into his arms at once.

"I'm so glad you could make it!" he shouted over the thumping bass.

"Happy birthday, Finn!" the couple cheered.

"We all got you a joint present," Thomas yelled, "but Kurti is going to have to cart it over later."

"Kurti? Cart? Oh, goodness, what have you come up with this time?"

Thomas and Janica's synchronized shrug made Finn narrow his eyes even more. He shook his head with a laugh and took Janica's hand.

"Come with me, I can't wait to introduce you to Kathrin."

Janica gave Thomas a knowing smile and they followed their host through the shiny, ultra-modern apartment. Janica was flattered that Finn was so eager for her to meet this Kathrin, and happy his new girlfriend appeared to have helped Finn stop obsessing about her illness.

They approached a group of three women, who were talking about the place where they all worked. Finn tapped the shoulder of a strikingly youthful-looking woman. Her round face practically lit up when she saw him. But when she noticed Janica and Thomas, she looked down, intimidated.

"What has he been telling her about us?" Thomas whispered to Janica.

"You should have seen your face when you met everyone the first time!" Janica teased.

Janica stepped closer to the shy girl and firmly shook her soft, warm hand.

"It's so nice to meet you, Kathrin. I'm guessing Finn already told you a few things about his little tribe?"

"Yes, he has," Kathrin replied, blinking nervously.

Her deep-brown eyes stood in interesting contrast to her light-blonde hair.

Thomas also shook her hand and said, "I'm still relatively new myself. They seem wilder than they are, trust me."

With another smile that lit up her face, Kathrin cast a glance at Finn, who was chatting with her coworkers.

"Finn said something very similar," she admitted.

"If you're ever not sure what's going on, just ask me. I remember what it feels like to be tested by them."

"You're scaring her," Janica objected.

"You're amazing people. But when you're all in the same room together, you turn into a tornado," Thomas retorted. He turned back to Kathrin, whose eyes were darting back and forth between him and Janica. "But before you know it, you're part of that twister, and never want to escape the vortex."

"Thomas teaches math and physics. I'm going to change the subject now, before he starts explaining the physical properties of a twister, or lectures you about the mathematical equation explaining its shape."

"Thank you. I mean . . ." Kathrin looked to Finn for help, but he was still engrossed in his conversation with her colleagues. "It's great to meet Finn's friends. But I'm afraid it's all a little overwhelming right now. Earlier, he introduced me to two women who look exactly the same. It's going to be so embarrassing if I keep mixing them up all the time."

"Here's a little hint: Susi is the one with the wedding ring," Thomas said.

"Oh, wow, thanks!"

"What do you do for a living?" Janica asked.

"I'm studying math, actually," she replied, giving Thomas one of her shy smiles. "I'm currently doing an internship at the company Finn works for."

"Where are you studying?" Thomas took a step closer while Janica, whose joints were hurting and who couldn't take the thumping bass, turned around and found a place to sit at the very back of the room. She was soon joined by Barbara, then Julia.

"What do you think of Kathrin?" Julia asked, handing Janica a bottle of water.

"Friendly, sweet, and a little shy."

"I think she'll relax soon."

"Hopefully before she meets Lars." Janica laughed.

"She already knows him from church! She lives in his part of town and has been to several of his services. By the way, he shaved his head again." Barbara brushed a hand over her own fuzzy hair. "His last sermon was about a lighthouse on a stormy shore—and he couldn't stop touching his shiny head."

She dug around in her huge, hopelessly cluttered handbag and pulled out a photograph.

"Look, they sent me the cover design. My YA novel is going to get promoted starting next week."

Julia and Janica bent over the photograph and admired the different blues of a lake and the wide sky above, and the solitary yellow balloon hovering in front of a few small clouds.

"You should be very proud of yourself," Janica said, handing the picture back to Barbara.

"Writing it was so much fun, and now I'm just enjoying the ride."

Thomas joined them, greeted Barbara and Julia, and joined in the gossip about the new girl.

"Have you noticed how Kathrin glows when she looks at Finn? Like a nuclear power plant!"

"Maybe we should have given Finn a hazmat suit for his birthday, since there's going to be so much excess energy around him," Julia joked.

"Too late!" Kurti scampered up. "The present is out in the garden. You should get out there so you don't miss out on Finn's face when he sees it."

"I'm going to take a video!" Julia giggled.

"Shouldn't we wait for Lars?"

"He's already outside with Angelo and Susi. Angelo is in love with Finn's present."

"OK," Kurti grinned. "I'll give you five minutes before I follow with the birthday boy and his nuclear power plant."

Thomas helped Janica to her feet. The friends pushed their way through the increasingly large and noisy crowd into the front hall, put on their winter coats, and left the house. They were greeted by icy air and a clear, starry sky. Lars, dressed up in a suit, was pushing a wheelbarrow full of straw. He nodded at them in greeting and headed toward Finn's huge shed, which was empty except for his lawn mower and a bicycle he rarely used. After a couple minutes, Kurti appeared in the doorway with Finn and Kathrin. They were followed by a handful of curious party guests.

Thomas waved Kathrin over, and the whole group struck up a rendition of "Happy Birthday" that was rather louder than it was tuneful.

Lars took a step forward and declared, "Our dear friend Finn: Last summer, just like every summer, we had to listen again and again to your complaints about having to mow this obscenely large lawn. We've had enough of your whining. So we found help. Never again, do you hear me, never again do we want to hear a single word about the speed of grass growth, the stubbornness of your old lawnmower, or how much you hate the smell of freshly cut grass, and how it makes you itchy."

"I'm getting a little worried!" Finn shouted above the loud music coming from inside.

"You should be!" Kurti whooped.

The group led Finn toward the shed. Angelo opened the door, and out came a shaggy, dark-brown Poitou donkey with a large red bow around its neck.

"Oh!" Kathrin gasped, and for a moment, Janica worried that it was all too much for the quiet math student.

But when she saw the elation on the woman's face, she knew Finn would have to compete with this long-eared furball for Kathrin's attention.

Chapter 38

That night, Janica sunk into bed and pulled the warm winter duvet up to her shoulders. Her knees, hips, and shoulders were throbbing with pain, and she felt more tired than she had in a long time. Yet, she smiled. She liked Kathrin, who may have been shy, but who replied honestly and openly when someone showed genuine interest in her.

Thomas came in, closed the bedroom door, and switched off the heater before slipping under the covers next to her, offering his shoulder as a pillow. Janica loved snuggling up against his warm body.

"Kathrin seems perfect for Finn," he said, pulling her closer.

His hand wandered down to her belly, where it slipped underneath the fabric and made its way back up. Janica enjoyed his touch, felt sparkling heat and a desire for more rushing through her body. But she knew she had to stop him immediately. An ice-cold hand grasped her heart when she pushed him away. Tears of frustration welled up in her eyes and she clenched her fists. For a long moment, Thomas didn't move, and the silence between them felt frostier than the icy air outside.

Then he placed both hands on her shoulder blades, and started rubbing the muscles gently. After a while, she rolled onto her stomach so he could continue his wonderful massage more easily.

"Is the pain that bad?" he asked in a low, soft voice.

"I'm sorry."

"Don't be, Janica. I always knew that that kind of intimacy between us would have to end."

"But this soon—" A sob escaped Janica's throat. "I had hoped . . ."

Icy cold and hot flashes took turns rolling through her body. Deep sadness and the feeling of being lost crashed over her like a sudden thunderstorm.

"Kathrin and Finn! I'm not going to be around to find out whether Kathrin choses the big donkey or the little one."

"Janica—"

"Did you know that Angelo and Susi got a call about a newborn? The mother is an alcohol and drug addict, and she's due in about six weeks. The baby will go through withdrawal, and there'll probably be some lasting effects, but our friends are going to give that child all their love and attention. And I won't see the baby grow up. I might not even be here by the time it arrives!"

"Darling—"

"Jenni and Lars have been talking on the phone a lot. Do you think they'll ever get together?" Janica trembled and clenched her fists again. "What about Kurti? He's a good man, but he's practically been scared of women ever since that last girl broke his heart. I don't want him to go through life on his own. He'd make such a caring husband and father."

"Should we try to set the poor guy up with someone?" Thomas asked.

Janica brushed his suggestion aside with an angry punch into the mattress.

"Julia! What about Julia? Our selfless little busy bee. She's always there for others and never asks for anything in return. Who's going to make her take time for herself when I'm not around anymore? And Barbara? And her book? I'll probably never even see a copy."

Thomas finished his massage, lay back down beside her, and pulled her on top of him, ignoring her attempts to resist.

"And I know: I can't change it!" she shouted. She gasped for air, her chest tight. "Getting all upset about it doesn't help! I know!"

Grief over missed opportunities, grief over all the small and big events she wouldn't live to see gripped her heart like it was caught in a vise.

Thomas stroked her short, tousled hair without a word.

"What about my parents? They're not young anymore. I always thought I'd take care of them like they took care of me when I was so sick as a child."

Janica sniffled, felt the sudden wetness under her nose, and sat up panicked. But Thomas was already handing her the paper towels.

"I'm dying, Thomas," she breathed, weeping into bloody towels as he held her close.

It took a long time for the blood let up. Thomas handed her wet wipes for her face, neck, and hands. Then he pulled her back against his chest, gave her a soft kiss on the forehead, and, now that she had fallen silent, found his voice again.

"What did you used to tell Rat about dying?"

"I beg your pardon?"

"Tell me, Janica."

"I used to tell her that it was like a caterpillar who had to spin its cocoon. Inside that cocoon, an amazing change happens. Everything old vanishes, and the caterpillar is reborn as a beautiful butterfly, with shimmering, healthy wings, so she can fly across the most colorful meadows."

"Rat used to worry a lot about Karsten and her dad, didn't she?"

"Yes, especially Karsten. Her illness made him so angry."

"And?"

"I know where you're going with this," Janica grumbled. But she could feel her frustration and her anger dissipating, as if the same wind that made the butterflies in her mind's eye dance had carried them away.

"Those butterflies forget what was. They aren't bothered by the past. They just spread their wings and enjoy the flight, the new world around them."

Janica turned her head and kissed Thomas's scruffy chin. "One time, I told Rat that it wouldn't feel longer than a single wing-flap until all her loved ones were reunited with her, because time works differently in eternity. But what if I'm wrong?"

"Even if you were, would that be so bad? Rat can 'fly' now, after all, even if it's only figurative. Her fear and pain are gone. Her broken body has been taken away, renewed. If the place you tell the children stories about really is as wonderful as you describe, they won't be bothered or burdened by what they leave behind, because that would mean they take their worries and grief with them—and wouldn't that contradict the very meaning of heaven?"

"Hmm," Janica replied.

She was tired but felt light and safe. She had opened the floodgates and let out all the built-up worries and fears. Thomas's words gave her comfort, and his closeness gave her peace. She curled up under the blanket and let herself drift off, his voice in her ear.

Chapter 39

Thomas leaned back in his chair and gave Janica, who was sitting in her wheelchair between Barbara and Julia, a searching look. His wife looked adorable with her short fiery-red locks, but her body was frail. It was difficult to get her to eat, and she struggled to make it the day without morphine. But he was reassured by the smile on her face. Since that night seven weeks ago, she hadn't railed against her fate again. Sometimes it frightened him how stoically she accepted each new deficiency, every additional weakness, as though it was the most natural thing on earth for a twenty-five-year-old to move like an arthritic woman in her nineties.

"It's a girl!" Susi burst out while Kurti, their host, was still pouring the champagne.

"She's very small, but otherwise healthy. They couldn't tell us how long she'll have to stay in the hospital. The withdrawal is terrible."

Susi fought back tears, and Angelo grasped her hand. He raised his glass and said, "To the mother, in the hope that she manages to get off the drugs."

The friends raised their glasses in silence, stretching their arms toward Janica, as she couldn't lift her arm well anymore. Lars, Thomas, and Steffen, who was joining their Honest and Positive game for the third time, stood up to clink glasses with everyone.

"The doctors are amazed by the little one. They say it's almost a miracle how healthy she is, how well developed her lungs are. One of the intensive care nurses says that, with some extra care, she might not be very different from other kids at all, despite the tough start."

Kurti was about to raise his glass again at the happy news, but Angelo stopped him.

"We think her middle name should be her mother's, but we'd like her first name to be Janica." He looked at Janica as if asking for permission.

"A lovely name," she replied. "What made you think of it?"

Barbara and Julia laughed out loud, and everyone smiled.

Janica slowly raised her glass and said, "To Janica, who will have the good fortune to grow up in such a wonderful home!"

The glasses clinked loudly, one spilling over and dripping onto the table. Thomas sought Janica's eye. Her voice had trembled slightly. Was she feeling grateful? Touched? Or was panic welling up because another Janica would be taking her place? Because she wouldn't be able to see the child who bore her name grow up?

"Steffen, your turn. What's new?" Finn asked, gracefully skipping Kathrin, who gave him a grateful smile and finally stopped nervously tapping her fingers.

"My ex-wife ended up losing her job because of the photograph in the paper. As you can imagine, our last meeting didn't go so well." Steffen sounded calm, almost indifferent, but Thomas could tell how upset he was by the way he cramped his thumbs in the belt loops of his jeans.

Lars said out loud what many of them were thinking: "You still care a lot about her, don't you?"

"I can't help it," Steffen admitted quietly.

"To Lara—that's her name, isn't it?" Kurti asked.

Steffen nodded and lowered his gaze.

"To Lara, who will hopefully find a new job she enjoys soon." Kurti didn't say more, knowing well that Steffen's other wishes were better left unspoken. Not every story had a happy ending.

Steffen cleared his throat and continued. "Unfortunately, some big shot from the department of internal affairs has stuck his nose in and wants to take the matter out of SFU hands. He's demanding a new investigation and threatening to indict me for manslaughter through culpable negligence at the workplace. I'm afraid he wants to turn the matter into political mudslinging."

"At the expense of you and the grieving family?"

"Nothing but pawns," someone growled.

"The positive: The press doesn't care anymore," Steffen continued. "Following the press release that stated the SFU agent responsible for the fatal shots had handed in his resignation, people lost interest. I guess everyone who demanded my head is satisfied that it rolled. I'm relieved. The SFU is out of the line of fire, and hopefully Lara and Marie, as well as the boy's family, will be left alone now. I applied for a job at the State Office of Criminal Investigation, and—if the same guy from internal affairs doesn't interfere—I might have an interesting new job soon."

"To decisions made and changes ahead, and to peace returning to the lives of so many!" Kurti's words were more confident than the look he gave Thomas. He seemed to have a fair idea how upset Steffen still was, especially now that everyone knew he'd never stopped loving his ex-wife.

Julia skipped her turn, saying she didn't have any news, and everyone turned to Janica, who simply said, "I can't do a day without morphine anymore."

"To morphine!" said Barbara, just as succinctly.

"On the bright side," Janica added, "I can still spend a few hours a week at the hospice. And the best thing is, my central nervous system hasn't been affected yet, so I can still tell when you jokers are messing with me!"

"To Janica's thick skull!" Angelo said, and this time the glasses clinked so loudly that Thomas thought some of them might break.

"Oh, and one more thing!" The room fell silent. "I'm lucky enough to see one more spring! The trees are blooming like never before, the daffodils and tulips are trying to outdo each other, and the hills and trees are once more covered in a rich green. The pear tree in our garden is one huge, white ocean of blossoms!"

The game continued around the table, and eventually the conversations continued in smaller groups. At some point, Thomas heard Janica say, "No, do not let Finn choose the flowers for my funeral. He likes to take things a bit too far. Julia, I'd like you to do it. Jenni has promised to take care of the music, and I've already talked to Lars about my sermon."

Thomas swallowed hard. That morning, Janica had insisted on visiting one of the city's cemeteries. She'd asked him to push her along the rows of graves in her red wheelchair, and eventually told him that she'd like an urn grave in the corner shaded by huge old horse-chestnut trees. Forced to avoid the sun all her life because of her sensitive skin, Janica loved the natural shade of wide, overhanging trees. She liked the chestnuts' white-and-red flowers, their large, rustling leaves, the change from the flower to the prickly-green fruit to the chestnut, and the gentle descent of their yellow-and-brown leaves in the fall.

Listening to her planning her own funeral like this took his breath away. It made her imminent death so much more real. And even though he couldn't explain exactly why, her confident handling of the arrangements made him love and admire her even more.

Fate had cheated them of the time it usually took young love to mature, to become the kind of love that turns two different people into true life partners. But that morning, together at the cemetery, Thomas suddenly felt they had reached that deep place it took other couples years—and often-tough setbacks and dark valleys—to reach.

It was as though he'd lived an entire life in these few short months with Janica by his side.

Chapter 40

April 30

Janica opened her eyes. Rays of sunshine fell on her face and made her sigh happily. She was much too warm under the covers for the first time in weeks. Usually she was freezing. But something was different today. She felt fresh, almost energetic, and when she quietly slipped out of the bed, trying not to wake Thomas, she found the pain in her joints surprisingly bearable, even though her last dose of morphine was hours ago.

Balou galloped through the door, greeted her with an eagerly wagging tail and a loving nudge with his nose, and she scratched behind his soft ears until he sprawled out on his back, sated.

Slowly, she walked into the bathroom and beamed at herself in the mirror, thrilled she'd managed the trip without dizzy spells, major pain, or any breaks.

Her short red curls were sticking out in all directions. A bad hair day. But who cared? At least she had hair again!

She washed, dressed, and walked to the patio. She struggled to open the heavy sliding door, but her effort was richly rewarded. Warm spring air enveloped her, heavy with the scent of the white lilac that grew beside the small patio and served as a privacy shield. A choir of birds greeted Janica at an incredible volume, as if they wanted to thank the sun, the colorful blossoms, and newly awakening nature in general.

Balou pushed past and circled the house several times to make absolutely sure that every bush, every trash can, the rain barrel, and the tricycle belonging to the child next door were still where they should be.

Janica gave a start when two strong arms wrapped themselves around her from behind, then she leaned back against Thomas, who whispered a good morning and a declaration of his love in her ear. Then he said, "You're rather adventurous this morning."

"I feel great."

"Then I think we should make the most of the day!"

"I have an appointment at the hospital, my port needs to be rinsed, and you've got school, Mr. Teacher."

"You reschedule your appointment for tomorrow, and I'm going to play hooky."

"You are?"

Thomas turned her around. He was wearing nothing but pajama pants and his hair was sticking out on one side of his head. Janica tried to smooth the stubborn strands, and let her hands wander down his unshaved cheeks and his neck to his chest, where she could feel his strong heartbeat.

"Until now, I haven't played my I'm-married-to-a-terminally-ill-woman card once. Today's the day!" Thomas declared, kissed her on the nose, and went into the house to make the call.

Janica leaned against the sliding door and listened as Thomas told his boss bluntly that his wife was having a very good day and he wanted to spend it with her. Evidently, he was granted permission, because he soon hung up and returned to her with a grin.

"He told me to have an unforgettable day with you. I'll take a quick shower and you think about where we're going for breakfast and what you'd like to do afterward."

Balou let out a low bark as if he was afraid they might forget about him.

Half an hour later, they were sitting on the patio of a café, wrapped in light blankets and eating breakfast, while Balou was lying under the table, keeping an eye on the curious sparrows that hopped around in search of crumbs. Pedestrians hurried past and children with backpacks ran toward their school, their cheerful laughter echoing down the street. Two elderly women arrived at the café and ordered coffee, but didn't pay the couple any further attention.

Thomas was pleased to see Janica consume half a glass of milk, half a bread roll, and a hard-boiled egg without having to force herself. She smiled at the small things that made Thomas happy these days, as she remembered all too well how serious and dull his life had once seemed. He crossed his hands behind his neck with contentment and stretched out his legs, displacing Balou from his observation post.

"So, what have you planned for today?"

Janica also leaned back and studied her short fingernails. She twisted her wedding ring several times and looked up.

"I considered so many things. I know several spots that, particularly now in spring, hold very special memories for me. But none of that is important. I can spend the day with you, and that's all that matters."

Thomas leaned forward and took her hand. There was more affection, gratitude, and sadness in his eyes than words could have begun to convey.

The arrival of the waiter broke the spell, and Thomas seemed confused as he paid the bill, taking a long time to resurface from the deep pool he'd fallen into.

He took Janica's hand and they walked to his car in silence. They drove for a good hour and parked at a deserted parking lot at the head of a hiking trail in the woods.

Janica climbed out of the car and inhaled the rich scent of damp soil and resinous tree trunks. The sky above the treetops was azure blue and almost cloudless. The ground was covered in a fresh layer of green and overgrown with tiny white flowers, as if it had rained stars in this forest last night.

Janica promptly whispered, "Starlight white!"

Thomas led her past the two wide, signposted hiking trails to a narrow path overgrown with tree roots and covered in leaves from last fall. They entered the mild green light of the mixed forest. Janica walked ahead with a euphoric smile on her face, enjoying the fact that it would have been ludicrous to bring the wheelchair here. She would walk on the soft, springy ground as far as her legs could carry her.

Thomas had put Balou on a leash and followed at a distance. He gave her time to soak up the feeling of independence and freedom she'd been deprived of these past months. She could gaze at the abundance of colors in peace, listen to the sounds of the forest, breathe in its scintillating scents.

After a few hundred yards, a tiny clearing opened up in front of them. Here, violet flowers competed with the white stars before both were replaced by yellow marsh marigolds, which craned their heads toward the warm sun at the edge of a small dark-green lake. A gentle slope led down to the water's edge.

Janica took the few steps to the center of the clearing, spun around, raised her arms cautiously but triumphantly, and called out, "Why haven't you brought me to this heavenly place before?"

Thomas tied Balou to a tree and walked over before answering her question. "This piece of land is part of Steffen's inheritance. I sold my share years ago to pay for the house. It was his and Lara's secret place. Now it's not being used at all."

"Are you saying no one ever comes here?"

"Maybe Steffen, from time to time, plus the forester and the animals."

"Wow!" She sighed, and wrapped her arms around his neck.

She stood up on her toes and pressed her body against his. She kissed him until he tore off first her cardigan, then her blouse, and laid her down in the grass.

"What are you doing to me?" he groaned, after he'd taken off his sweater and she'd pulled his head back down to her.

"Only what your boss told us to do." She laughed.

Janica spun around once more underneath the trees at the edge of the clearing. Her eyes wandered from the surface of the lake, which reflected the light of the evening sun, to the tops of the trees against the sky, and finally back down to the soft grass, where she and Thomas had made love and then held each other silently for a long time, lost in the bliss of their togetherness. Then they had talked, and paused, and talked some more. But now it was time to say good-bye to this special place. An oasis that couldn't be more magical, especially since Janica knew she'd never see it again.

Balou, who had been waiting patiently, greeted Thomas with wild exuberance, and the two jogged ahead.

Janica slowly meandered along the path, surrounded by the birdsong, the creaking of branches, and the rustle of the leaves in the wind. But with each step away from the dark lake and its untouched shore, she could feel the energy drain from her body. Her knees began to ache, her hips made an awful cracking sound, and the pain in her shoulders suddenly seemed to radiate in all directions: into her neck and head, into her chest and belly. Janica panted and clutched a young birch tree for support as a dizzy spell threatened to throw her to the ground. She wanted to call out for Thomas, but all she could manage was a hoarse croak. She sank to her knees. Tears shot to her eyes. Had this day been her swan song? One last hurrah before a swift and total decline?

She heard Balou barking in the distance. He sounded agitated, almost angry. At that moment, without any control or warning, she wet herself.

The icy cold had returned to her body. The movements of the birch tree's slender branches above her head suddenly appeared menacing, as if they were trying to hit her.

The barking came closer. The blurry monster racing toward her was Balou. He had broken free and was dragging the leash behind him. A short while later, Thomas fell to his knees in front of her.

"Janica!" he gasped, pulled her close, and turned her so her head rested on his lap.

"It hurts," she moaned. Her eyes begged him for help.

"Balou completely lost it."

"H–he came to my bed j–just before my nose started bleeding the first time," she stammered, placing her hand on the restless dog's head.

Thomas didn't say anything, just stroked her back and brushed stubborn curls from her face. "I'm going to give you a piggyback ride to the car and then we're going to the hospital."

"I wet myself," she said.

"So?" he grumbled, pulled her to her trembling legs, and lifted her onto his back.

She was embarrassed about her wet pants, but there was no other way. She would have to get used to losing control of one bodily function after another. Assuming she even had time to get used to anything. She clung to Thomas as well as her shoulders permitted, and closed her eyes until he gently set her down on the passenger seat.

He sat down behind the wheel, started the car, and took the corners of the winding country road more gently than ever in his life. Janica thanked him with a smile.

Chapter 41

May 1

Thomas hated leaving Janica alone in the hospital, but the nurse had told him in no uncertain terms that he was disturbing the woman's sleep. Back home, Thomas took Balou for a long walk while he talked to Steffen.

His brother had called, despite the late hour, because he'd visited Marie at her grandparents' and fought with Lara. The fight hadn't been about his unannounced visit, or being trapped at her folks' place, or the loss of her job, but how warmly her parents had welcomed him. Yet again, in her presence, they'd told him how sorry they were that their daughter had kicked him out. Steffen was deeply upset, fearing the argument had slammed shut the door he'd felt open a crack over the last few weeks. Thomas was glad that Steffen wasn't bottling up this latest unhappy event, even if all he could do was listen.

When they finished talking, Thomas drove aimlessly through the dark streets. Eventually, he turned toward the suburb where Lars worked and lived, and, at about half past midnight, parked outside the parsonage, which was far too large for a single man.

He leaned on the steering wheel and looked at the house. To his relief, he saw lights on, so he locked Balou in the car with the windows cracked and walked up to ring the bell. A few moments later, Lars opened the door, wearing sweatpants and a T-shirt that was much too tight.

He was holding his cell phone against one ear, and when he recognized his visitor, said, "Hey, Jenni, let me call you back tomorrow."

But before Lars could hang up, Thomas took the phone from his hand.

"Jenni, it's me, Thomas."

"What happened?" she asked with alarm.

"Janica's at the hospital."

"I'll be there tomorrow, I just need to cancel an interview."

"She wouldn't want—"

"I don't care. She's my sister!" Jenni hung up.

Lars had closed the door and was ushering Thomas past the office into his den, which was sparsely and soberly decorated.

"Coffee? Water? Beer?"

Thomas shook his head and sank into the oversized leather couch. Lars sat down in the other corner.

"Janni?" he asked, and Thomas told him about their day, not leaving anything out, even though he had to lower his eyes to his knotted hands when he confessed they'd made love in the forest clearing.

"It's my fault!" he cried, clenching his fists. He felt like running, but there was nowhere to hide. "I asked too much of her. The long walk, the whole day outdoors . . . and then I couldn't even control myself and . . . it's my fault!"

"What's your fault?"

"Everything!" Thomas snarled, jumped to his feet, and started pacing.

"Janica's good day? Her appetite? Her strength and energy? The romantic clearing? The—"

"Stop it!" Thomas yelled, but immediately raised his hand in apology. "Of course not. That was a gift!"

"A gift, I see."

"Yes. And all I could do was waste that gift on . . . on—"

"Accepting another gift that God gives people who love each other?"

Thomas made a growling noise. He was still pacing, but his steps slowed.

"The day would have been perfect if I'd just controlled myself. What do you think triggered her bladder failure? I know enough about female anatomy . . . I'm not completely stupid."

"It had to happen sooner or later. Janica probably expected it, but maybe she chose to ignore the warning signs today—"

"Oh, stop it!"

Thomas spun around and stormed down the hallway to the front door. He paused at the door, pressed his hands against the cold glass, and then his forehead, too. He'd made the decision to come here instead of going home to his empty, lonely house. At home, no one would have challenged him; he would have been left alone. But he had sought out someone to talk to because he needed someone to hold up a mirror, needed a voice of reason to help him calm the chaos in his mind.

He pushed himself off the door and walked back to the den, where Lars was still sitting on the couch, waiting. His gaze was attentive and empathetic, not at all reproachful or pitying. Thomas sunk back into his seat.

"I feel guilty."

"That may be. But *are* you guilty?"

"I know that Janica's body is going to fail more and more. But today, it was almost like before her illness. I just wanted to . . ." Thomas dug his elbows into his thighs and buried his face in his hands.

"Hold on to the moment? You were given a wonderful day. And Janica gave you what you'd both been wishing for."

"She's been in too much pain lately. She's turned me down me several times."

"Couldn't she have done the same today?"

"She should have!"

"Or maybe she just did what she wanted, too?"

Thomas closed his eyes and returned to the clearing in his mind. Janica had taken the initiative. She had kissed him and pressed her body against his, refused to let him go, and encouraged every step. But was that really the truth or was his memory playing tricks to make him feel better? He could feel her lips on his, her arms in his neck as she pulled him down to her. Slowly, he raised his head. For the first time in ages, she had felt well enough to be with him. How could he diminish that wonderful gift by wishing it undone and tearing himself to pieces?

"She's just incredible," he whispered, and saw Lars's worried face relax into an affectionate smile. Thomas was completely unprepared for the tears flooding his eyes. "She's dying, Lars. She's dying."

"Yes, she's dying," Lars confirmed, and let them sit in silence with the terrible fact.

Thomas felt infinitely grateful for this silence. Silent sobs shook his body and he buried his face in his hands again. He was overwhelmed by his pain, his fears, and the gnawing uncertainty inside him. He surrendered to the grief and cried uncontrollably. He felt a hand on his shoulder. A simple touch, telling him that what he was doing was right and OK. And that he wasn't alone.

An hour later, Thomas and Lars were sitting down for a small meal, and Thomas listened with fascination as his host told him happy stories about Janica. The more Lars told him, the more grateful Thomas felt for having been allowed to know her. He could tell how much Lars loved this woman, even though it was a different kind of love than his. She would leave a great emptiness behind. Not just for him and her family, but also Lars, Barbara, Julia, and the others. Janica had left a mark on many people's hearts, and Thomas was comforted to realize it would remain there forever.

Janica

I felt like glass in a frame that was twisting and exerting too much pressure on its precious contents. The glass tried to yield, to adapt its shape, but that only worked up to a certain point before the first crack appeared. It was tiny, barely visible. But the pressure increased and the crack grew larger, creeping over the glass like a spiderweb until it shattered. I felt shattered.

My body was giving up, allowing the inevitable to happen. I was plagued by wild dreams. About caterpillars that struggled not to turn into butterflies, even though that was their destiny. They didn't seem to understand that their lives as colorful winged creatures would be so much easier. A white rat whispered it to them, but only some listened. Another time, trains raced through my dreams. They always rolled into a dark, narrow tunnel. The darkness threatened to smother me until Sven appeared, smiling, and pointed to the bright light up ahead. Or I was outside a huge city built of gemstones and pearls, but I couldn't find a way in. A girl with long black hair came skipping past, leaving a trail of beads in the soft grass, beckoning.

The dreams came and went. They were neither nightmares nor the kind of thing you'd want to remember. They were just images living in my head. Like long-forgotten memories or hidden knowledge buried deep inside.

Once, I dreamt of a little red-haired girl in a pink princess dress. She danced until the skirt's many layers whirled through the air, as if there was nothing more beautiful, more liberating, more important. The girl was beautiful to watch—graceful, bursting with energy and life. I couldn't see her face, but I knew who she was.

After that dream, I awoke in terrible pain that made me scream until a nurse came with morphine. Then I drifted into blackness. Into nothingness, emptiness. I glided through the darkness, strangely relaxed even though something inside me told me to be afraid of this nothingness, this emptiness. But I wasn't. Why? I don't know. Perhaps because, even in the darkness, I remembered my previous dreams? They were my solace; they gave me the courage to go on. I felt protected, held.

Thomas kissed me awake. Like a prince woke his princess. And he gave me a fairy-tale castle. I have no idea how he, my family, and my friends managed it, but I didn't have to stay at the hospital. They brought me to the place that was like a second home to me, even though I shouldn't really be here.

My life might be short compared to that of other people, but it was filled with gifts that I saw where others only closed their eyes or shook their heads, lost heart, gave up. It was my *life. And it was a good life.*

Chapter 42

"I'm going to *walk* in!" Janica decided, grinning defiantly at a concerned-looking Thomas and a grinning Werner.

Stubbornly, she heaved herself out of the "graduation-bunch-of-ranunculus red" wheelchair, pushed the electric door opener, and waited for the door to swing open before stepping into the round room. Rays of sunshine fell through the pointed skylight in a golden ribbon and painted magical rainbows on the white walls.

The few people in the room fell silent. Flavio, the most recent regular at the hospice, waved to her. His bronze-colored skin looked gray, but his brown eyes sparkled. Liana, one of Janica's newer friends, slowly walked toward her. She, her mother, and her two sisters would be going home in a few days. At the farthest table, a tall teenage girl turned to check out the new arrivals. Jessika was also back, looking haggard. Sitting next to her was a girl whose chubbiness made Jessika seem even more emaciated. When she turned around, Janica noticed her unflattering glasses and pimply skin.

Janica gave the girl a smile full of admiration and gratitude, remembering how her own classmates had abandoned her, unable to fit death and suffering into their youthful understanding of the world. But this mousy girl had the guts to face the roaring monster threatening her friend. Jessika could consider herself lucky.

Janica made it to the middle of the room, directly beneath the skylight, before her legs gave out. Thomas held her until Werner arrived with the wheelchair.

"Stubborn girl," he whispered.

"But look how far I made it!"

"Well done." Werner laughed and wheeled her through the door that led to the bedrooms.

Janica had been assigned the large corner room with three instead of just one window and even a tiny patio. Two trolleys stood beside the wide bed, holding everything she'd need in the coming weeks. Or days?

She looked around with a smile. Thomas had hung the butterfly-swarm picture on the bathroom door, photographs of her friends and family stood neatly arranged along the sill of the double window, and at the far end, closest to her bed, was one of their wedding pictures.

A vase stood on the dresser, holding long-stemmed roses so big that Janica gaped at them in amazement.

"Salmon with a hint of sunrise orange," she declared. "From Finn?"

"That's right," Werner said. He pushed the IV pole behind the bed. "Do you want to unpack right away or—"

"I'd like to go back to the round room, please. I really want to meet Jessika's friend."

"I've got to get to work." Thomas leaned over to kiss Janica, then clapped Werner on the shoulder in farewell. "Please make sure she doesn't do anything stupid."

"We're a children's hospice, we're used to herding cats!"

"We should have thought of that argument during the battle with the insurance company. Our appeal might have gone through quicker."

"Dr. Kraus and Helga really gave it their all. They bombarded that company with petitions from every parent whose child has ever passed through here. And you—"

Thomas placed his hand on Werner's shoulder again, silencing him. Janica noticed, but didn't ask. She had a vague idea of the schemes and battles going on behind her back these last few months. Like her wedding, or the fact that she was permitted to stay at the children's hospice where she'd volunteered for years. There was probably a lot more she didn't know about, but she didn't mind. She loved surprises and hoped she'd live to see a few more.

Jessika smiled at Janica, a smile that made Janica feel like she'd swallowed a peach pit—it slid down her throat and sat uncomfortably in her stomach. Jessika had given up. The fight was too hard, the path too long and spiked with too many obstacles, tears, too much pain. The girl's arresting silver-gray eyes looked sunken, telling of the massive artillery attacks the doctors had launched against the tumor, and also of the tumor's rebellious strength, the power and agility of this guerilla band of rogue cells. War was raging inside Jessika, but she was no longer willing to be the battlefield. Her longing for peace was too great.

Janica looked at the black scarf on Jessika's head and frowned, unable to remember what color her hair had been.

Janica turned to the chubby friend. It was clear that she was trying, but she couldn't manage to keep the conversation flowing.

"Hi there! I'm Janica. I'm very pleased to meet a friend of Jessika's!"

"I'm Michaela. Are you—I mean—aren't there just kids here?"

"Nice to meet you, Michaela."

Janica placed a hand on the girl's ice-cold fingers for a moment and saw Jessika lean back in her seat, relieved that someone was taking care of her friend. But her face remained unmoving, mask-like. Her beautiful eyes reflected nothing but the chaos raging inside the body that held them prisoner.

"I used to help here as a volunteer. Now I need help, too, so my friends and the staff made it possible for me to stay."

"That's . . . good," Michaela said with uncertainty, and blinked nervously several times. Then she pulled up her shoulders. "Everything I say comes out wrong. Of course it isn't good that you're staying here—"

"Don't worry, Michaela. I understand. It's really hard to talk to sick people, especially since we're on an emotional roller coaster. One minute we're way up high, then down low, sometimes we're scared, then euphoric. What we like now or think we need, we might hate in an hour."

Michaela looked at her friend, but Jessika had closed her eyes tight, so she turned back to Janica with helplessness in her black-flecked, brown eyes. *The reverse of the black leopard's coat at the zoo,* Janica thought.

"Are you two friends from school?" Janica asked, sighing inwardly.

"No, we're neighbors." Michaela hesitated briefly, glanced at her distant friend once more, and shrugged. She straightened up and pushed her glasses higher on her nose. "I used to get teased by all the kids for being fat. All except Jessika. So one day, I asked if she'd help me. You know, Jessika does track and field and she's really good."

Janica saw Jessika flinch and fold her arms across her skinny chest. Her haggard body must have once held enormous power. Janica gave Michaela an encouraging nod.

"She won all the district tournaments. You should see her run! As fast as the wind, and for so long. She jumps hurdles I can barely see over." Michaela's voice was full of admiration, and she was speaking more confidently now. "She used to train very hard, and every time she went for a run in the woods or anywhere else no one would be able to see me, I'd go along. At the start, she would run a lap almost three times before I made it around once, but I got better. And I lost weight."

Michaela sighed. Quietly, turning to Jessika, she added, "I miss you. I hope you can run with me again soon."

Jessika leaned forward, folded her arms on her legs, and buried her face in them. Underneath her thin shirt, her spine stuck out like a miniature mountain range.

Michaela gaped at her with wide eyes and flushed red. Panic was burning in her eyes like a wildfire.

Janica ignored the pain in her shoulders and elbows and placed her hand soothingly on Michaela's again. She wished she had more strength and that her thoughts wouldn't keep fluttering away like startled crows. She would love to help Jessika and her sweet, frightened friend, if only her own pain and weakness would let her.

"I had no idea Jessika was such an athlete. Long-distance running and hurdles? That takes a whole lot of stamina."

"And a huge amount of willpower just to get yourself out there," Michaela gushed, and added, following a deep breath, "I know what I'm talking about, even though I'm light years away from Jessika."

"I have enormous admiration for people like that," Janica replied, thinking of all the young people she'd known in this place who'd run endlessly long distances and surmounted impossibly high hurdles day in and day out.

"After a while, your lungs burn and your legs want to give out, right?" Janica continued. "But the finish line is still so far away. And there's everything outside: the people cheering for your competition, drowning out the voices cheering for you? The searing heat of the sun beating down on you, or a drenching, cold rain. And the other runners, bumping into you or blocking your way. And those hurdles. They seem higher and higher the longer you've been running, don't they?"

Michaela looked at Jessika, as if expecting a reply, but the girl merely buried her head even deeper in her arms, as though she knew their eyes were on her.

"Jessika always stays totally calm. I've never seen anything get her down. She never gives up!" The damp sparkle in Michaela's eyes suggested she'd caught on to Janica's metaphor.

"So you always made it to the finish, Jessika?" Janica put all her admiration into the question.

The girl nodded weakly, unwilling to give up her hunched posture. A shiver ran down her body.

"She doesn't always come in first," Michaela continued, full of pride for her friend, "but always near the front. Her room is just full of trophies!"

Janica said nothing. She didn't need to stress the point that Jessika possessed the ideal preconditions to have a shot at winning the hardest race of her life. Winning might mean one day returning to her old life as a runner, or it might mean reaching the end of her life with dignity and peace. Jessika was smart and, after all this time being sick, sensitized to reading between the lines of seemingly superficial conversations. Janica would have loved to give Jessika's neighbor a big hug. The generous young woman could prove to be Jessika's life preserver in the middle of a raging ocean.

As if she had heard these thoughts, Jessika lifted her head. The twitching muscles in her face revealed an inner struggle, but then she asked Michaela, "How was your history exam? The one you were so worried about?"

Janica leaned back in her wheelchair, her heart flooding with relief. Then she heard twelve-year-old Liana snarl at her mother, her younger sisters, and one of the nurses in frustration and pain, saying that she just wanted to be left alone. Nothing new in this world.

Chapter 43

May 16

Annabelle was back. Not skipping or dancing—in a wheelchair, bald, adorned with countless bead necklaces and bracelets, her skin ashen and her eyes slightly yellow. But those eyes still sparkled.

No one who listened to her or looked into her dainty face would have guessed that she knew why she was here: to die. Looking at her mother, however, it was obvious. The pain of loss already ate away at her like a vulture ripping through a carcass.

Annabelle visited Janica whenever she was permitted and had enough strength. Janica had been bound to her bed since the day Annabelle arrived, in too much pain even to use her wheelchair, despite all the morphine. Even speaking was difficult, so Annabelle did all the talking. Janica enjoyed the babbling, albeit noticeably weaker, voice. Annabelle kept her informed about happenings in the round room, how Jessika was, who was fighting again, about Liana's permanent bad mood, and about Flavio's attempts to flirt with the new student nurse, even though she was about eight years his senior. Annabelle told her when people came and went, about new patients and those who were back yet again. But most of all, Annabelle told her about the magnificent palace of pearls the two of them would soon move into. In the child's imagination, the house with doors made of diamonds grew more amazing and colorful every day. And, deep in her heart, Janica knew that even the girl's wildest exaggerations didn't come near the magnificence of her future home. She just knew it, held on to it, used it to pull herself up when the self-pity, incomprehension, and thousands of unanswered questions threatened to smother the sparks of acceptance, contentment, and hope.

Today, once again, Annabelle was babbling away. Janica had her eyes shut, enjoying the shower of words like the spray of a waterfall running down mossy-rock ledges on a hot summer's day. Then, a knock on the door. Janica struggled to lift her leaden eyelids. Julia scurried into the room as quickly as ever, waving to her, while Kurti spoke with Annabelle, then wheeled her to the round room.

Janica felt warmth streaming through her heart. Julia and Kurti might not know it, but they were going to become a couple. Did they realize it yet? Were they coming here together to let Janica be the first to see the love that had sprouted from their years of friendship?

"Hello, best friend," Julia said as she bent over her and planted a kiss on her forehead.

"Hello, friend with pink, glittering love butterflies in her stomach."

Julia giggled and winked at her conspiratorially. She moved two chairs next to the bed and sat down, pulling up her knees and resting her heels on the seat. The two women gazed at each other in silence, united in a mix of joy and sweet pain, not needing any words.

Kurti returned via the open patio door and was, to Janica's boundless joy, leading Balou. The huge wolfhound spun around and licked Janica's hand maniacally.

"Officially, he's staying in a kennel outside, but unofficially . . ." Kurti grinned and didn't finish the sentence, but Janica understood. Another of the many loving gifts from her friends and the hospice staff.

"The children aren't supposed to find out," Kurti added in his broad Bavarian accent. "Werner said something about 'herding cats *and* dogs' and a 'petting zoo.'" He gave a cheerful laugh and sat down beside Julia, brushing her shoulder as if by accident.

There was another knock on the door. Susi poked her head in, and, when she spotted her friends, grinned and pushed in a stroller. Angelo followed and closed the door behind them.

Janica painstakingly pushed herself up a little higher and used the button to raise the bed's head slightly. She didn't dare move too much for fear of the crippling pain in her hip.

"Janica, meet Janica!" Angelo announced, brimming with excitement. Very gently, he lifted a tiny baby from the stroller, gave it a long, loving look, and placed it on Janica's stomach, keeping his hand underneath the little head.

While the friends greeted each other noisily, Janica focused entirely on the tiny person in her lap. She placed one hand on the rapidly rising and falling chest of the dainty girl with black fluff on her head, which appeared big compared to the rest of her body. Janica felt the breath flow into the body and out again, found the fast-beating, strong heart, and happiness pulsed through her own body in the same rhythm. The girl's tiny white fingers twitched in her sleep, revealing the perfection of this miracle.

"I hope you know how lucky you are," she whispered, and smiled as a corner of the tiny mouth curled up. It looked like the hint of an understanding smile, like a promise to love Susi and Angelo for her big namesake.

Balou nudged the tiny feet inside the cream-colored footie pajamas with his damp nose. One ear up, one ear down, head cocked to one side, he watched the tiny creature with fascination. Since there was no reaction, he tried a second nudge, this time a little harder. The sleeping baby pulled up her legs and made a soft, happy noise, and the dog replied with a delighted yelp. Then he turned his attention to Thomas, who at this moment came through the patio door.

The noise level in the room rose even higher, but Janica didn't take her eyes off the tiny creature. After a while, Kurti knelt in front of the bed and very carefully rested his arms on the mattress, trying not to disturb the baby or the delicate woman.

"Janica?"

She tore her eyes away from the girl and looked into Kurti's angular face with its kind brown eyes. It took her a few moments to fight her way back from the world of simplest existence that she had shared with little Janica.

Kurti had an uncommonly wistful smile on his face and a wet gleam in his eyes. He blinked desperately to stop the tears, but they stubbornly rolled down his stubbly cheeks. She didn't object when Julia took the child from her. It was too much to focus on more than one person at a time, especially since Kurti's sorrowful expression demanded her all.

"My boss is very sorry, but he needs to send me to Genoa for business."

"When?"

Janica's chest suddenly felt tight. Her toes and fingers went numb and she saw tiny white stars on Kurti's face, but she forced herself to breathe slowly, in and out again. She wasn't ready! She didn't want to say good-bye yet. Not to Kurti. Not to her friends. Not to her family. Not to Thomas. Janica swallowed several times, trying hard to push her rising panic down into the depths of her ravaged body. She hated having to say good-bye. To her apartment, her parents' farm, the horses, the colors of spring, sunrises and sunsets. Good-bye to the sight of a full moon.

But that wasn't true. She wanted those good-byes! Wanted this slow, thoughtful leave-taking. Wanted to feel all the emotions that showed her she was still alive. Wanted to help her loved ones let her go.

"I'm flying out tomorrow. I'll be gone for two weeks." Kurti took a deep breath. "I know two weeks isn't a long time—"

"But they can mean a whole life," Janica replied, hoping Kurti could hear her above the noise of her friends and the now-crying baby.

Slowly, careful to hide the pain the movement caused her, Janica raised her hand and placed it against Kurti's cheek. Kurti pressed his lips together. His tears rolled over her fingers like dull pearls and landed on her sunshine-yellow sheet.

"We'll meet again in a better place," he whispered, his voice failing. "Until then, my sweet friend!"

Kurti turned his head away, kissed the palm of Janica's hand, and left with Julia a short while later.

Chapter 44

Steffen shifted uncomfortably on the worn-out brown cushion of the metal chair. The high ceiling and the bare, gray walls of the hallway added to his uneasiness. He stared at one of the lightbulbs, which flickered as though winking at him.

Today, they'd decide whether the disciplinary action against him would go to court or not. Behind the heavy paneled door, a handful of men and women were discussing what would become of him, his career, his family. A year ago, these same people had already analyzed every detail of that confusing night with the hostages. Together with him, with him and his lawyer, without him. Now his fate lay in their hands.

Steffen stretched his legs across the shiny floor tiles. He shouldn't be in this cold, impersonal building but with Lara, who was still suffering from the loss of her job and being cooped up with her judgmental parents. He wished he was with little Marie, who'd been torn from her home and school, with poor Janica, and with his brother, who needed him now more than ever.

Steffen tried to breathe deeply to calm his heart rate and his mind, just like they'd taught him in training.

The sound of approaching footsteps made him turn from the winking light. He recognized the boy's father immediately. The man walked slightly stooped, as though weighed down by sorrow, and his suit hung loose, looking two sizes too large. His face was a mask of pain and anger. Steffen jumped to his feet. When he saw the man's eyes staring straight past him, the clenched fists and pinched mouth, Steffen's pity for the man turned into sheer panic.

What was going on here? Why had they brought the child's father in again? Was there new evidence in an investigation Steffen knew nothing about? Shouldn't his lawyer be aware of this? Something was seriously wrong here!

The father and two other men with him reached the door. One of the two lawyers—they could only be lawyers—held the door for his client, then followed him through. The second lawyer, a wiry man in his late fifties with huge glasses and an expensive suit, turned and gave Steffen an inscrutable look before pulling the door firmly shut.

Steffen staggered backward and fell into his chair. He felt the old familiar panic rising up in him; his whole body started to shake, and he doubled over. He couldn't stop the flood of images from that fateful night. He saw the father, wild with despair, fighting two of his colleagues; he heard the voices through his earpiece, saw the flashes behind the dark windows, then the silent scream of the father as he fell to his knees. Once again, the silhouette of the man in the window appeared, practically begging to put an end to the whole affair.

The door opened. As if through a dense fog, Steffen heard someone call his name. He stood up mechanically, fear rattling him to the core, and staggered across the hall.

Before he could reach the room, Steffen found himself standing in front of the father of the dead boy and his two lawyers. The lawyers retreated a few steps. The father frowned and gave him a strangely worried look before closing the door again. Steffen stared at the hand held out to him for several seconds before he understood. Trembling, he took the man's hand.

"Peter Neumeyer," the father said with a deep, hoarse voice, as if recovering from a fierce argument.

"I know," Steffen stuttered, and forced himself to give his name, too. The man nodded. They had never really met.

"I insisted on this meeting," Neumeyer informed him, cutting off Steffen, who'd opened his mouth to ask a question. "It's time this nightmare came to an end. For you and for me and my family."

"I—"

"Whatever happened that night, it wasn't your fault. That lunatic was holding my family hostage and had fired his gun. You and your colleagues were trying to help. What would have happened if you hadn't taken him out? Perhaps I would have lost my wife and my other children as well as Philipp. Don't get me wrong: I don't think I'll ever stop being angry about what happened. I find it very difficult to talk to you. But you don't deserve to be hounded by the media like this, and neither do we. We just want to grieve our son in peace." Neumeyer took a deep breath but continued immediately, unwilling to be interrupted. "Your mission and your intention back then was to help, and that's what you did. For that, I'm grateful. And that's precisely what I just said in there. Hopefully, I made myself sufficiently clear this time."

Steffen felt dizzy, and not only because of his panic attack. He opened his mouth but once again was waved off. Was Neumeyer trying to save him from saying something rash that might get him in trouble?

"I suspect you've been told not to apologize to me or my family in any way, because it could be interpreted as an admission of guilt?"

Steffen dared to hint at a nod. Neumeyer held out his hand to him for a second time. Steffen gazed down at for a moment, then looked up into the man's eyes. They shook hands, understanding each other without words.

Followed by his lawyers, Neumeyer turned and walked down the corridor, each step heavy with grief.

Steffen felt shaken and amazed. For several minutes, he stood perfectly still outside the door. Then a jolt ran through his body. The three men were long gone; several women in stylish suits carrying files had hurried past, and the flickering light had given up the ghost. Relief washed over him, enveloped his aching heart like a healing balm. The man's tacit forgiveness had freed him at last from his heavy burden.

Steffen straightened his shoulders, took a deep breath, and raised his eyes to the door in front of him. No matter what the decision today, he had just received a good verdict.

Chapter 45

"And here I thought nothing could lay old Kurti low."

Thomas winked at Janica, pushed the blanket aside, and gently sat down on the mattress.

"I know something that'll lay *you* low in a minute," Janica retorted with a hint of mischief and self-mockery, and Thomas's heart did a little dance.

Then he smelled what she meant. "The smell of the great, wide world," he quipped.

"I'm going to ring for a nurse to help me get cleaned up. Perhaps you'd like to take Balou for a little walk?"

"I'll take care of it."

"Thomas!"

He shook his head, leaned over her, and planted a kiss on her pale, sunken cheek. How he missed her freckles. But death stole more and more of what he loved so dearly each day.

"The new orderly is on tonight."

Janica flinched, and Thomas went to open the low cupboard with the care supplies. She had never said a word about the new staff member, but Thomas had noticed she didn't like his superficial way, how he was rougher than the other orderlies. He knew she was uncomfortable being seen naked and in awkward situations by the man.

"You don't need to—"

"But I'd like to."

He pulled back the feather-light blanket, which sometimes still felt too heavy for Janica's spindly body.

He opened the sticky tabs of the incontinence pants and waited while she laboriously turned on her side, panting with the effort.

He did what needed to be done, massaged cream into her skin with gentle strokes, and helped her roll back to her back. Thomas disposed of the garbage and put his sneakers on.

"I'm going for a run with Balou. I won't be long."

Exhausted from the procedure, Janica nodded gently. Her bluish eyelids remained closed. Her once-more curly eyelashes crowned them like golden fluff, but couldn't disguise the lifelessness of this human husk, this body once brimming with a love for life and thirst for adventure. Balou had already run outside and was barking expectantly, but Thomas's eyes rested for a long moment on the small body underneath the blanket.

"I love you!" he said, not knowing whether she could hear.

He closed the screen door softly, clipped the long leather leash to the dog's collar, and jogged from the hospice's gardens out into the fields beyond. He pushed himself to run faster than usual, welcoming the discomfort that would mask the pain in his soul.

Janica had given him a chance to escape all this. She had cut him loose early, tried to spare him. Had he been a fool not to accept her gift? Why had he burdened himself with loving a woman whose life was running out like sand in an hourglass, who receded further and further until she was just a bright, tiny dot like the stars above his head?

His breath came in gasps. His legs worked in the right rhythm, but his heart kept skipping beats. Balou looked up at him repeatedly, as if worried.

Thomas let out a loud scream. Wild, angry, tormented by questions he should have worked out months ago. Balou scampered back, then growled dangerously.

Thomas hadn't wanted to let go of Janica back then, and didn't want to do so now or ever. She had given him so much, and now it was his turn to give—with both hands. She would live on in his memory. The gift was not letting her go, but holding her close. Even if she would soon be no more than a distant, glimmering star, it would be his star, the star he knew better than anyone else on earth. No, he didn't want to miss a day, not a second of what he was going through right now, because pain and grief were part of life. There would be easier and happier times again, and he knew he would experience them more intensely, more thankfully, and more joyously than before.

Suddenly, a voice in his head whispered that it was all nonsense, that he should keep running, never turn back. This tempting voice, sweet as honey, grew more insistent, louder. Why should he burden himself with yet more pain and suffering? Hadn't he done enough? What was stopping him from turning his back on all this, getting back to everyday life already? Laughter, parties, a routine of work and weekends: the pleasant existence of so many around him.

Thomas stopped dead in his tracks. His legs trembled, his lungs burned, his heart raced, and his drenched T-shirt clung to his back. Gasping for breath, he leaned forward and braced his hands on his knees, thigh muscles twitching. He prayed that he wouldn't succumb to this tempting voice with its false promises of an easy way out. Those promises might come true here on earth, but not beyond.

Balou nuzzled up to his side, tongue hanging far out of his mouth, and seemed to look at him with profound confusion.

"It's ridiculous to run away from love. Right, my friend?"

Balou tilted his head and gave a short yelp. It sounded strangely sorrowful and understanding at the same time.

Thomas forced himself to stand up. He gazed down the dark path, dimly lit by the stars and a sliver of moon, back toward the orange glow of lit windows and the occasional blue flickering of a TV screen. Everyday life. Even the death of loved ones was part of it—no matter how far he ran. His parents had been taken, one of his colleagues at work, Rat and Derja, and now it was Janica's turn. And one day it would be his turn, too. There was no use trying to run from this part of human existence. Pretending death didn't exist wouldn't make it go away. Wasn't it better to accept it, deprive it of some of its power, use its inescapable presence as a reminder to appreciate every day?

"Come on, let's get back to Janica."

Balou barked once and took off. Thomas followed at a slower pace, his legs still heavy. His heart, though, felt a little lighter.

Janica was awake when Thomas got out of the shower. Following his return, he'd cleaned her up twice more, then convinced her to drink some of the nutritious liquid food.

Balou was lying on the mat in front of the patio door and wagged his tail sleepily against the ground when Thomas crossed the room to close the window. He sat carefully on the edge of the bed and hoped Janica would indicate that he could lie beside her for a few precious minutes until the weight of his body on the mattress made her too uncomfortable.

"Balou is wiped out," she sighed, extending her fingers in his direction.

"He's not the only one." Thomas chuckled.

As gently as he could, he lay down beside her, and she pushed her face into the crook of his neck. A warm feeling spread through him at her touch. He tried not to move, and closed his eyes to shut out the sight of the IV pole, the glowing medical devices. He breathed in her scent, felt the warmth of her body and her breath tickling his throat. These small things that brought him joy, and he captured them deep in his heart so he could treasure them for a long time to come.

"You're like my angel," Janica whispered.

Frowning with confusion, Thomas recalled the night when this red-haired bundle of energy had saved his brother's life and brought Steffen safely home. Her bubbly, contagious liveliness, the force with which she'd entered their lives, the mysterious road to the otherworldly family farm . . . How many times had he wondered whether Janica was a visitor from heaven, come down to show the Hejduk brothers the colors of life before disappearing again? Wasn't that precisely what she was doing right now? Was her task on this earth fulfilled? Would she return to heaven?

"I'd make a pretty crappy angel."

"What could possibly make you think that?" she asked. "Why do you think I wanted to throw you out of my life when the cancer came back?"

"To protect me?"

Janica's body was wracked by a reluctant laugh, followed immediately by a groan that cut him to the quick.

"Didn't it even occur to you that maybe I was trying to protect *myself*? Protect myself from being abandoned by you in a moment like this? Because you might reach the point when you can no longer handle watching me fall apart—knowing there's nothing you can do to stop it. There's nothing fun about changing soiled sheets while the person in bed snarls at you, makes you feel like you can't do anything right. It's awful to spend your time trying to make me take tiny sips of that yucky nutrition drink. Not everyone has the patience, but you do! You do everything for me, when others would have run long ago. You tell me the most wonderful things about my red curls, my eyelashes, and my eyes, and you make me feel like you even love the pointy bones that are digging mercilessly into your side right now."

"I love every single pointy bone of yours. But I'm still going to keep telling my students not to starve themselves or read those terrible magazines that put anorexic models on the covers!"

"You do that, my strong, wonderful angel!" Janica giggled, and, with a huge effort, gave him a kiss on his chin.

Chapter 46

The days seemed confusingly long to Janica, even though she kept nodding off. She assumed it was due to the loss of a day-and-night rhythm, the immobility that imprisoned her in her own body, the pain that had taken up residence in every single cell. She denied herself extra doses of morphine whenever possible, trying to spend her final days as alert as possible.

Thomas had taken leave from school, wanting to be with her around the clock. Finn stopped by for a few minutes after work each night. Kathrin came with him twice, but both times, she burst into tears as soon as she saw Janica, and had to wait outside with Balou. Janica thought her sensitive soul was a gift, but also sensed that Finn's girlfriend carried a deep-seated fear of death in her heart.

Lars's visits were balm for Janica's soul. The goofy pastor didn't mince words: He broached serious subjects as well as easy ones, and made Janica smile—most of all because she got to hear Thomas laugh. Lars never left without saying a prayer with her and Thomas, which always brought her peace.

Julia and Barbara took turns visiting around lunchtime, forcing Thomas out to have an hour by himself. They fed Janica—or tried, at least—and chatted at her about everything going on in their lives. As soon as Thomas returned, they said good-bye as though it was the last time, and were very visibly happy every time they got to visit Janica again two days later.

Angelo and Susi called once a day. Little Janica was keeping them busier than they had expected. The child, born with so many challenges, barely slept and demanded their full and constant attention.

Janica's parents spent a whole day with their daughter, and together they Skyped with Jenni. She was currently recording an album in New York, and it had taken all of Janica's powers of persuasion to keep her sister from canceling the long-scheduled project.

Helga and Werner came by several times a day, nearly bursting with their desire to look after her.

But most of all she enjoyed the brief visits from Annabelle and Jessika. She talked with Jessika about her running and took pleasure in the hopeful gleam in the silver-gray eyes when they fantasized about future competitions and victories. Once, Lars joined them, and Jessika was amazed to learn that even the Bible spoke of a race and winning a prize. Lars wrote down the passage for her, and from then on, she carried the scrap of notepaper around like her greatest treasure.

Janica smiled as she thought of the conversation, and tried cautiously to shift her weight. Thomas was sitting at the table in the now-cluttered room with his back to her, reading something on the Internet. His laptop hummed discreetly while Balou snored much less so, and through the open patio door, she could hear the rustle of the leaves in the wind, and the concert of the birds searching for partners and places to nest.

On this day, every breath had seemed a little harder than the one before. Janica felt the rattling in her windpipe more than she heard it. Several times, she had to fight back panic at the feeling that she could neither get enough oxygen in nor squeeze the air back out of her lungs. Breathing, the most natural thing in the world for every healthy person, became the hardest work Janica had ever done. Carefully, she lifted her hand and felt for the glacier-ice-blue necklace with the single white bead in the middle, which she'd asked to wear today. Her eyes paused on the slightly hunched back of her husband. Tears crept to her tired, cloudy eyes.

With great effort, she squeezed the air from the few pulmonary sacs that still worked. "Thomas?"

"Just a moment."

He raised his hand, asking her to wait. Could she? How many moments did she have left?

Suddenly, Balou was at her side. He did what he wasn't allowed to do and what he hadn't tried until then: placed his front paws on the bed and brought his head close to hers. He whimpered and nudged her cheek. Thomas spun around. Janica saw how he turned pale, his hands began to tremble, and his shoulders slumped forward. She tried desperately to give him an encouraging smile, but had no idea whether she succeeded.

He was by her side in a heartbeat. Sitting down next to Balou, he clasped her hand in one of his while grabbing his smartphone with the other. Everything was spinning before Janica's eyes. Werner was suddenly there, raising the head of Janica's bed despite her pain. He moved calmly and injected something through the port.

Thomas called Janica's parents and Jenni, then he bent over and kissed her forehead for what seemed like several long minutes. His hand brushed over her short curls as gently as a breath of wind, and whispered in her ear words of thanks and boundless love. The pressure on her chest eased slightly and the crackling in her lungs lessened a little. Janica thanked Werner with her eyes. He nodded.

Janica didn't know whether she had slept for a long time, or just briefly, or even at all, but suddenly Petra was standing by her bed.

She had put Annabelle on a bed with wheels and pushed her into the already-crammed room. In response to Werner's questioning look, Janica closed her eyes in agreement and he permitted the visitors to stay for a few minutes.

Annabelle's mother cried uncontrollably. She leaned over Janica and kissed both her sunken, cold cheeks, as if Janica was a member of the family, as if they had been friends since childhood. "Thank you for everything," she managed to say before leaving the room.

Annabelle, lying beside her now, looked at her from wide eyes. Was she trying to understand what it felt like, what it looked like, this thing that was going to happen to her in the next few days, too?

"You're going before me?" she asked incredulously and with a husky voice with nothing childlike about it.

"Yes," Janica said, finding the voice she'd thought was gone.

"Then you'll go through the gate of precious gemstones first?"

"Yes."

"All right. Then we'll just do it the other way round."

"Yes."

"You pick me up and show me everything. And then you take me to my room next to yours. Don't forget to reserve it for me."

"The one who built the city has had our rooms ready for a long time."

"It's true, right? No more pain? We can dance and jump and play, and make bead necklaces?"

"Yes."

"That's good," Annabelle sighed. Her voice sounded distant, as if, in her mind, she was already in this better world.

Janica focused on her breathing, traced the searing pain that seemed to tear her joints apart, and wondered how much longer it would be like this. How much longer would she have to bear this torture?

When she woke up again, it was dark. A muted lamp on the windowsill gave just enough light for her to make out silhouettes. Annabelle was gone, and Heidi and Peter were sitting there instead. They were holding each other, crying, whispering words of comfort back and forth. Janica turned her head heavily and spotted Thomas. He was staring at the lamp like it held all the light left in the world. His left hand was resting on Balou's head. As if he sensed Janica's eyes on him, the dog looked up and turned his head in her direction.

"Jenni?" Janica managed between two painful breaths.

Her parents and Thomas winced. Heidi grasped her hand and squeezed it much too hard, but Janica didn't say anything. Was there a good kind of pain?

"She's on her way. But it'll be a few hours yet."

Janica's next breath was a drawn-out sigh. A few hours? Good, important hours. Agonizing, difficult hours.

Thomas bent over and placed his head beside Janica's.

"Don't leave me. Please don't leave me," she heard him whisper.

His despair was tangible, hovering in the air that smelled of medicine or some essential oil. Janica couldn't place it. But it didn't matter. Things like that didn't matter any longer.

"Let me go," she whispered back, but wasn't sure whether she actually said the words out loud or just thought them.

She was on her way to another world, but her family and friends had to stay in this one, where they had to bear pain and grief.

"Dr. Kraus is in her office," her father told her, lovingly stroking her arm, which she knew was nothing but bones, sinews, and skin like parchment. But that wasn't important any longer, either.

"Wait," Janica gasped. "For Jenni."

"She wouldn't want you to suffer unnecessarily," Peter objected gently.

"Wait," Janica repeated. This one word would have been an agonizing scream if she'd still had the strength.

"All right. We'll wait, my little heroine," Peter replied, his voice breaking.

He said something else, but Janica didn't catch it as she drifted off into a merciful slumber.

"*Amazing grace . . .*" softly sung, but in a full, beautiful, and wonderfully familiar voice lured Janica back from a dreamless sleep to the presence of her loved ones.

> *Through many dangers, toils, and snares,*
> *I have already come:*
> *'Tis grace that brought me safe thus far,*
> *And grace will lead me home.*

Jenni sang songs of comfort and hope for her—songs against fear and failure, just like she had when they were children. Before Janica's first bout of cancer, during, and after. Janica kept her eyes closed, barely able to make out colors and sharp outlines any more, and gave herself over to the colorful carousel of her emotions and memories.

> *Yes, when this flesh and heart shall fail,*
> *And mortal life shall cease:*
> *I shall possess, within the veil,*
> *A life of joy and peace.*

Jenni finished the song with a quiet sob.

"Please—keep—singing," Janica gasped, giving away that she was awake, but also that breathing was even more difficult than earlier.

"I'm getting Dr. Kraus," Peter announced.

She felt him glide out of the dark room like a shadow. He was fetching help, but also the final good-bye. For a moment, Janica wished she was lying in the middle of a colorful meadow of flowers. She longed for the rich green of leaves. For the bright yellow of canola, the deeper shade of the sunflower, the soft red of the poppy, the strong violet of cornflowers. She would have loved to see the small yellow mounds in the center of daisies, surrounded by their white stars, the bumblebees and honeybees in their striped dress, drinking the delicious nectar and carrying the life-giving pollen away on their legs. She thirsted for the deep blue of the sky. At the same time, she felt grateful to be here in these familiar surroundings—with her loved ones, and not alone.

The doctor brought a stool, sat, and gave Janica a loving smile.

"You know better than anyone what I can offer you, what the drugs do."

Janica didn't dare to speak, but gave her consent with a determined fluttering of her eyelids.

"Are you ready?"

This time she forced herself to utter a loud and clear "Yes."

"I'll be back in a few minutes, then. It's time to say good-bye," she said, looking at Heidi, Peter, Jenni, and Thomas.

When Janica found the strength to open her eyelids, her gaze sought Thomas. The love of her life.

Janica

It was time to say good-bye. I was sad, yes. It's human nature to cling to the life we know. But I wasn't unhappy. My life was very short compared to some others. But if I think of the journeys of my friends at the hospice, my time on this earth was a long one. There are countless different perspectives from which to view and judge a life.

Perhaps you think me weird or very old-fashioned, but I'm glad I could enjoy the hope of a life after death—even look forward to it. What would I be without it? Who would I be without it? A thing that had come from nothing and would go back to nothing? I wasn't just a fleeting thought, a grain of dust in a huge universe—a coincidence, a whim of nature. No, I am loved!

And with this deep, warm, and complete knowledge, I accepted the inevitable. This uncharted and unknown, this final moment opens a door. I was ready to step through it.

If you like, you can imagine me in a light sundress—pink, maybe— dancing through a meadow bursting with colors. I spread my arms and turn my freckled, laughing face toward the warm sun. My red curls float around my shoulders. I don't feel any more pain, have escaped my broken body like a butterfly its cocoon. Perhaps you see me fluttering in the wind across the meadow with Rat, flying over silver-sparkling rivers and blue-shadowed mountains. Imagine me and Annabelle exploring our eternal city decorated with pearls and gemstones, and how we string one glittering bead after the other on endlessly long strings. One bead for every laugh, one for every happy moment, one for every person we love.

Imagine me as I am in this special place, as you like me best, as you would like to see me. But never forget the happy, relieved smile on my face. Because in that night, I no longer heard Thomas's "I love you," or that of my parents and my sister. But I heard precisely those words from a booming yet gentle, an all-encompassing and everlasting, a through-and-through benevolent voice. I felt free, even before the final word was spoken.

Chapter 47

May 29

Thomas's eyes followed Petra, walking hunched over despite her young age, and her husband, Pierre. They were leaving the shady gravesite beneath the huge chestnut tree to attend their daughter's urn burial. Annabelle had followed Janica by just a few hours.

Funeral guests shook his hand. He didn't know many of them but assumed they were relatives of the children and teenagers Janica had meant so much to in their short lives. Among them were Rat's father and brother, Derja's veiled mother, and also the families of Flavio, Liana, and Sven. Sven embraced him without a word. Tears ran freely down his once-again round, healthy-looking face.

Barbara gave him a brief hug and whispered something he didn't understand, as he seemed to be enclosed in a glass bell, which kept his feelings on the inside and every well-meaning word on the outside. She put a book in his hand, and when he looked down, he realized it was her YA novel. A bright-green Post-it caught his eye and made him turn the first few pages to the dedication.

For Janica, who always stayed a trusting, happy child in her heart, who touched our hearts, and will live on in them forever.

He looked up for Barbara, but she was already on her way out of the cemetery. He would talk to her later, or call her, or see her at the friends' next get-together.

They'd all had coffee together after the memorial service about a week ago. Thomas had asked Peter and Heidi to let him and Balou stay at the farm with them for a few days, and they had gladly taken him in. Jenni, who'd performed three songs during today's brief funeral service and one by the grave, hugged him tightly.

"I'll be home for two more days," she whispered, and he smiled, knowing she'd be happy to tell him many more stories from Janica's childhood.

He would soak them up like a sponge in a rain shower, lock them up deep inside him, live off them until the desperate agony in his heart had eased to a bearable pain and, eventually, a beautiful memory—or so he hoped.

"We'll wait by the car," Peter said quietly.

Thomas nodded absentmindedly and knelt down on the dry ground in front of the urn, which was painted with white daisies on a blue background. Countless bouquets and flowers surrounded it in a display of colors that would have delighted Janica. One bunch of roses with massive wine-red, almost black, blossoms had clearly come from Finn. The pretty, petite bouquet of soft-orange ranunculus, interwoven by several colorful bead necklaces, must have been left by Petra and Pierre.

Next to the chestnut trees, a cemetery worker stood waiting to lower the urn into the ground. But Thomas didn't want to be rushed. He'd had several weeks to get used to the idea of saying good-bye to

Janica, but then, when the moment had actually come, the reality and finality of it had hit him like a baseball bat.

He understood now what it meant when people said their heart was broken. It wasn't merely a phrase to express grief and loss. The part of his heart with which he'd loved his wife had broken in two, like a delicate glass sculpture. The glass was still there, but hairline cracks had deepened until they couldn't hold out against the pressure of pain any longer and shattered. Its shards stabbed him, sending waves of despair and loneliness through his soul.

Thomas didn't know whether it was silly to address Janica with words, but she had taught him to live in the moment, not to worry about what others thought of him, and use every gift he had been given.

"You showed me the colors of this world. I promise you I'll always carry them in my heart."

Steffen watched Thomas kneeling in the shadow of the chestnut tree. He should probably go to his brother's side, put a hand on his shoulder, show him he wasn't alone—that there was someone who understood his pain, at least to some extent. But he couldn't. To his boundless surprise, he had spotted his wife and daughter among the many guests at the burial. Now he was watching them slowly walk away between the boxwood hedges and gravestones. What were they doing here? How did they know Janica, a woman who hadn't been one of their mutual friends, about whom he had never breathed a word?

Reluctantly, he turned his eyes back to Thomas, whose lips were moving; perhaps he was praying. His brother's shoulders weren't sagging as frighteningly as during the previous days, and his face seemed much less gray. He seemed ready following this final step, the lowering of the urn, to look ahead.

Determined, Steffen turned around and chased after Lara and Marie. Thomas had long ago ceased to be the traumatized boy he had been when their parents died. Steffen didn't have to protect him anymore. This past year, they had actually swapped roles.

Steffen started jogging, trying to catch up with the two women who meant the most in the world to him. Had he ever realized how much he loved and needed Lara before she'd kicked him out? Had he even known what love was? Maybe he did now, after having watched his vulnerable, quiet brother give his heart to a woman who would leave him so quickly. Of course, one could only speculate about how bright their love would have burned after five, ten, or fifteen years of marriage. But Steffen suspected it would have stood the test of time, especially in view of Thomas's extraordinary display of dedication these last few traumatic weeks. Was that what love looked like? Putting yourself second, supporting your partner without reservations, suffering through tough times side by side, working on yourself, celebrating everything you had in common while giving your partner the freedom to retain their idiosyncrasies? He, Steffen, had given up far too soon, had focused too much on what had seemed important to *him*. Thomas and Janica hadn't been granted the time to emerge from their dark valley and climb to sunny heights again, to continue their way strengthened by their shared experience, grateful and happy. But other couples did get the chance. He might get the chance.

"Lara? Marie?"

They didn't hear him, because they were too close to the busy main road now.

He sped up, and began to sweat in his black suit under the glaring May sun. "Larissa!" he shouted, and this time she and her daughter turned around, stopped, and waited for him to catch up.

Marie beamed and let him pick her up, while Lara gave him a quizzical look.

"I saw you at Janica's funeral," he started, and shook his head at himself. Of course he had, that's why they were all here. "I didn't know you knew her."

"But Daddy, I told you about her," Marie scolded, tapping her small index finger on his cheek.

"You did?" he asked, not taking his eyes off Lara's pretty, round face.

"'Course I did. You kept asking me questions about Mommy's new friend."

"*She* was the new friend?"

Now his daughter had his undivided attention. He remembered the jealousy and incomprehension he'd felt when he'd thought Lara might be dating a woman. His suspicion had never been confirmed, especially since the ominous friend had disappeared from Lara and Marie's life at some point. Now he knew why.

Steffen gave a crooked grin as everything fell into place. Now that he knew the truth, Steffen remembered Janica mentioning a Larissa a number of times, and that she had a little girl. He hadn't thought anything of it. To him, Larissa had always been Lara.

While the leaves of a linden tree rustled softly above them, Lara turned to him. She smiled like she hadn't in a long time: open, friendly, and affectionate, without any trace of reproach or mistrust.

"One day, Janica came by our house while she was out walking her dog, and Moppel went crazy when he saw the gigantic wolfhound. We got to talking. When she walked past the next time, Janica let herself into the yard to play with Marie. That's how it started. For a long time, I didn't know that she was basically my sister-in-law—I mean—" Lara broke off and looked down sadly. "I'm so sorry for Thomas . . . and you."

"And I'm sorry for you and Marie. Janica was a very special person."

"Yes!" his daughter whispered reverently.

She squirmed out of his arms and he gently let her down on the path covered with red gravel. She started inspecting the nearby gravestones.

"May I walk you and Marie home?"

Lara watched her daughter for several long moments before turning her gaze to the tiny yellow-green flowers of the linden tree.

"Why not?" she replied.

Steffen's heart leapt. He called Marie and grasped her dainty hand tightly, burning with the desire to never let it go again, to watch the girl grow up every single day. For a brief moment, his thoughts turned to the children in Janica's hospice, to the fathers who came and the ones who stayed away. He hadn't only hurt Lara and Marie, but himself, too. How could he have been so blind?

Hand in hand, father and daughter followed Lara through the elaborate iron gate and out onto the sidewalk.

"You do realize that your house is too far away from Janica's apartment for it to be part of her normal route, even with her bike."

"But she was there," Marie said, unfazed.

Lara smiled at him, and a telltale gleam appeared in those expressive eyes in which Steffen was drowning all over again.

Chapter 48

June 14

Thomas threw his schoolbag on the couch and braced himself for Balou's exuberant greeting. He patted the dog's shaggy gray coat and, after taking a sip of water and changing into sneakers, grabbed the leash.

His shoulders rose high as he took a deep breath. The couch, the animal, the leash, the huge dining table . . . all reminded him of the life that had withered away like a rose without water.

His eyes went to the large framed photograph in the hallway, where he saw it every time he walked from one room to another. It was a uniquely wonderful and crazy picture, symbolizing the symbiosis of pure joie de vivre and impending death. There was Janica in her wedding dress and him in his suit among their bald-headed friends. No one was looking into the camera, because the moment the photographer had pushed the button, everyone had burst out laughing at one of Peter's jokes.

Thomas winced when the doorbell rang. Balou began to bark with excitement. Poised like a sprinter on the starting block, he waited for the door to open so he could attack the visitor with love.

Thomas did him the favor and the dog lunged at Kurti. He was standing with his legs apart, knowingly braced for the bear.

"How are you, Thomas?"

"Um, hi!" Thomas replied as all of Janica's friends pushed through the door.

"Got any weekend plans?" Finn asked, and grinned at Kathrin.

Before Thomas had a chance to reply, Werner said, "Pack a bag. We're having a barbecue by the lake tonight. We're going to camp out there till Sunday."

Frowning, Thomas looked from one person to the next. He opened his mouth to protest, but closed it again without a word. He knew this ambush had come at a decisive point in his life after Janica. Either he would return to the old solitary life he'd led before the red-haired whirlwind had turned it upside down, or he would take his first steps on his own into the world Janica had opened up to him.

"Give me ten minutes," he said, and was met with deafening cheers, the frightened cries of Angelo and Susi's baby, and enthusiastic barking from Balou.

He packed in a rush and walked out to the patio. He grabbed the small green watering can and turned to the flowerpot with the strawberries he had given Janica for her birthday. Amazed, he studied the walnut-sized fruit between the rich green leaves. Where had this strawberry suddenly come from? Hadn't they all been green yesterday?

The strawberry was shockingly red. But how could Janica's strawberries be anything but?

"Janica's first strawberry," he whispered, and jumped when Lars said, "Enjoy it. She would have wanted you to have the first one."

"It reminds you of life, doesn't it?"

"You should've become a pastor," Lars teased.

Thomas grinned up at him, then folded his arms in mock indignation. "Lars, if you don't herd that mob of strange creatures out of my house this minute, I'll give you a sermon about the biochemistry of strawberry plants. Give me a few minutes and I'll be right behind you guys."

Lars looked down at him with admiring eyes, speechless for once, and headed inside. Thomas stood there, his chest full of broken glass, but the shards beginning to twinkle with a wild array of colors.

Acknowledgments

I would like to thank Susanne Bronner, Karen Hauck and her daughter Elisabeth, Carola Bauser, and Beate Lange-Alber for reading my manuscript and providing much valuable critical, as well as enthusiastic, feedback. My special thanks go to the future Frau Dr. Med. Sarah Winter for all her helpful tips about the illnesses mentioned in the book and everything connected with them. Thank you, also, to all the orderlies, nurses, and doctors you "pestered" on my behalf.

I am responsible for any inaccuracies, deviations, or mistakes; some information has been adapted to fit the storyline. Here I ask for your understanding.

About the Author

Photo © 2015 Christoph Büchle

Noa C. Walker is a child of the late 1960s. She loves the mountains as well as the seaside, which is why she can often be found with her laptop near the Bavarian Alps or by the North Sea. She enjoys watching people in cafés, busy streets, and squares, and from time to time her observations end up in her novels.

About the Translator

Photo © Martin Pfanner

Lisa Reinhardt grew up in South Germany. When she was seven, her mother took an English course and asked Lisa to quiz her on irregular verbs every day. Thus, Lisa's love and passion for the English language were born. Following high school, she moved to New Zealand and studied English and linguistics at the University of Otago. She now lives with her husband and daughter on a farm as remote and magical as the one in this book.

23607044R00176

Printed in Great Britain
by Amazon